Approved June 6, 1996

American Society of Civil Engineers

Minimum Design Loads for Buildings and Other Structures

Revision of ANSI/ASCE 7-93

Published by American Society of Civil Engineers
1801 Alexander Bell Drive
Reston, Virginia 20191-4400

ABSTRACT

ASCE standard, *Minimum Design Loads for Buildings and Other Structures* (ASCE 7-95 a revision of ANSI/ASCE 7-93), gives requirements for dead, live, soil, flood, wind, snow, rain, ice, and earthquake loads, and their combinations, that are suitable for inclusion in building codes and other documents. The major revision of this standard involves the section on wind loads. This section has been greatly expanded to include the latest information in the field of wind load engineering. Requirements have been added for flood loads and ice loads. An appendix on serviceability requirements has also been added. The structural load requirements provided by this standard are intended for use by architects, structural engineers, and those engaged in preparing and administering local building codes.

Library of Congress Cataloging-in-Publication Data

Minimum design loads for buildings and other structures/American Society of Civil Engineers
     p.   cm.
   "ASCE 7-95"
   "Revision of ANSI/ASCE 7-93."
   "Approved September 1995."
   "Published December 1995."
   Includes bibliographical references and index.
   ISBN 0-7844-0092-X
  1. Structural engineering—United States. 2. Standards, Engineering—United States. I. American Society of Civil Engineers.
  TH851.M56 1996   94-3854
  624.1'72—dc20   CIP

STANDARDS

In April 1980, the Board of Direction approved ASCE Rules for Standards Committees to govern the writing and maintenance of standards developed by the Society. All such standards are developed by a consensus standards process managed by the Management Group F (MGF), Codes and Standards. The consensus process includes balloting by the balanced standards committee made up of Society members and non-members, balloting by the membership of ASCE as a whole and balloting by the public. All standards are updated or reaffirmed by the same process at intervals not exceeding five years.

The following standards have been issued:

ANSI/ASCE 1-82 N-725 Guidelines for Design and Analysis of Nuclear Safety Related Earth Structures

ANSI/ASCE 2-91 Measurement of Oxygen Transfer in Clean Water

ANSI/ASCE 3-91 Standard for the Structural Design of Composite Slabs and ANSI/ASCE 9-91 Standard Practice for the Construction and Inspection of Composite Slabs

ASCE 4-86 Seismic Analysis of Safety-Related Nuclear Structures

Building Code Requirements for Masonry Structures (ACI530-95/ASCE5-95/TMS402-95) and Specifications for Masonry Structures (ACI530.1-95/ASCE6-95/TMS602-95)

Specifications for Masonry Structures (ACI530-95/ASCE6-95/TMS602-95)

ANSI/ASCE 7-93 Minimum Design Loads for Building and Other Structures

ANSI/ASCE 8-90 Standard Specification for the Design of Cold-Formed Stainless Steel Structural Members

ANSI/ASCE 9-91 listed with ASCE 3-91

ANSI/ASCE 10-90 Design of Latticed Steel Transmission Structures

ANSI/ASCE 11-90 Guideline for Structural Condition Assessment of Existing Buildings

ANSI/ASCE 12-91 Guideline for the Design of Urban Subsurface Drainage

ASCE 13-93 Standard Guidelines for Installation of Urban Subsurface Drainage

ASCE 14-93 Standard Guidelines for Operation and Maintenance of Urban Subsurface Drainage

ASCE 15-93 Standard Practice for Direct Design of Buried Precast Concrete Pipe Using Standard Installations (SIDD)

ASCE 16-95 Standard for Load and Resistance Factor Design (LRFD) of Engineered Wood Construction

FOREWORD

The material presented in this publication has been prepared in accordance with recognized engineering principles. This Standard and Commentary should not be used without first securing competent advice with respect to their suitability for any given application. The publication of the material contained herein is not intended as a representation or warranty on the part of the American Society of Civil Engineers, or of any other person named herein, that this information is suitable for any general or particular use or promises freedom from infringement of any patent or patents. Anyone making use of this information assumes all liability from such use.

ACKNOWLEDGEMENTS

The American Society of Civil Engineers (ASCE) acknowledges the work of the Minimum Design Loads on Buildings and Other Structures Standards Committee of the Management Group F, Codes and Standards. This group comprises individuals from many backgrounds including: consulting engineering, research, construction industry, education, government, design and private practice. This revision of the standard began in 1989 and incorporates information as described in the commentary.

This Standard was prepared through the consensus standards process by balloting in compliance with procedures of ASCE's Management Group F, Codes and Standards. Those individuals who serve on the Standards Committee are:

Kharaiti L. Abrol
Kenneth R. Andreason
Demirtas C. Bayar
John E. Breen
David G. Brinker
Ray A. Bucklin
Howard S. Burton
James R. Cagley
Robert Caldwell
Jack E. Cermak
Charles W. Chambliss
Kevin C.K. Cheung
Edward Cohen
James S. Cohen
Ross B. Corotis
Jay H. Crandell
Stanley W. Crawley
Amitabha Datta
Charles A. De Angelis
Susan Dowty
Donald Dusenberry
Bruce R. Ellingwood
Edward R. Estes, Jr.
John W. Foss
Raymond R. Fox
Theodore Galambos
Robert A. Garbini
Satyendra K. Ghosh
Lonrenzo Gonzalez
David S. Gromala
John L. Gross
Charles H. Gutberlet, Jr.
Robert D. Hanson
Gilliam S. Harris
James R. Harris
Arthur L. Held
Mark B. Hogan
Scott Humphreys
Nicholas Isyumov
A. Harry Karabinis
D. J. L. Kennedy
Randy Kissell

Arthur S. Koenig
Uno Kula
Edward M. Laatsch
James G. MacGregor
Ian Mackinlay
Harry W. Martin
Rush Masih
George M. Matsumura
Murvan M. Maxwell
William McGuire
Douglas K. McLeod
Richard McConnell
Kishor C. Mehta
Rick Mendlen
Joseph J. Messersmith, Jr.
Arthur Monsey
Walter P. Moore, Jr., Chair
Arthur J. Mullkoff
Joe N. Nunnery
Michael O'Rourke
Clifford Oliver
Alan B. Peabody
Dale C. Perry
Clarkson W. Pinkham
Robert D. Prince
Robert Ratay
Mayasandra K. Ravindra
Lawrence D. Reaveley
Ramon Riba
Abraham J. Rokach
William D. Rome
Herbert S. Saffir
Andrew Scanlon
Ashvin A. Shah
William L. Shoemaker
John H. Showalter, Jr.
Emil Simiu
Thomas L. Smith
David C. Soderquist
Irwin J. Speyer
Theodore Stathopoulos
Frank W. Stockwell

Donald R. Strand
John G. Tawresey
John C. Theiss
Harry B. Thomas
Wayne Tobiasson
Brian E. Trimble
Joseph V. Tyrrell
Thomas R. Tyson
Joseph W. Vellozzi
Richard A. Vognild
Frank J. Walter, Jr.
Marius B. Wechsler
Lyle L. Wilson
Joseph A. Wintz, III
Edwin G. Zacher

Task Committee on General Provisions
John E. Breen
Donald Dusenberry
John L. Gross, Chair
William McGuire
Irwin J. Speyer
John G. Tawresey

Task Committee on Load Combinations
Ross B. Corotis
Bruce R. Ellingwood
Theodore Galambos, Chair
D. J. L. Kennedy
James G. MacGregor
Clarkson W. Pinkham
Andrew Scanlon

Task Committee on Live Loads
James R. Cagley, Chair
Ross B. Corotis
Charles A. DeAngelis
Raymond R. Fox
Gilliam S. Harris
Joseph Hartman

Contents

List of Tables

List of Figures

Conversion Factors—Inch-Pound Units to SI (Metric) Units

To convert from	to	Multiply by
pounds-force	kilonewtons (kN)	4.448 222 E−03
pounds-force per linear foot	kilonewtons per meter (kN/m)	1.459 390 E−02
pounds-force per square foot	kilonewtons per square meter (kN/m^2)	4.788 026 E−02
pounds per cubic foot	kilonewtons per cubic meter (kN/m^3)	1.570 875 E−01
slug	kilogram (kg)	1.459 390 E+01
pounds per cubic foot	kilograms per cubic meter (kN/m^3)	1.601 846 E+01
feet	meters (m)	3.048 000 E−01
inches	millimeters (mm)	2.540 000 E+01
miles	kilometers (km)	1.609 344 E+00
square feet	square meters (m^2)	9.290 304 E−02
square inches	square millimeters (mm^2)	6.451 600 E+02
miles per hour	kilometers per hour (km/h)	1.609 344 E+00
feet per second	meters per second (m/s)	3.048 000 E−01
feet per second per second	meters per second squared (m/s^2)	3.048 000 E−01
inches per hour	millimeters per hour (mm/h)	2.540 020 E+01
gallons per minute	cubic meters per second (m^3/s)	6.309 020 E−05
°F · h · sq ft/Btu	kelvin square meter per watt (K · m^2/W)	1.762 280 E−01
degree Fahrenheit	degree Celsius (°C)	$t_c = (t_f - 32)/1.8$

Note: This table includes most units used throughout this Standard. For additional conversion factors see ASTM E380-93 "Standard Practice for Use of the International System of Units (The Modernized Metric System)."

American Society of Civil Engineers Standard
Minimum Design Loads for Buildings and Other Structures

1. General

*1.1 Scope

This standard provides minimum load requirements for the design of buildings and other structures that are subject to building code requirements. Loads and appropriate load combinations, which have been developed to be used together, are set forth for strength design and allowable stress design. For design strengths and allowable stress limits, design specifications for conventional structural materials used in buildings and modifications contained in this standard shall be followed.

1.2 Definitions

The following definitions apply to the provisions of the entire standard.

Allowable stress design: a method of proportioning structural members, such that elastically computed stresses produced in the members by nominal loads do not exceed specified allowable stresses (also called working stress design).

Authority having jurisdiction: the organization, political subdivision, office or individual charged with the responsibility of administering and enforcing the provisions of this standard.

Buildings: structures, usually enclosed by walls and a roof, constructed to provide support or shelter for an intended occupancy.

Design strength: the product of the nominal strength and a resistance factor.

Essential facilities: buildings and other structures that are intended to remain operational in the event of extreme environmental loading from wind, snow, or earthquakes.

Factored load: the product of the nominal load and a load factor.

Limit state: a condition beyond which a structure or member becomes unfit for service and is judged either to be no longer useful for its intended func-

tion (serviceability limit state) or to be unsafe (strength limit state).

Load effects: forces and deformations produced in structural members by the applied loads.

Load factor: a factor that accounts for deviations of the actual load from the nominal load, for uncertainties in the analysis that transforms the load into a load effect, and for the probability that more than one extreme load will occur simultaneously.

Loads: forces or other actions that result from the weight of all building materials, occupants and their possessions, environmental effects, differential movement, and restrained dimensional changes. Permanent loads are those loads in which variations over time are rare or of small magnitude. All other loads are variable loads (see also nominal loads).

Nominal loads: the magnitudes of the loads specified in Sections 3–9 (dead, live, soil, wind, snow, rain, flood, and earthquake) of this standard.

Nominal strength: the capacity of a structure or member to resist the effects of loads, as determined by computations using specified material strengths and dimensions and formulas derived from accepted principles of structural mechanics or by field tests or laboratory tests of scaled models, allowing for modeling effects and differences between laboratory and field conditions.

Occupancy: the purpose for which a building or other structure, or part thereof, is used or intended to be used.

Other structures: structures, other than buildings, for which loads are specified in this standard.

P-delta effect: the second order effect on shears and moments of frame members induced by axial loads on a laterally displaced building frame.

Resistance factor: a factor that accounts for deviations of the actual strength from the nominal strength and the manner and consequences of failure (also called strength reduction factor).

Strength design: a method of proportioning structural members such that the computed forces produced in the members by the factored loads do not exceed the member design strength (also called load and resistance factor design).

Temporary facilities: buildings or other structures that are to be in service for a limited time and have a limited exposure period for environmental loadings.

1.3 Basic Requirements

*1.3.1 Strength. Buildings and other structures, and all parts thereof, shall be designed and constructed to support safely the factored loads in load combinations defined in this document without exceeding the appropriate strength limit states for the materials of construction. Alternatively, buildings and other structures, and all parts thereof, shall be designed and constructed to support safely the nominal loads in load combinations defined in this document without exceeding the appropriate specified allowable stresses for the materials of construction.

*1.3.2 Serviceability. Structural systems and members thereof shall be designed to have adequate stiffness to limit deflections, lateral drift, vibration, or any other deformations that adversely affect the intended use and performance of buildings and other structures.

*1.3.3 Self-Straining Forces. Provision shall be made for anticipated self-straining forces arising from differential settlements of foundations and from restrained dimensional changes due to temperature, moisture, shrinkage, creep, and similar effects.

1.3.4 Analysis. Load effects on individual structural members shall be determined by methods of structural analysis that take into account equilibrium, general stability, geometric compatibility, and both short- and long-term material properties. Members that tend to accumulate residual deformations under repeated service loads shall have included in their analysis the added eccentricities expected to occur during their service life.

*1.4 General Structural Integrity

Buildings and other structures shall be designed to sustain local damage with the structural system as a whole remaining stable and not being damaged to an extent disproportionate to the original local damage. This shall be achieved through an arrangement of the structural elements that provides stability to the entire structural system by transferring loads from any locally damaged region to adjacent regions capable of resisting those loads without collapse. This shall be accomplished by providing sufficient continuity, redundancy, or energy-dissipating capacity (ductility), or a combination thereof, in the members of the structure.

*1.5 Classification of Buildings and Other Structures

Buildings and other structures shall be classified, based on the nature of occupancy, according to Table 1-1 for the purposes of applying wind,

TABLE 1-1
Classification of Buildings and Other Structures for Wind, Snow, and Earthquake Loads

Nature of Occupancy	Category
Buildings and other structures that represent a low hazard to human life in the event of failure	I
including, but not limited to: • Agricultural facilities • Certain temporary facilities • Minor storage facilities	I
All buildings and other structures except those listed in Categories I, III, and IV	II
Buildings and other structures that represent a substantial hazard to human life in the event of failure including, but not limited to: • Buildings and other structures where more than 300 people congregate in one area • Buildings and other structures with elementary school, secondary school, or day-care facilities with capacity greater than 250 • Buildings and other structures with a capacity greater than 500 for colleges or adult education facilities • Health-care facilities with a capacity of 50 or more resident patients but not having surgery or emergency treatment facilities • Jails and detention facilities • Power generating stations and other public utility facilities not included in Category IV • Buildings and other structures containing sufficient quantities of toxic or explosive substances to be dangerous to the public if released	III
Buildings and other structures designated as essential facilities including, but not limited to: • Hospitals and other health-care facilities having surgery or emergency treatment facilities • Fire, rescue and police stations and emergency vehicle garages • Designated earthquake, hurricane, or other emergency shelters • Communications centers and other facilities required for emergency response • Power generating stations and other public utility facilities required in an emergency • Buildings and other structures having critical national defense functions	IV

snow, and earthquake provisions. The categories range from I to IV, where category I represents buildings and other structures with a low hazard to human life in the event of failure and category IV represents essential facilities. Each building or other structure shall be assigned to the highest applicable category.

When buildings or other structures have multiple uses (occupancies), the relationship between the uses of various parts of the building or other structure and the independence of the structural systems for those various parts shall be examined. The classification for each independent structural system of a multiple use building or other structure shall be that of the highest usage group in any part of the building or other structure that is dependent on that basic structural system.

1.6 Additions and Alterations to Existing Structures

When an existing building or other structure is enlarged or otherwise altered, structural members affected shall be strengthened if necessary so that the factored loads defined in this document will be supported without exceeding the specified design strength for the materials of construction. When using allowable stress design, strengthening is required when the stresses due to nominal loads exceed the specified allowable stresses for the materials of construction.

*1.7 Load Tests

A load test of any construction shall be conducted when required by the authority having jurisdiction whenever there is reason to question its safety for the intended occupancy or use.

*2. Combinations of Loads

2.1 General

Buildings and other structures shall be designed using the provisions of either 2.3 or 2.4. Either 2.3 or 2.4 shall be used exclusively for proportioning elements of a particular construction material throughout the structure.

2.2 Symbols and Notation

D = dead load;
E = earthquake load;
F = load due to fluids with well-defined pressures and maximum heights;
F_a = flood load;
H = load due to the weight and lateral pressure of soil and water in soil;
L = live load;
L_r = roof live load;
R = rain load;
S = snow load;
T = self-straining force;
W = wind load.

2.3 Combining Factored Loads Using Strength Design

*2.3.1 Applicability. The load combinations and load factors given in 2.3.2 shall be used only in those cases in which they are specifically authorized by the applicable material design standard.

*2.3.2 Basic Combinations. Structures, components, and foundations shall be designed so that their design strength equals or exceeds the effects of the factored loads in the following combinations:

1. $1.4D$
2. $1.2(D + F + T) + 1.6(L + H) + 0.5(L_r \text{ or } S \text{ or } R)$
3. $1.2D + 1.6(L_r \text{ or } S \text{ or } R) + (0.5L \text{ or } 0.8W)$
4. $1.2D + 1.3W + 0.5L + 0.5(L_r \text{ or } S \text{ or } R)$
5. $1.2D + 1.0E + 0.5L + 0.2S$
6. $0.9D + (1.3W \text{ or } 1.0E)$

Exception: The load factor on L in combinations 3–5 shall equal 1.0 for garages, areas occupied as places of public assembly, and all areas where the live load is greater than 100 lb/sq ft (pounds-force per square foot) (4.79 kN/m²).

Each relevant strength limit state shall be investigated. Effects of one or more loads not acting shall be investigated. The most unfavorable effects from both wind and earthquake loads shall be investigated, where appropriate, but they need not be considered to act simultaneously. Refer to Section 9.2.2.6 for specific definition of the earthquake load effect E.[1]

2.3.3 Other Load Combinations. The structural effects of F_a shall be investigated in design using the same load factors as used for L (live load) in the basic combinations of 2 and 4 of 2.3.2. The structural effects of F_a shall also be included when investigating the overturning and sliding in the basic combination 6 using a load factor of 0.5 when wind also occurs and 1.6 when acting alone.

---

[1]The same E from Section 9 is used for both Sections 2.3.2 and Sec. 2.4.1. Refer to the Commentary for Section 9.

2.4 Combining Nominal Loads Using Allowable Stress Design

*2.4.1 Basic Combinations.
Loads listed herein shall be considered to act in the following combinations, whichever produces the most unfavorable effect in the building, foundation, or structural member being considered. Effects of one or more loads not acting shall be investigated.

1. D
2. $D + L + F + H + T + (L_r \text{ or } S \text{ or } R)$
3. $D + (W \text{ or } E)$
4. $D + L + (L_r \text{ or } S \text{ or } R) + (W \text{ or } E)$

The most unfavorable effects from both wind and earthquake loads shall be investigated, where appropriate, but they need not be assumed to act simultaneously. Refer to Section 9.2.2.6 for the specific definition of the earthquake load effect E.[1]

2.4.2 Other Load Combinations.
The structural effects of F_a shall be investigated in design.

*2.4.3 Load Reduction.
When structural effects due to two or more loads in combination with dead load, but excluding earthquake load, are investigated in load combinations of Sections 2.4.1 and 2.4.2, the combined effects shall comply with both of the following requirements: (a) The combined effects due to the two or more loads multiplied by 0.75 plus effects due to dead loads shall not be less than the effects from the load combination of the dead load plus the load producing the largest effects; and (b) the allowable stress shall not be increased to account for these combinations.

The load combinations including earthquake loads shall follow the requirements in Section 9.

2.4.4 Overturning and Sliding.
Buildings and other structures shall be designed so that the overturning moment due to lateral forces (wind or flood) acting singly or in combination does not exceed two-thirds of the dead load stabilizing moment unless the building or structure is anchored to resist the excess moment. The base shear due to lateral forces (wind or flood) shall not exceed two-thirds of the total resisting force due to friction and adhesion unless the building or structure is anchored to resist the excess sliding force.

2.4.5 Counteracting Loads.
Stress reversals shall be accounted for where the effects of design loads counteract one another in a structural member or joint.

*2.5 Load Combinations for Extraordinary Events.
Where required by the applicable code, standard, or the authority having jurisdiction, strength and stability shall be checked to ensure that structures are capable of withstanding the effects of extraordinary (i.e. low-probability) events such as fires, explosions, and vehicular impact.

3. Dead Loads

3.1 Definition
Dead loads consist of the weight of all materials of construction incorporated into the building, including but not limited to walls, floors, roofs, ceilings, stairways, built-in partitions, finishes, cladding, and other similarly incorporated architectural and structural items, and fixed service equipment, including the weight of cranes.

*3.2 Weights of Materials and Constructions
In determining dead loads for purposes of design, the actual weights of materials and constructions shall be used, provided that in the absence of definite information, values approved by the authority having jurisdiction shall be used.

3.3 Weight of Fixed Service Equipment
In determining dead loads for purposes of design, the weight of fixed service equipment, such as plumbing stacks and risers, electrical feeders, and heating, ventilating, and air conditioning systems, shall be included.

4. Live Loads

4.1 Definition
Live loads are those loads produced by the use and occupancy of the building or other structure and do not include construction or environmental loads such as wind load, snow load, rain load, earthquake load, flood load, or dead load. Live loads on a roof are those produced (1) During maintenance by workers, equipment, and materials; and (2) during the life of the structure by movable objects such as planters and by people.

*4.2 Uniformly Distributed Loads

*4.2.1 Required Live Loads.
The live loads used in the design of buildings and other structures shall be the maximum loads expected by the intended use or occupancy but shall in no case be

less than the minimum uniformly distributed unit loads required by Table 4-1.

4.2.2 Provision for Partitions. In office buildings or other buildings, where partitions will be erected or rearranged, provision for partition weight shall be made, whether or not partitions are shown on the plans, unless the specified live load exceeds 80 lb/sq ft (3.83 kN/m²).

*4.3 Concentrated Loads

Floors and other similar surfaces shall be designed to support safely the uniformly distributed live loads prescribed in 4.2 or the concentrated load, in pounds (kN), given in Table 4-1, whichever produces the greater load effects. Unless otherwise specified, the indicated concentration shall be assumed to be uniformly distributed over an area 2.5 ft (762 mm) square [6.25 sq ft (0.58 m²)] and shall be located so as to produce the maximum load effects in the structural members.

Any single panel point of the lower chord of exposed roof trusses or any point along the primary structural members supporting roofs over manufacturing, commercial storage and warehousing, and commercial garage floors shall be capable of carrying safely a suspended concentrated load of not less than 2,000 lb (poundforce) (8.90 kN) in addition to dead load. For all other occupancies, a load of 200 lb (0.89 kN) shall be used instead of 2,000 lb (8.90 kN).

*4.4 Loads on Handrails, Guardrail Systems, Grab Bar Systems, and Vehicle Barrier Systems

4.4.1 Definitions

Handrail: a rail grasped by hand for guidance and support. A handrail assembly includes the handrail, supporting attachments, and structures.

Guardrail system: a system of building components near open sides of an elevated surface for the purpose of minimizing the possibility of a fall from the elevated surface by people, equipment, or material.

Grab bar system: a bar provided to support body weight in locations such as toilets, showers, and tub enclosures.

Vehicle barrier system: a system of building components near open sides of a garage floor or ramp, or building walls that act as restraints for vehicles.

*4.4.2 Loads

A. Handrail assemblies and guardrail systems shall be designed to resist a load of 50 lb/ft (pound-force per linear foot) (0.73 kN/m) applied in any direction at the top and to transfer this load through the supports to the structure. For one- and two-family dwellings, the minimum load shall be 20 lb/ft (0.29 kN/m).

Further, all handrail assemblies and guardrail systems shall be able to resist a single concentrated load of 200 lb (0.89 kN), applied in any direction at any point along the top, and have attachment devices and supporting structure to transfer this loading to appropriate structural elements of the building. This load need not be assumed to act concurrently with the loads specified in the preceding paragraph.

Intermediate rails (all those except the handrail), balusters, and panel fillers shall be designed to withstand a horizontally applied normal load of 50 lb (0.22 kN) on an area not to exceed 1 ft square (305 mm square) including openings and space between rails. Reactions due to this loading are not required to be superimposed with those of either preceding paragraph.

B. Grab bar systems shall be designed to resist a single concentrated load of 250 lb (1.11 kN) applied in any direction at any point.

C. Vehicle barrier systems for passenger cars shall be designed to resist a single load of 6,000 lb (26.70 kN) applied horizontally in any direction to the barrier system, and shall have anchorages or attachments capable of transferring this load to the structure. For design of the system the load shall be assumed to act at a minimum height of 1 ft 6 in. (460 mm) above the floor or ramp surface on an area not to exceed 1 ft square (305 mm square), and is not required to be assumed to act concurrently with any handrail or guardrail loadings specified in the preceding paragraphs of 4.4.2. Garages accommodating trucks and buses shall be designed in accordance with an approved method which contains provision for traffic railings.

4.5 Loads Not Specified

For occupancies or uses not designated in 4.2 or 4.3, the live load shall be determined in accordance with a method approved by the authority having jurisdiction.

*4.6 Partial Loading

The full intensity of the appropriately reduced live load applied only to a portion of a structure

TABLE 4-1
Minimum Uniformly Distributed Live Loads, L_o and Minimum Concentrated Live Loads

Occupancy or Use	Uniform psf (kN/m²)	Conc. lb. (kN)
Apartments (see residential)		
Access floor systems		
Office use	50 (2.4)	2,000 (8.9)
Computer use	100 (4.79)	2,000 (8.9)
Armories and drill rooms	150 (7.18)	
Assembly areas and theaters		
Fixed seats (fastened to floor)	60 (2.87)	
Lobbies	100 (4.79)	
Movable seats	100 (4.79)	
Platforms (assembly)	100 (4.79)	
Stage floors	150 (7.18)	
Balconies (exterior)	100 (4.79)	
On one- and two-family residences only, and not exceeding 100 sq ft (9.3 m²)	60 (2.87)	
Bowling alleys, poolrooms and similar recreational areas	75 (3.59)	
Corridors		
First floor	100 (4.79)	
Other floors, same as occupancy served except as indicated		
Dance halls and ballrooms	100 (4.79)	
Decks (patio and roof)		
Same as area served, or for the type of occupancy accommodated		
Dining rooms and restaurants	100 (4.79)	
Dwellings (see residential)		
Elevator machine room grating (on area of 4 sq in) (2,580 mm²)		300 (1.33)
Finish light floor plate construction		
(on area of 1 sq in.) (645 mm²)		200 (0.89)
Fire escapes	100 (4.79)	
On single-family dwellings only	40 (1.92)	
Garages (passenger cars only)	50 (2.40)	Note 1
Trucks and buses	Note 2	
Grandstands (see stadium and arena bleachers)		
Gymnasiums, main floors and balconies	100 (4.79)[4]	
Handrails, guardrails and grab bars	See Section 4.4	
Hospitals		
Operating rooms, laboratories	60 (2.87)	1,000 (4.45)
Private rooms	40 (1.92)	1,000 (4.45)
Wards	40 (1.92)	1,000 (4.45)
Corridors above first floor	80 (3.83)	1,000 (4.45)
Hotels (see residential)		
Libraries		
Reading rooms	60 (2.87)	1,000 (4.45)
Stack rooms	150 (7.18)[3]	1,000 (4.45)
Corridors above first floor	80 (3.83)	1,000 (4.45)
Manufacturing		
Light	125 (6.00)	2,000 (8.90)
Heavy	250 (11.97)	3,000 (13.40)
Marquees and Canopies	75 (3.59)	
Office Buildings		
File and computer rooms shall be designed for heavier loads based on anticipated occupancy		
Lobbies and first floor corridors	100 (4.79)	2,000 (8.90)
Offices	50 (2.40)	2,000 (8.90)
Corridors above first floor	80 (3.83)	2,000 (8.90)
Penal Institutions		
Cell blocks	40 (1.92)	
Corridors	100 (4.79)	
Residential		
Dwellings (one- and two-family)		
Uninhabitable attics without storage	10 (0.48)	
Uninhabitable attics with storage	20 (0.96)	
Habitable attics and sleeping areas	30 (1.44)	
All other areas except balconies	40 (1.92)	
Hotels and multifamily houses		
Private rooms and corridors serving them	40 (1.92)	
Public rooms and corridors serving them	100 (4.79)	

TABLE 4-1 *(continued)*
Minimum Uniformly Distributed Live Loads, L_o and Minimum Concentrated Live Loads

Occupancy or Use	Uniform psf (kN/m²)	Conc. lbs. (kN)
Reviewing stands, grandstands and bleachers	100 (4.79)[4]	
Roofs	See Sections 4.3 and 4.9	
Schools		
Classrooms	40 (1.92)	1,000 (4.45)
Corridors above first floor	80 (3.83)	1,000 (4.45)
First floor corridors	100 (4.79)	1,000 (4.45)
Scuttles, skylight ribs, and accessible ceilings		200 (9.58)
Sidewalks, vehicular driveways, and yards, subject to trucking	250 (11.97)[5]	8,000 (35.60)[6]
Stadiums and Arenas		
Bleachers	100 (4.79)[4]	
Fixed Seats (fastened to floor)	60 (2.87)[4]	
Stairs and exitways	100 (4.79)	Note 7
Storage areas above ceilings	20 (0.96)	
Storage warehouses (shall be designed for heavier loads if required for anticipated storage)		
Light	125 (6.00)	
Heavy	250 (11.97)	
Stores		
Retail		
First floor	100 (4.79)	1,000 (4.45)
Upper floors	75 (3.59)	1,000 (4.45)
Wholesale, all floors	125 (6.00)	1,000 (4.45)
Vehicle barriers	See Section 4.4	
Walkways and elevated platforms (other than exitways)	60 (2.87)	
Yards and terraces, pedestrians	100 (4.79)	

[1]Floors in garages or portions of building used for the storage of motor vehicles shall be designed for the uniformly distributed live loads of Table 4-1 or the following concentrated load: (1) for passenger cars accommodating not more than nine passengers, 2,000 lb (8.90 kN) acting on an area of 20 sq in. (12,900 mm²); and (2) mechanical parking structures without slab or deck, passenger car only, 1,500 lb (6.70 kN) per wheel.

[2]Garages accommodating trucks and buses shall be designed in accordance with an approved method which contains provisions for truck and bus loadings.

[3]The weight of books and shelving shall be computed using an assumed density of 65 lb/cu ft (pounds per cubic foot, sometimes abbreviated pcf) (10.21 kN/m³) and converted to a uniformly distributed load; this load shall be used if it exceeds 150 lb/sq ft (7.18 kN/m²).

[4]In addition to the vertical live loads, horizontal swaying forces parallel and normal to the length of seats shall be included in the design according to the requirements of ANSI/NFPA 102.

[5]Other uniform loads in accordance with an approved method which contains provisions for truck loadings shall also be considered where appropriate.

[6]The concentrated wheel load shall be applied on an area of 20 sq in. (12,900 mm²).

[7]Minimum concentrated load on stair treads [on area of 4 sq. in. (2,580 mm²)] is 300 lb (1.33 kN).

or member shall be considered accounted for if it produces a more unfavorable effect than the same intensity applied over the full structure or member.

*4.7 Impact Loads

The live loads specified in 4.2.1 and 4.4.2 shall be assumed to include adequate allowance for ordinary impact conditions. Provision shall be made in the structural design for uses and loads that involve unusual vibration and impact forces.

4.7.1 Elevators. All elevator loads shall be increased by 100% for impact and the structural supports shall be designed within the limits of deflection prescribed by ANSI/ASME A17.1 and ANSI/ASME A17.2.

4.7.2 Machinery. For the purpose of design, the weight of machinery and moving loads shall be increased as follows to allow for impact: (1) elevator machinery, 100%; (2) light machinery, shaft- or motor-driven, 20%; (3) reciprocating machinery or power-driven units, 50%; and (4) hangers for floors or balconies, 33%. All percentages shall be increased where specified by the manufacturer.

*4.8 Reduction in Live Loads

*4.8.1 Permissible Reduction. Unless the limitations of 4.8.2 are met, members having an influence area of 400 ft² (37.16 m²) or more shall not

7

be designed for a reduced live load determined by applying the following equation:

$$L = L_o \left(0.25 + \frac{15}{\sqrt{A_I}} \right) \qquad \text{(Eq. 4-1)}$$

$$\left[\text{in SI: } L = L_o \left(0.25 + \frac{4.57}{\sqrt{A_I}} \right) \right]$$

where L = reduced design live load per square foot of area (per square meter of area) supported by the member; L_o = unreduced design live load per square foot of area (per square meter of area) supported by the member (see Table 4-1); and A_I = influence area, in square feet (square meters). The influence area, A_I, in terms of tributary area shall be as follows: for other than cantilevered construction, the influence area is four times the tributary area for a column, two times the tributary area for a beam, and equal to the panel area for a two-way slab. For edge columns and beams, influence area is half that of the respective interior members, and for corner columns influence area is a quarter that of the respective interior members. For members supporting cantilevered construction, for a one-way slab and a precast T-beam, the influence is the same as the tributary area.

The reduced design live load shall be not less than 50% of the unit live load L_o for members supporting one floor nor less than 40% of the unit live load L_o for members supporting two or more floors.

*4.8.2 Limitations on Live-Load Reduction. For live loads of 100 lb/sq ft (4.79 kN/m²) or less, no reduction shall be made for areas to be occupied as places of public assembly, for garages except as noted later, for one-way slabs, or for roofs except as specified in 4.11. For live loads that exceed 100 lb/sq ft (4.79 kN/m²) and in garages for passenger cars only, design live loads on members supporting two or more floors are not prohibited from being reduced 20%, but live loads in other cases shall not be reduced except as approved by the authority having jurisdiction.

*4.9 Minimum Roof Live Loads

*4.9.1 Flat, Pitched, and Curved Roofs. Ordinary flat, pitched, and curved roofs shall be designed for the live loads specified in Eq. (4-2) or other controlling combinations of loads as discussed in Section 2, whichever produces the greater load. In structures such as greenhouses, where special scaffolding is used as a work surface for workmen and materials during maintenance and repair operations, a lower roof load than specified in Eq. (4-2) shall not be used unless approved by the authority having jurisdiction.

$$L_r = 20 R_1 R_2 \quad \text{where } 12 \le L_r \le 20 \qquad \text{(Eq. 4-2)}$$
$$[\text{in SI: } L_r = 0.96 R_1 R_2 \quad \text{where } 0.58 \le L_r \le 0.96]$$

where L_r = roof live load per square foot of horizontal projection in pounds per square foot (kN/m²).

The reduction factors R_1 and R_2 shall be determined as follows:

$$R_1 = 1 \qquad \qquad \text{for } A_t \le 200 \text{ sq ft } (18.58 \text{ m}^2)$$
$$R_1 = 1.2 - 0.001 A_t \qquad \text{for } 200 \text{ sq ft} < A_t < 600 \text{ sq ft}$$
$$[\text{in SI: } \quad 1.2 - 0.01076 A_t \quad \text{for } 18.58 \text{ m}^2 < A_t < 55.74 \text{ m}^2]$$
$$R_1 = 0.6 \qquad \qquad \text{for } A_t \ge 600 \text{ sq ft } (55.74 \text{ m}^2)$$

where A_t = tributary area in square feet (square meters) supported by any structural member and

$$R_2 = 1 \qquad \qquad \text{for } F \le 4$$
$$R_2 = 1.2 - 0.05 F \qquad \text{for } 4 < F < 12$$
$$R_2 = 0.6 \qquad \qquad \text{for } F \ge 12$$

where, for a pitched roof, F = number of inches of rise per foot (in SI: $F = 0.12 \times$ slope, with slope expressed in percentage points) and, for an arch or dome, F = rise-to-span ratio multiplied by 32.

*4.9.2 Special-Purpose Roofs. Roofs used for promenade purposes shall be designed for a minimum live load of 60 lb/sq ft (2.87 kN/m²). Roofs used for roof gardens or assembly purposes shall be designed for a minimum live load of 100 lb/sq ft (4.79 kN/m²). Roofs used for other special purposes shall be designed for appropriate loads, as directed or approved by the authority having jurisdiction.

*4.10 Crane Loads

The crane live load shall be the rated capacity of the crane. Design loads for the runway beams, including connections and support brackets, of moving bridge cranes and monorail cranes shall include the maximum wheel loads of the crane and the vertical impact, lateral, and longitudinal forces induced by the moving crane.

4.10.1 Maximum Wheel Load. The maximum wheel loads shall be the wheel loads produced by the weight of the bridge, as applicable, plus the sum of the rated capacity and the weight of the trolley with the trolley positioned on its runway at the location where the resulting load effect is maximum.

4.10.2 Vertical Impact Force. The maximum wheel loads of the crane shall be increased by the percentages shown below to determine the induced vertical impact or vibration force:

Monorail cranes (powered) 25
Cab-operated or remotely operated bridge
 cranes (powered) 25
Pendant-operated bridge cranes (powered) . . . 10
Bridge cranes or monorail cranes with
 hand-geared bridge, trolley and hoist 0

4.10.3 Lateral Force. The lateral force on crane runway beams with electrically powered trolleys shall be calculated as 20% of the sum of the rated capacity of the crane and the weight of the hoist and trolley. The lateral force shall be assumed to act horizontally at the traction surface of a runway beam, in either direction perpendicular to the beam, and shall be distributed with due regard to the lateral stiffness of the runway beam and supporting structure.

4.10.4 Longitudinal Force. The longitudinal force on crane runway beams, except for bridge cranes with hand-geared bridges, shall be calculated as 10% of the maximum wheel loads of the crane. The longitudinal force shall be assumed to act horizontally at the traction surface of a runway beam, in either direction parallel to the beam.

4.11 References

[1] American National Standard Practice for the Inspection of Elevators, Escalators, and Moving Walks (Inspectors' Manual), ANSI A17.2-1988.

[2] American National Standard Safety Code for Elevators and Escalators, ANSI/ASME A17.1-1993.

[3] American National Standard for Assembly Seating, Tents, and Air-Supported Structures, ANSI/NFPA 102-1992.

5. Soil and Hydrostatic Pressure and Flood Loads

*5.1 Pressure on Basement Walls

In the design of basement walls and similar approximately vertical structures below grade, provision shall be made for the lateral pressure of adjacent soil. Due allowance shall be made for possible surcharge from fixed or moving loads. When a portion or the whole of the adjacent soil is below a free-water surface, computations shall be based on the weight of the soil diminished by buoyancy, plus full hydrostatic pressure.

Basement walls shall be designed to resist lateral soil loads. Soil loads specified in Table 5-1 shall be used as the minimum design lateral soil loads unless specified otherwise in a soil investigation report approved by the authority having jurisdiction. The lateral pressure from surcharge loads shall be added to the lateral earth pressure load. The lateral pressure shall be increased if soils with expansion potential are present at the site as determined by a geotechnical investigation.

*5.2 Uplift on Floors and Foundations

In the design of basement floors and similar approximately horizontal elements below grade, the upward pressure of water, where applicable, shall be taken as the full hydrostatic pressure applied over the entire area. The hydrostatic head shall be measured from the underside of the construction. Any other upward loads shall be included in the design.

Where expansive soils are present under foundations or slabs-on-ground, the foundations, slabs, and other components shall be designed to tolerate the movement or resist the upward pressures caused by the expansive soils, or the expansive soil shall be removed or stabilized around and beneath the structure.

*5.3 Flood Loads

The provisions of this section apply to buildings and other structures located in areas prone to flooding as defined on a flood hazard map.

5.3.1 Definitions. The following definitions apply to the provisions of Section 5.3.

Base Flood: the flood having a 1% chance of being equalled or exceeded in any given year.

Base Flood Elevation: the elevation of flooding, including wave height, having a 1% chance of being equalled or exceeded in any given year.

Area of Special Flood Hazard: the land in the flood plain within a community subject to a one percent or greater chance of flooding in any given year. These areas are designated as either special flood hazard areas (*A* Zones) or coastal high hazard areas (*V* Zones) on a Flood Hazard Map. Special flood hazard areas include areas subject to mudflows, flood-related erosion and alluvial fan flooding.

TABLE 5-1
Design Lateral Soil Load

Description of Backfill Material	Unified Soil Classification	Design Lateral Soil Load[a] psf per foot of depth (kN/m² per meter of depth)
Well-graded, clean gravels; gravel-sand mixes	GW	35 (5.50)[c]
Poorly graded clean gravels; gravel-sand mixes	GP	35 (5.50)[c]
Silty gravels, poorly graded gravel-sand mixes	GM	35 (5.50)[c]
Clayey gravels, poorly graded gravel-and-clay mixes	GC	45 (7.07)[c]
Well-graded, clean sands: gravelly sand mixes	SW	35 (5.50)[c]
Poorly graded clean sands: sand-gravel mixes	SP	35 (5.50)[c]
Silty sands, poorly graded sand-silt mixes	SM	45 (7.07)[c]
Sand-silt clay mix with plastic fines	SM-SC	85 (13.36)[d]
Clayey sands, poorly graded sand-clay mixes	SC	85 (13.36)[d]
Inorganic silts and clayey silts	ML	85 (13.36)[d]
Mixture of inorganic silt and clay	ML-CL	85 (13.36)[d]
Inorganic clays of low to medium plasticity	CL	100 (15.72)
Organic silts and silt clays, low plasticity	OL	—[b]
Inorganic clayey silts, elastic silts	MH	—[b]
Inorganic clays of high plasticity	CH	—[b]
Organic clays and silty clays	OH	—[b]

[a]Design lateral soil loads are given for moist conditions for the specified soils at their optimum densities. Actual field conditions shall govern. Submerged or saturated soil pressures shall include the weight of the buoyant soil plus the hydrostatic loads.

[b]Unsuitable as backfill material.

[c]For relatively rigid walls, as when braced by floors, the design lateral soil load shall be increased for sand and gravel type soils to 60 psf per foot (9.43 kN/m² per meter) of depth. Basement walls extending not more than 8 feet (2.44 m) below grade and supporting light floor systems are not considered as being relatively rigid walls.

[d]For relatively rigid walls, as when braced by floors, the design lateral load shall be increased for silt and clay type soils to 100 psf per foot (15.72 kN/m² per meter) of depth. Basement walls extending not more than 8 feet (2.44 m) below grade and supporting light floor systems are not considered as being relatively rigid walls.

Special Flood Hazard Areas (A Zone): Areas which have been determined as prone to flooding but not subject to wave heights of more than 3 ft (0.91 m) or high velocity wave action are designated as *A* Zones on the flood hazard map.

Coastal High Hazard Areas (V Zone): Coastal areas which have been determined as prone to flooding and subject to wave heights in excess of 3 ft (0.91 m) or subject to high-velocity wave action from storms or seismic sources are designated as *V* Zones on the flood hazard map.

Flood Hazard Map: an official map approved by an authority having jurisdiction where the boundaries of the flood, mudslide and related erosion areas having special hazards have been designated as various zones as determined by a detailed study.

5.3.2 Design Requirements

5.3.2.1 Design Loads. Structural systems of buildings or other structures shall be designed, constructed, connected and anchored to resist floatation, collapse and permanent lateral movement due to action of wind loads and loads from flooding associated with the base flood including hydrostatic, hydrodynamic, and impact loads (see Section 2).

5.3.2.2 Breakaway Walls. When walls and partitions located below the base flood elevation in a coastal high-hazard zone are required to break away such walls and their connections to the structure shall be designed for not less than 10 psf (0.48 kN/m²) nor more than 20 psf (0.96 kN/m²), except if the design wind load is greater, on the vertical projected area. Breakaway walls which exceed a design loading resistance of 20 psf (0.96 kN/m²) shall not be used unless the design meets the following conditions:

1. Breakaway wall collapse shall result from a water load less than that which occurs during the base flood; and
2. The elevated portion of the building and supporting foundation system shall resist collapse, displacement, and other structural damage due to the effects of wind and water loads acting simultaneously on all building components (structural and non-structural).

5.3.3 Loads During Flooding

5.3.3.1 Load Basis. In areas of special flood hazard the structural design shall be based on the 100-year flood.

5.3.3.2 Hydrostatic Loads. Hydrostatic loads caused by a depth of water to the level of the base flood elevation shall be applied over all surfaces involved, both above and below ground level, except that for surfaces exposed to free water, the design depth shall be increased by 1 ft (0.30 m).

Reduced uplift and lateral loads on surfaces of enclosed spaces below the base flood elevation shall apply only if provision is made for entry and exit of floodwater (see Section 5.3.4.4).

5.3.3.3 Hydrodynamic Loads. Where water velocities do not exceed 10 ft/sec (3.05 m/s), dynamic effects of the moving water shall be converted into equivalent hydrostatic loads by increasing the base flood elevation for design purposes by an equivalent surcharge depth, d_h, on the headwater side and above the ground level only, equal to:

$$d_n = \frac{aV^2}{2g}$$ (Eq. 5-1)

Where

V = average velocity of water in feet per second (meters per second)

g = acceleration due to gravity, 32.2 ft/sec/sec (9.81 m/s²)

a = coefficient of drag or shape factor (not less than 1.25).

The equivalent surcharge depth shall be added to the base flood elevation design depth and the resultant hydrostatic pressures applied to, and uniformly distributed across, the vertical projected area of the building or structure which is perpendicular to the flow. Surfaces parallel to the flow or surfaces wetted by the tailwater shall be considered subject to the hydrostatic pressures for depths to the base flood elevation only.

In coastal high hazard zones the hydrodynamic loads of both water velocity and waves shall be accounted for. Wave runup on walls below the base flood elevation shall be accounted for in the design. In riverine flood plains and coastal flood plains outside the *V* Zone the magnitude and application of hydrodynamic loads shall be determined by a detailed analysis utilizing basic concepts of fluid mechanics. In coastal flood plains landward of the *V* Zone waves are less than 3 ft high (0.91 m).

Wave loads are those loads which result from water waves propagating over the water surface and striking a building or other structure. Design and construction of buildings and other structures

subject to wave loads shall account for the following loads: waves breaking on any portion of the building or structure; uplift forces caused by shoaling waves beneath a building or structure, or portion thereof; wave runup striking any portion of the building or structure; wave-induced drag and inertia forces; wave-induced scour at the base of a building or structure, or its foundation. Wave loads shall be included for both *V* and *A* Zones.

5.3.3.4 Impact Loads. Impact loads are those which result from debris, ice and any object transported by floodwaters striking against buildings and structures or parts thereof.

Minimum impact load is a concentrated load acting horizontally at the most critical location at or below the base flood elevation produced by a 1,000 lb (4.5 kN) object travelling at the velocity of the floodwater and acting on a 1 sq ft (0.09 m²) surface of the structure. It shall be assumed that the velocity of the object is reduced to zero in 1 sec.

5.3.4 Special Flood Hazard Areas—A Zones. The following aspects of *A* Zone design and construction shall be accounted for in the design: elevation above the base flood elevation, anchorage, floodproofing, enclosures below the base flood elevation, and scour.

5.3.4.1 Elevation. Buildings or structures within a special flood hazard area shall be elevated so that the lowest habitable floor, including basement, is located at or above the base flood elevation.

Exception: Nonresidential buildings floodproofed in accordance with Section 5.3.4.3 or 5.3.4.4.

All structural components subject to hydrostatic and hydrodynamic loads and impact loads from water-borne objects during the occurrence of flooding to the base flood elevation shall be capable of resisting such forces, including the effect of buoyancy.

5.3.4.2 Anchorage. The structural systems of buildings or other structures shall be designed, connected and anchored to prevent floatation, collapse and permanent lateral movement resulting from wind loads, impact loads, hydrodynamic loads and hydrostatic loads, including the effects of buoyancy, from flooding equal to the base flood elevation.

5.3.4.3 Nonresidential Flood-resistant Construction. As an alternative to meeting the elevation provision of Section 5.3.4.1, nonresidential buildings or other structures located in non-coastal high hazard areas shall be floodproofed so that the structure is watertight. Walls and floors below an elevation one foot (0.30 m) above the base flood elevation shall be substantially impermeable to the passage of water. Openings below the base flood elevation shall be provided with watertight closures and shall have adequate structural capacity to resist all applicable loads.

5.3.4.4 Enclosures below Base Flood Elevation. Enclosed spaces below the base flood elevation shall not be used for any purpose other than parking of vehicles, building access or storage. Enclosed spaces which do not meet the requirements of Section 5.3.4.3 shall be provided with vents, valves, or other openings which will automatically equalize the hydrostatic forces on exterior and interior walls by allowing for the entry and exit of flood waters.

To provide for equalization of hydrostatic forces a minimum of two openings having a total net area of not less than one square inch for every square foot (0.007 m² for every square meter) of enclosed area subject to flooding shall be provided. The bottom of all openings shall not be higher than 12 in. (0.30 m) above grade. Openings shall not be equipped with screens, louvers, valves, or other coverings or devices unless they permit the automatic entry and exit of floodwaters.

5.3.4.5 Scour. The effects of scour shall be included in the design of the foundations of buildings or other structures in special flood hazard areas—*A* Zones.

Foundation embedment shall be below the depth of potential scour.

*5.3.5 Coastal High Hazard Areas—V Zones. Loadings in *V* Zones are more severe than loadings in *A* Zones, and the design shall take into account the following: elevation above the base flood elevation, foundation type, obstructions below the base flood elevation, and the effects of erosion and scour.

*5.3.5.1 Elevation. Buildings or structures erected within a coastal high hazard area shall be elevated so that the lowest portion of the lowest horizontal structural members supporting the lowest floor with the exception of footings, mat or raft foundations, piles, pile caps, columns, grade beams, and bracing shall be located at or above the base flood elevation.

Buildings or structures erected in coastal high hazard areas shall be supported on piles or columns. The piles or columns and their foundation and structure attached thereto shall be anchored to resist floatation, collapse and permanent lateral

movement due to the effects of wind, water, and impact loads acting simultaneously on all building components.

All structural components subject to wind loads, hydrostatic and hydrodynamic loads and impact loads from water-borne objects during the occurrence of flooding to the base flood elevation shall be capable of resisting such forces, including the effects of buoyancy.

5.3.5.2 Space below Base Flood Elevation. Spaces below the base flood elevation shall be free of obstruction.

Exceptions:

1. Footings, mat or raft foundations, piles, pile caps, columns, grade beams, and bracing that provide structural support for the building.
2. Structural systems of entrances and required exits.
3. Incidental storage of portable or mobile items that are readily moveable in the event of a storm.
4. Walls or partitions shall not be used to enclose all or part of the space, unless they are not part of the structural support of the building and are designed to breakaway or collapse without causing collapse, displacement or other damage to the structural system of the building in accordance with Section 5.3.2.2. Insect screening, open wood lattice, and similar screening, which allow the passage of water, shall not be used unless these systems comply with Section 5.3.2.2.

*5.3.5.3 Erosion and Scour. The effects of long-term erosion, storm-induced erosion and local scour shall be included in the design of foundations of buildings or other structures in coastal high-hazard areas. Foundation embedment shall be below the depth of potential scour.

6. Wind Loads

6.1 General

Provisions for the determination of wind loads on buildings and other structures are described in the following subsections. These provisions apply to the calculation of wind loads for main wind-force resisting systems and for individual structural components and cladding of buildings and other structures. Specific requirements are given for using wind-tunnel investigations to determine wind loading and structural response for buildings or other structures having irregular geometric shapes, response characteristics, or site locations with shielding or channeling effects that warrant specific investigation, or to establish more accurate wind loading.

6.2 Definitions

The following definitions apply only to the provisions of Section 6:

*Basic wind speed, V: 3-second gust speed at 33 ft (10 m) above the ground in Exposure C (see 6.5.3.1) and associated with an annual probability of 0.02 of being equaled or exceeded (50-year mean recurrence interval).

Building, enclosed: a building that does not comply with the requirements for open or partially enclosed buildings.

Building, open: a structure having all walls at least 80% open.

Building, partially enclosed: a building that complies with both of the following conditions:

1. the total area of openings in a wall that receives positive external pressure exceeds the sum of the areas of openings in the balance of the building envelope (walls and roof) by more than 10%; and
2. the total area of openings in a wall that receives positive external pressure exceeds 4 sq ft (0.37 m^2) or 1% of the area of that wall, whichever is smaller, and the percentage of openings in the balance of the building envelope does not exceed 20%

These conditions are expressed by the following equations:

1. $A_o > 1.10A_{oi}$
2. $A_o > 4$ sq ft (0.37 m^2) or $> 0.01A_g$, whichever is smaller, and $A_{oi}/A_{gi} \leq 0.20$ where:

   A_o = the total area of openings in a wall that receives positive external pressure, in sq ft (m^2);
   A_g = the gross area of that wall in which A_o is identified, in sq ft (m^2);
   A_{oi} = the sum of the areas of openings in the building envelope (walls and roof) not including A_o, in sq ft (m^2);
   A_{gi} = the sum of the gross surface areas of the building envelope (walls and roof) not including A_g, in sq ft (m^2).

Building, low-rise: enclosed or partially enclosed buildings which comply with the following conditions:

1. mean roof height h less than or equal to 60 ft (18 m);
2. mean roof height h does not exceed least horizontal dimension.

*Components and cladding: elements that do not qualify as part of the main wind-force resisting system.

Design force, F: equivalent static force to be used in the determination of wind loads for open buildings and other structures.

Design pressure, p: equivalent static pressure to be used in the determination of wind loads for buildings. The pressure is denoted as:

p_z = pressure that varies with height in accordance with the velocity pressure q_z evaluated at height z, or
p_h = pressure that is uniform with respect to height as determined by the velocity pressure q_h evaluated at mean roof height h.

*Effective wind area: the area used to determine GC_p. For components and cladding panels, the effective wind area in Figs. 6-5 through 6-8 is the span length multiplied by an effective width that need not be less than one-third the span length. For cladding fasteners, the effective wind area shall not be greater than the area that is tributary to an individual fastener.

*Flexible buildings and other structures: Slender buildings and other structures that have a fundamental natural frequency less than 1 Hz. Included are buildings and other structures that have a height h exceeding four times the least horizontal dimension.

*Importance factor, I: a factor that accounts for the degree of hazard to human life and damage to property.

*Main wind-force resisting system: an assemblage of structural elements assigned to provide support and stability for the overall structure. The system generally receives wind loading from more than one surface.

Recognized literature: published research findings and technical papers that are approved by the authority having jurisdiction.

6.3 Symbols and Notation

The following symbols and notation apply only to the provisions of Section 6:

A = effective wind area, in square feet (sq meters).

a = width of pressure coefficient zone, in feet (meters).

A_f = area of open buildings and other structures either normal to the surface or projected on a plane normal to the wind direction, in square feet (sq meters).

B = horizontal dimension of a building measured normal to wind direction, in feet (meters).

C_f = force coefficient to be used in the determination of wind loads for other structures.

C_p = external pressure coefficient to be used in the determination of wind loads for buildings.

D = diameter of a circular structure or member, in feet (meters).

D' = depth of protruding elements such as ribs and spoilers, in feet (meters).

G = gust effect factor.

G_f = gust effect factor for main wind-force resisting systems of flexible buildings and other structures.

GC_p = product of external pressure coefficient and gust effect factor to be used in the determination of wind loads for buildings.

GC_{pf} = product of the equivalent external pressure coefficient and gust effect factor to be used in the determination of wind loads for main wind-force resisting system of low-rise buildings.

GC_{pi} = product of internal pressure coefficient and gust effect factor to be used in the determination of wind loads for buildings.

H = height of hill or escarpment in Fig. 6-2, in feet (meters).

h = mean roof height of a building or height of other structure, except that eave height shall be used for roof angle θ of less than or equal to 10°, in feet (meters).

I = importance factor.

K_1, K_2, K_3 = multipliers in Fig. 6-2 to obtain K_{zt}.

K_h = velocity pressure exposure coefficient evaluated at height $z = h$.

K_z = velocity pressure exposure coefficient evaluated at height z.

K_{zt} = topographic factor.

L = horizontal dimension of a building measured parallel to the wind direction, in feet (meters).

L_h = distance upwind of crest of hill or escarpment in Fig. 6-2 to where the difference in ground elevation is half the height of hill or escarpment, in feet (meters).

M = larger dimension of sign, in feet (meters).

N = smaller dimension of sign, in feet (meters).

p = design pressure to be used in the determination of wind loads for buildings, in pounds per square foot (N/m^2).

p_h = design pressure evaluated at height $z = h$, in pounds per square foot (N/m^2).

p_L = wind pressure acting on leeward face in Fig. 6-9.

p_W = wind pressure acting on windward face in Fig. 6-9.

p_z = design pressure evaluated at height z above ground, in pounds per square foot (N/m^2).

q = velocity pressure, in pounds per square foot (N/m^2).

q_h = velocity pressure evaluated at height $z = h$, in pounds per square foot (N/m^2).

q_z = velocity pressure evaluated at height z above ground, in pounds per square foot (N/m^2).

r = rise-to-span ratio for arched roofs.

$*V$ = basic wind speed obtained from Fig. 6-1, in miles per hour (meters per second). The basic wind speed corresponds to a 3-sec. gust speed at 33 ft (10 m) above ground in exposure category C and is associated with an annual probability of 0.02 of being equaled or exceeded (50-year mean recurrence interval).

W = width of building in Figs. 6-5C and 6-7A and width of span in Figs. 6-6 and 6-7B, in feet (meters).

X = distance to center of pressure from windward edge in Table 6-6, in feet (meters).

x = distance upwind or downwind of crest in Fig. 6-2, in feet (meters).

z = height above ground level, in feet (meters).

ϵ = ratio of solid area to gross area for open sign, face of a trussed tower, or lattice structure.

θ = angle of plane of roof from horizontal, in degrees.

ν = height-to-width ratio for solid sign.

6.4 Calculation of Wind Loads
6.4.1 General
6.4.1.1 Allowed procedures. The design wind loads for buildings and other structures as a whole or for individual components and cladding thereof shall be determined using one of the following procedures: (1) Analytical procedure in accordance with 6.4.2; or (2) wind-tunnel procedure in accordance with 6.4.3.

6.4.1.2 Minimum design wind loading. The wind load used in the design of the main wind-force resisting system shall be not less than 10 lb/sq ft (0.48 kN/m²) multiplied by the area of the building or structure projected on a vertical plane normal to the wind direction. In the calculation of design wind loads for components and cladding for buildings, the algebraic sum of the pressures acting on opposite faces shall be taken into account. The design pressure for components and cladding of buildings shall be not less than 10 lb/sq ft (0.48 kN/m²) acting in either direction normal to the surface. The design force for open buildings and other structures shall be not less than 10 lb/sq ft (0.48 kN/m²) multiplied by the area A_f.

6.4.2 Analytical Procedure. Design wind pressures and design wind forces shall be determined in accordance with the appropriate equations given in Table 6-1 using the following procedure:

1. A velocity pressure q (q_z or q_h) is determined in accordance with the provisions of 6.5.
2. A gust effect factor G is determined in accordance with the provisions of 6.6.
3. Appropriate pressure or force coefficients are selected from the provisions of 6.7.

The equations given in Table 6-1 are for determination of: (1) Wind loading on main wind-force resisting systems; and (2) wind loading on individual components and cladding.

6.4.2.1 Limitations of analytical procedure. The provisions of 6.4.2 take into consideration the load magnification effect caused by gusts in resonance with along-wind vibrations of flexible buildings and other structures but do not include allowances for across-wind loading, vortex shedding, or

instability due to galloping or flutter. The designer shall refer to recognized literature for documentation pertaining to wind load effects, or use the wind-tunnel procedure of 6.4.3, for site locations for which channeling effects or buffeting in the wake of upwind obstructions warrant special consideration, or for those buildings and other structures having unusual geometric shapes or response characteristics.

6.4.2.2 Air-permeable cladding. Design pressures determined from Section 6.4.2 shall be used, unless approved test data or recognized literature demonstrate lower loads for the type of air-permeable cladding being considered.

6.4.2.3 Application of pressures and forces. Design pressures, p, shall be assumed to act in a direction normal to the surface considered. Design forces, F, shall be assumed to act on the gross structure or components and cladding in accordance with Tables 6-6 through 6-10 and shall be considered to vary with respect to height in accordance with the velocity pressure q_z.

6.4.3 Wind-Tunnel Procedure. Wind-tunnel tests or similar tests employing fluids other than air shall be used for the determination of design wind loads in accordance with 6.4.3.1.

6.4.3.1 Test conditions. Tests for the determination of mean and fluctuating forces and pressures shall be considered to be properly conducted only if all of the following conditions are satisfied:

1. the natural atmospheric boundary layer has been modeled to account for the variation of wind speed with height;
2. the relevant macro (integral) length and micro length scales of the longitudinal component of atmospheric turbulence are modeled to approximately the same scale as that used to model the building or other structure;
3. the modeled building or other structure and surrounding structures and topography are geometrically similar to their full-scale counterparts;
4. the projected area of the modeled building or other structure and surroundings is less than 8% of the test section cross-sectional area unless correction is made for blockage;
5. the longitudinal pressure gradient in the wind tunnel test section is accounted for;
6. Reynolds number effects on pressures and forces are minimized; and
7. response characteristics of the wind tunnel instrumentation are consistent with the required measurements.

TABLE 6-1
Design Wind Pressure, p (psf) (N/m^2), and Forces, F (lb) (N)

Design wind loading	Low-rise buildings	Buildings of all heights	Open buildings and other structures
Main wind-force resisting systems	$p = q_h[(GC_{pf}) - (GC_{pi})]^{*\#\S}$ q_h: at mean roof height using *Exposure C for all terrain* GC_{pf}: given in Fig. 6-4 GC_{pi}: given in Table 6-4	$p = qGC_p - q_h(GC_{pi})^{*\#}$ q: q_z for windward wall at height z *above ground* q_h for leeward wall, side walls and roof at mean roof height G: given in 6.6.1 C_p: given in Fig. 6-3 GC_{pi}: given in Table 6-4	$F = q_z GC_f A_f$ q_z: at height z above ground G: given in 6.6.1 C_f: given in Tables 6-6 through 6-10 A_f: projected area normal to wind†

Buildings and Low-Rise Buildings

Components and cladding‡	h ≤ 60 ft (18 m)	h > 60 ft (18 m)	
	$p = q_h[(GC_p) - (GC_{pi})]^*$ q_h: at mean roof height using Exposure C for all terrain GC_p: given in Figs. 6-5, 6-6 and 6-7 GC_{pi}: given in Table 6-4	$p = q[(GC_p) - (GC_{pi})]^{*\S\S}$ q: q_z for positive pressure at height z above ground q_h for negative pressure at mean roof height GC_p: given in Fig. 6-8 GC_{pi}: given in Table 6-4	$F = q_z GC_f A_f$ q_z: at height z above ground G: given in 6.6.1 C_f: given in Tables 6-6 through 6-10 A_f: projected area normal to wind†

Flexible Buildings and Other Structures (f < 1 Hz. Includes buildings and structures with height/least horizontal dimension > 4)

	Buildings		Other Structures
Main wind-force resisting systems	$p = qG_f C_p^{*\#}$ q: q_z for windward wall at height z above ground q_h for leeward wall at mean roof height G_f: obtained by rational analysis C_p: given in Fig. 6-3		$F = q_z G_f C_f A_f$ q_z: at height z above ground G_f: obtained by rational analysis C_f: given in Tables 6-6 through 6-10 A_f: projected area normal to wind†
Components and cladding‡	$p = q[(GC_p) - (GC_{pi})]^*$ q: q_z for positive pressure at height z above ground q_h for negative pressure at mean roof height GC_p: given in Fig. 6-8 GC_{pi}: given in Table 6-4		$F = q_z GC_f A_f$ q_z: at height z above ground G: given in 6.6.1 C_f: given in Tables 6-6 through 6-10 A_f: projected area normal to wind†

*Positive pressure acts toward surface and negative pressure acts away from surface; values of external and internal pressures shall be combined algebraically to determine most critical load.

#Pressure shall be applied simultaneously on windward and leeward walls and on roof surfaces as shown in Figs. 6-3 and 6-4.

†A_f is the projected area normal to the wind except where C_f is given for the surface area.

‡Major structural components supporting tributary areas greater than 700 sq ft (65 m²) shall be permitted to be designed using the provisions for main wind-force resisting systems.

§Low-rise buildings shall be permitted to be designed in accordance with the provisions for buildings in 6.5.3.2.2.

§§In the design of components and cladding for buildings having a mean roof height h, 60 ft (18 m) < h < 90 ft (27 m), GC_p values of Figs. 6-5, 6-6, and 6-7 shall be used only if the height-to-width ratio is 1 or less and q is taken as q_h and Exposure C (see 6.5.3.3.1) is used for all terrain.

6.4.3.2 Dynamic response. Tests for the purpose of determining the dynamic response of a building or other structure shall be in accordance with 6.4.3.1. The structural model and associated analysis shall account for mass distribution, stiffness, and damping.

6.5 Velocity Pressure

*6.5.1 Procedure for Calculating Velocity Pressure. The velocity pressure q_z shall be calculated from the formula.

$$q_z = 0.00256 K_z K_{zt} V^2 I \, (\text{lb/sq ft})$$
$$[\text{In SI: } q_z = 0.613 K_z K_{zt} V^2 I \, (\text{N/m}^2)] \qquad (\text{Eq. 6-1})$$

where the basic wind speed V is selected in accordance with the provisions of 6.5.2, the importance factor I is set forth in Table 6-2, and the velocity pressure exposure coefficient K_z is given in Table 6-3 in accordance with the provisions of 6.5.3. Provisions of 6.5.5 shall be used to determine K_{zt} where applicable, but K_{zt} shall not be less than 1.0. The numerical coefficient 0.00256 (or 0.613 in SI) shall be used except where sufficient climatic data are available to justify the selection of a different value of this factor for a specific design application.

*6.5.2 Selection of Basic Wind Speed. The basic wind speed V used in the determination of design wind loads on buildings and other structures shall be as given in Fig. 6-1 except as provided in 6.5.2.1 and 6.5.2.2.

*6.5.2.1 Special wind regions. The basic wind speed shall be increased where records or experience indicate that the wind speeds are higher than those reflected in Fig. 6-1. Mountainous terrain, gorges and special regions shown in Fig. 6-1 shall be examined for unusual wind conditions. The authority having jurisdiction shall, if necessary, adjust the values given in Fig. 6-1 to account for higher local wind speeds. Such ad-

TABLE 6-2
Importance Factor, *I* (Wind Loads)

Category	I
I	0.87
II	1.00
III	1.15
IV	1.15

NOTE:
1. The building and structure classification categories are listed in Table 1-1.

TABLE 6-3
Velocity Pressure Exposure Coefficients, K_h and K_z

Height above ground level, z					
ft	(m)	A	B	C	D
0-15	(0-4.6)	0.32	0.57	0.85	1.03
20	(6.1)	0.36	0.62	0.90	1.08
25	(7.6)	0.39	0.66	0.94	1.12
30	(9.1)	0.42	0.70	0.98	1.16
40	(12.2)	0.47	0.76	1.04	1.22
50	(15.2)	0.52	0.81	1.09	1.27
60	(18)	0.55	0.85	1.13	1.31
70	(21.3)	0.59	0.89	1.17	1.34
80	(24.4)	0.62	0.93	1.21	1.38
90	(27.4)	0.65	0.96	1.24	1.40
100	(30.5)	0.68	0.99	1.26	1.43
120	(36.6)	0.73	1.04	1.31	1.48
140	(42.7)	0.78	1.09	1.36	1.52
160	(48.8)	0.82	1.13	1.39	1.55
180	(54.9)	0.86	1.17	1.43	1.58
200	(61.0)	0.90	1.20	1.46	1.61
250	(76.2)	0.98	1.28	1.53	1.68
300	(91.4)	1.05	1.35	1.59	1.73
350	(106.7)	1.12	1.41	1.64	1.78
400	(121.9)	1.18	1.47	1.69	1.82
450	(137.2)	1.24	1.52	1.73	1.86
500	(152.4)	1.29	1.56	1.77	1.89

NOTES:
1. Linear interpolation for intermediate values of height z is acceptable.

2. For values of height z greater than 500 ft (152.4 m), K_z shall be calculated from Eq. (C3).

3. Exposure categories are defined in 6.5.3.

justment shall be based on meteorological information and an estimate of the basic wind speed obtained in accordance with the provisions of 6.5.2.2.

*6.5.2.2 Estimation of basic wind speeds from regional climatic data. Regional climatic data shall only be used in lieu of the basic wind speeds given in Fig. 6-1 when: (1) Approved extreme-value statistical-analysis procedures have been employed in reducing the data; (2) and the length of record, sampling errror, averaging time, anemometer height, data quality, and terrain exposure have been taken into account.

*6.5.2.3 Limitation. Tornadoes have not been considered in developing the basic wind-speed distributions.

*6.5.3 Exposure Categories

6.5.3.1 General. An exposure category that adequately reflects the characteristics of ground surface irregularities shall be determined for the site at which the building or structure is to be constructed. Account shall be taken of variations in ground surface roughness that arise from natural topography and vegetation as well as from

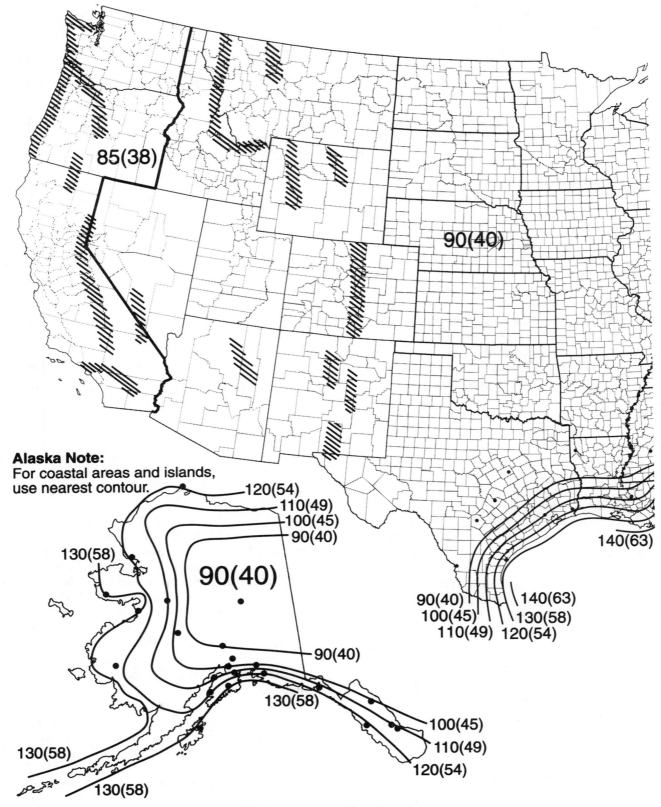

FIG. 6-1. Basic Wind Speed

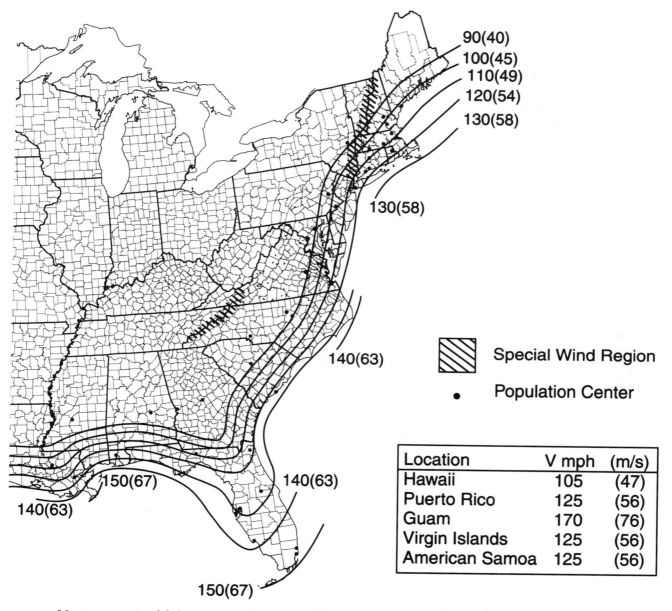

Location	V mph	(m/s)
Hawaii	105	(47)
Puerto Rico	125	(56)
Guam	170	(76)
Virgin Islands	125	(56)
American Samoa	125	(56)

Notes: 1. Values are 3-second gust speeds in miles per hour (m/s) at 33 ft (10m) above ground for Exposure C category and are associated with an annual probability of 0.02.

2. Linear interpolation between wind speed contours is permitted.

3. Islands and coastal areas shall use wind speed contour of coastal area.

4. Mountainous terrain, gorges, ocean promontories, and special wind regions shall be examined for unusual wind conditions.

K₁ MULTIPLIER

H/L_h	2-D Ridge	2-D Escarpment	3-D Axisym. Hill
0.10	0.14	0.09	0.11
0.15	0.22	0.13	0.16
0.20	0.29	0.17	0.21
0.25	0.36	0.21	0.26
0.30	0.43	0.26	0.32
0.35	0.51	0.30	0.37
0.40	0.58	0.34	0.42
0.45	0.65	0.38	0.47
0.50	0.72	0.43	0.53

K₂ MULTIPLIER

x/L_h	2-D escarpment Downwind of Crest	All Others Cases
0.00	1.00	1.00
0.50	0.88	0.67
1.00	0.75	0.33
1.50	0.63	0.00
2.00	0.50	0.00
2.50	0.38	0.00
3.00	0.25	0.00
3.50	0.13	0.00
4.00	0.00	0.00

K₃ MULTIPLIER

z/L_h	2-D Ridge	2-D Escarpment	3-D Axisym. Hill
0.00	1.00	1.00	1.00
0.10	0.74	0.78	0.67
0.20	0.55	0.61	0.45
0.30	0.41	0.47	0.30
0.40	0.30	0.37	0.20
0.50	0.22	0.29	0.14
0.60	0.17	0.22	0.09
0.70	0.12	0.17	0.06
0.80	0.09	0.14	0.04
0.90	0.07	0.11	0.03
1.00	0.05	0.08	0.02
1.50	0.01	0.02	0.00
2.00	0.00	0.00	0.00

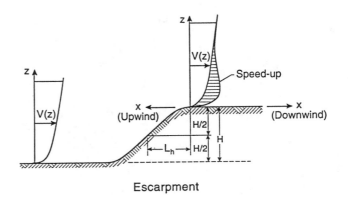

2-D Ridge or 3-D Axisymmetrical Hill

Escarpment

NOTES:
1. For values of H/L_h, x/L_h and z/L_h other than those shown, linear interpolation is permitted.
2. For $H/L_h > 0.5$, assume $H/L_h = 0.5$, and substitute $2H$ for L_h in x/L_h and z/L_h.
3. Multipliers are based on the assumption that wind approaches the hill or escarpment along the direction of maximum slope.
4. Effect of wind speed-up shall not be required to be accounted for when $H/L_h < 0.2$ or when $H < 15$ ft (4.5 m) for Exposure D, or < 30 ft (9 m) for Exposure C, or < 60 ft (18 m) for all other exposures.
5. Notation:
   H: Height of hill or escarpment relative to the upwind terrain, in feet (meters).
   L_h: Distance upwind of crest to where the difference in ground elevation is half the height of hill or escarpment, in feet (meters).
   K_1: Factor to account for shape of topographic feature and maximum speed-up effect.
   K_2: Factor to account for reduction in speed-up with distance upwind or downwind of crest.
   K_3: Factor to account for reduction in speed-up with height above local terrain.
   x: Distance (upwind or downwind) from the crest to the building site, in feet (meters).
   z: Height above local ground level, in feet (meters).

FIG. 6-2. Multipliers for Obtaining Topographic Factor K_{zt}

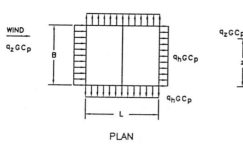

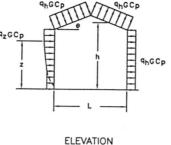

PLAN

ELEVATION

Wall Pressure Coefficients, C_p

Surface	L/B	C_p	Use With
Windward Wall	All values	0.8	q_z
Leeward wall	0-1	−0.5	
	2	−0.3	q_h
	≥4	−0.2	
Side walls	All values	−0.7	q_h

Roof Pressure Coefficients, C_p, for Use with q_h

Wind direction	h/L	Windward Angle, θ (degrees)								Leeward Angle, θ (degrees)		
		10	15	20	25	30	35	45	≥60#	10	15	≥ 20
Normal to ridge for θ ≥ 10°	≤0.25	−0.7 / 0.0*	−0.5 / 0.2	−0.3 / 0.3	−0.2 / 0.3	−0.2 / 0.4	0.0* / 0.5		0.01 θ	−0.3	−0.5	−0.6
	0.5	−0.9	−0.7	−0.4 / 0.0*	−0.3 / 0.2	−0.2 / 0.2	−0.2 / 0.3	0.0* / 0.4	0.01 θ	−0.5	−0.5	−0.6
	≥1.0	−1.3**	−1.0	−0.7	−0.5 / 0.0*	−0.3 / 0.2	−0.2 / 0.2	0.0* / 0.3	0.01 θ	−0.7	−0.6	−0.6

Wind direction	h/L	Horiz distance from windward edge		
Normal to ridge for θ < 10° and Parallel to ridge for all θ	≤ 0.5	0 to h/2	−0.9	
		h/2 to h	−0.9	
		h to 2h	−0.5	
		>2h	−0.3	
	≥ 1.0	0 to h/2	−1.3**	
		>h/2	−0.7	

*Value is provided for interpolation purposes.

**Value can be reduced linearly with area over which it is applicable as follows:

Area (sq ft)	Reduction Factor
≤ 100 (9.29 sq m)	1.0
250 (23.23 sq m)	0.9
≥1000 (92.9 sq m)	0.8

NOTES:
1. Plus and minus signs signify pressures acting toward and away from the surfaces, respectively.
2. Linear interpolation is permitted for values of L/B, h/L and θ other than shown. Interpolation shall only be carried out between values of the same sign. Where no value of the same sign is given, assume 0.0 for interpolation purposes.
3. Where two values of C_p are listed, this indicates that the windward roof slope is subjected to either positive or negative pressures and the roof structure shall be designed for both conditions. Interpolation for intermediate ratios of h/L in this case shall only be carried out between C_p values of like sign.
4. For monoslope roofs, entire roof surface is either a windward or leeward surface.
5. For flexible buildings use appropriate G_f as determined by rational analysis.
6. Refer to Table 6-5 for arched roofs.
7. Notation:
   B: Horizontal dimension of building, in feet (meter), measured normal to wind direction.
   L: Horizontal dimension of building, in feet (meter), measured parallel to wind direction.
   h: Mean roof height in feet (meters), except that eave height shall be used for θ ≤ 10 degrees.
   z: Height above ground, in feet (meters).
   G: Gust effect factor.
   q_z, q_h: Velocity pressure, in pounds per square foot (N/m²), evaluated at respective height.
   θ: Angle of plane of roof from horizontal, in degrees.

For roof slopes greater than 80°, use $C_p = 0.8$.

FIG. 6-3. External Pressure Coefficients, C_p, for Loads on Main Wind-Force Resisting Systems for Enclosed or Partially Enclosed Buildings of All Heights

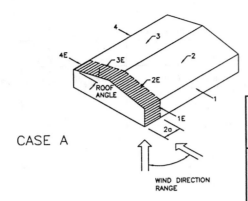

CASE A

WIND DIRECTION RANGE

CASE A

Roof Angle θ (degrees)	Building Surface							
	1	2	3	4	1E	2E	3E	4E
0-5	0.40	−0.69	−0.37	−0.29	0.61	−1.07	−0.53	−0.43
20	0.53	−0.69	−0.48	−0.43	0.80	−1.07	−0.69	−0.64
30-45	0.56	0.21	−0.43	−0.37	0.69	0.27	−0.53	−0.48
90	0.56	0.56	−0.37	−0.37	0.69	0.69	−0.48	−0.48

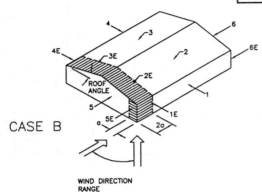

CASE B

WIND DIRECTION RANGE

CASE B

Roof Angle θ (degrees)	Building Surface											
	1	2	3	4	5	6	1E	2E	3E	4E	5E	6E
0-90	−0.45	−0.69	−0.37	−0.45	0.40	−0.29	−0.48	−1.07	−0.53	−0.48	0.61	−0.43

NOTES:
1. Case A and Case B are required as two separate loading conditions to generate the wind actions, including torsion, to be resisted by the main wind-force resisting system.
2. To obtain the critical wind actions, the building shall be rotated in 90° degree increments so that each corner in turn becomes the windward corner while the loading patterns in the sketches remain fixed. For the design of structural systems providing lateral resistance in the direction parallel to the ridge line, Load Case A shall be based on θ = 0°.
3. Plus and minus signs signify pressures acting toward and away from the surfaces, respectively.
4. For Case A loading the following restrictions apply:
   a. The roof pressure coefficient GC_{pf}, when negative in zone 2, shall be applied in zone 2 for a distance from the edge of roof equal to 0.5 times the horizontal dimension of the building measured perpendicular to the eave line or 2.5h, whichever is less; the remainder of zone 2 extending to the ridge line shall use the pressure coefficient GC_{pf} for zone 3.
   b. Except for moment-resisting frames, the total horizontal shear shall not be less than that determined by neglecting wind forces on roof surfaces.
5. Combinations of external and internal pressures (see Table 6-4) shall be evaluated as required to obtain the most severe loadings.
6. For buildings sited within Exposure B, calculated pressures shall be multiplied by 0.85.
7. For values of θ other than those shown, linear interpolation is permitted.
8. Notation:
   a: 10 percent of least horizontal dimension or 0.4h, whichever is smaller, but not less than either 4% of least horizontal dimension or 3 ft (1 m).
   h: Mean roof height, in feet (meters), except that eave height shall be used for θ ≤ 10°.
   θ: Angle of plane of roof from horizontal, in degrees.

FIG. 6-4. External Pressure Coefficients, GC_{pf}, for Loads on Main Wind-Forced Resisting Systems for Enclosed or Partially Enclosed Low-Rise Buildings with Mean Roof Height h Less than or Equal to 60 ft (18 m)

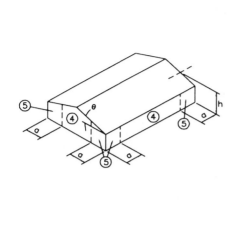

FIG. 6-5A Walls

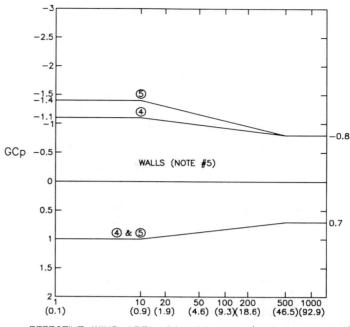

EFFECTIVE WIND AREA, SQUARE FEET (SQUARE METERS)

NOTES:
1. Vertical scale denotes GC_p to be used with q_h based on Exposure C.
2. Horizontal scale denotes effective wind area, in square feet (square meters).
3. Plus and minus signs signify pressures acting toward and away from the surfaces, respectively.
4. Each component shall be designed for maximum positive and negative pressures.
5. Values of GC_p for walls shall be reduced by 10% when $\theta \leq 10°$.
6. If a parapet equal to or higher than 3 ft (1 m) is provided around the perimeter of the roof with $\theta \leq 10°$, Zone 3 shall be treated as Zone 2.
7. Values of GC_p for roof overhangs include pressure contributions from both upper and lower surfaces.
8. For hipped roofs with $10 < \theta \leq 30°$, edge/ridge strips and pressure coefficients for ridges of gabled roofs shall apply on each hip.
9. On the lower level of flat, stepped roofs shown in Fig. 6-5C, the zone designations and pressure coefficients shown in Fig. 6-5B ($\theta \leq 10°$) shall apply, except that at the roof-upper wall intersection(s), Zone 3 shall be treated as Zone 2 and Zone 2 shall be treated as Zone 1. Positive values of GC_p equal to those for walls in Fig. 6-5A shall apply on the cross-hatched areas shown in Fig. 6-5C.
10. For buildings sited within Exposure B, calculated pressures shall be multiplied by 0.85.
11. Notation:
    a: 10 percent of least horizontal dimension or $0.4h$, whichever is smaller, but not less than either 4% of least horizontal dimension or 3 ft (1 m).
    b: $1.5h_1$ in Fig. 6-5C, but not greater than 100 ft (30.5 m).
    h: Mean roof height, in feet (meters), except that eave height shall be used for $\theta \leq 0°$.
    h_i: h_1 or h_2 in Fig. 6-5C; $h = h_1 + h_2$; $h_1 \geq 10$ ft (3.1 m); $h_i/h = 0.3$ to 0.7.
    W: Building width in Fig. 6-5C.
    W_i: W_1 or W_2 or W_3 in Fig. 6-5C. $W = W_1 + W_2$ or $W_1 + W_2 + W_3$; $W_i/W = 0.25$ to 0.75.
    θ: Angle of plane of roof from horizontal, in degrees.

*FIG. 6-5. External Pressure Coefficients, GC_p, for Loads on Building Components and Cladding for Enclosed or Partially Enclosed Buildings with Mean Roof Height h Less than or Equal to 60 ft (18 m)

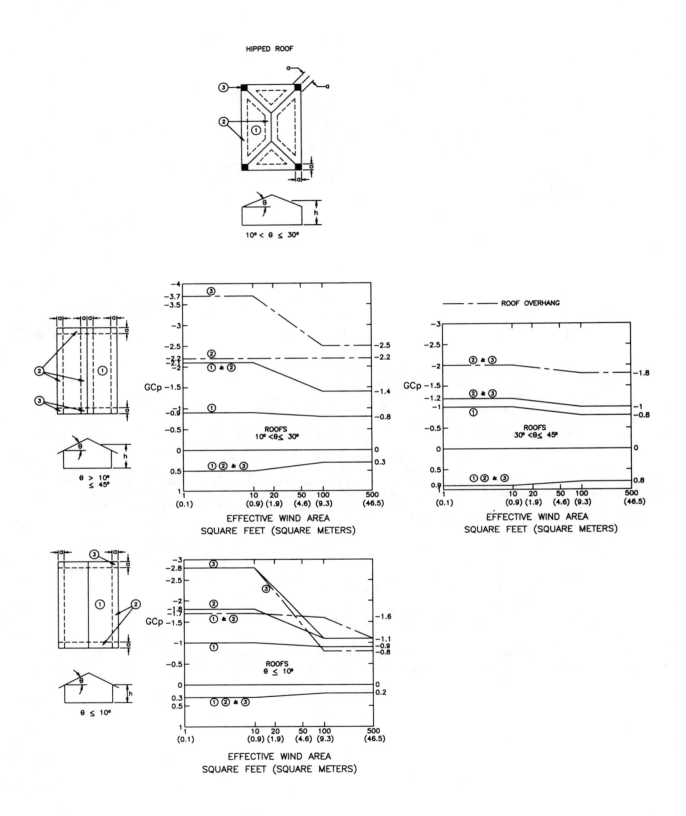

FIG. 6-5B. Gabled and Hipped Roofs (Refer to Notes on Fig. 6-5)

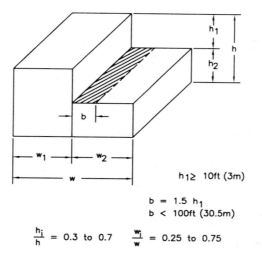

$h_1 \geq$ 10ft (3m)

$b = 1.5\, h_1$
$b < $ 100ft (30.5m)

$\dfrac{h_i}{h}$ = 0.3 to 0.7 $\dfrac{w_i}{w}$ = 0.25 to 0.75

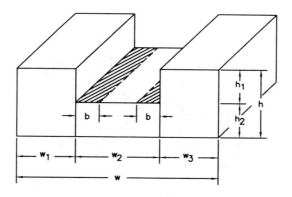

FIG. 6-5C. Stepped Roofs (Refer to Notes on Fig. 6-5)

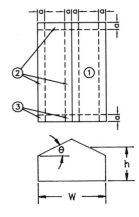

Plan and Elevation of
a Single-Span Module

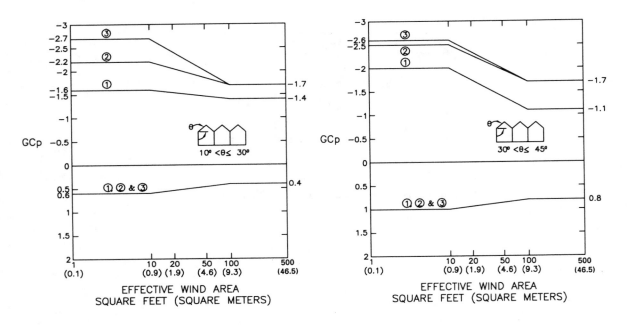

EFFECTIVE WIND AREA
SQUARE FEET (SQUARE METERS)

NOTES:
1. Vertical scale denotes GC_p to be used with q_h based on Exposure C.
2. Horizontal scale denotes effective wind area A, in square feet (square meters).
3. Plus and minus signs signify pressures acting toward and away from the surfaces, respectively.
4. Each component shall be designed for maximum positive and negative pressures.
5. For $\theta \leq 10°$, values of GC_p from Fig. 6-5B shall be used.
6. For buildings sited within Exposure B, calculated pressures shall be multiplied by 0.85.
7. Notation:
   a: 10% of least horizontal dimension of a single-span module or $0.4h$, whichever is smaller, but not less than either 4 percent of least horizontal dimension of a single-span module or 3 ft (1 m).
   h: Mean roof height, in feet (meters).
   W: Building width, in feet (meters).
   θ: Angle of plane of roof from horizontal, in degrees.

*FIG. 6-6. External Pressure Coefficients, GC_p, for Loads on Building Components and Cladding for Multispan Gabled Roofs (with Two or More Spans) on Enclosed or Partially Enclosed Buildings with Mean Roof Height, h, Less than or Equal to 60 ft (18 m)

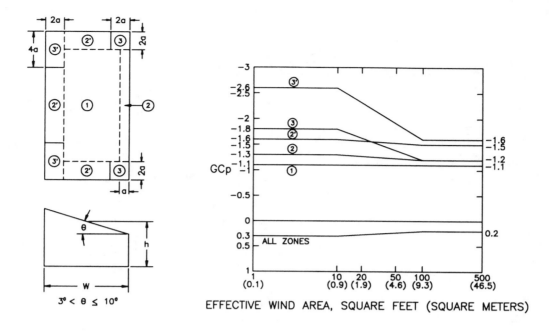

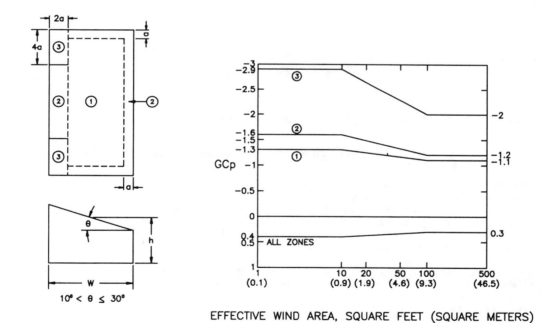

FIG. 6-7A. Monoslope Roofs (Refer to notes on page 28).

FIG. 6-7. External Pressure Coefficients, GC_p, for Loads on Building Components and Cladding for Monoslope Roofs and Sawtooth Roofs with Two or More Spans on Enclosed or Partially Enclosed Buildings with Mean Roof Height, h, Less than or Equal to 60 ft (18 m)

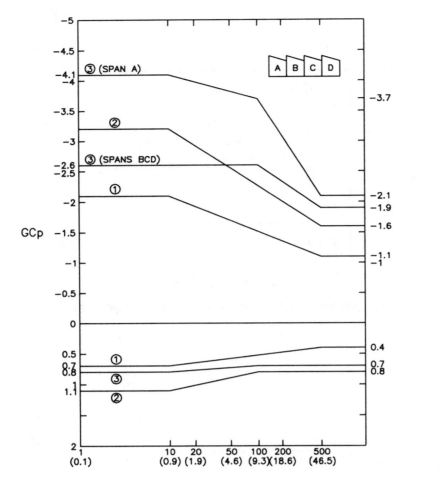

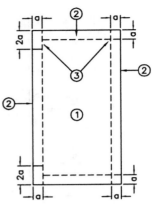

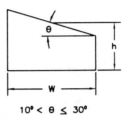

EFFECTIVE WIND AREA, SQUARE FEET (SQUARE METERS)

FIG. 6-7B. Sawtooth Roofs—Two or More Spans

NOTES for Figures 6-7A and 6-7B:

1. Vertical scale denotes GC_p to be used with q_h based on Exposure C.
2. Horizontal scale denotes effective wind area A, in square feet (square meters).
3. Plus and minus signs signify pressures acting toward and away from the surfaces, respectively.
4. Each component shall be designed for maximum positive and negative pressures.
5. For $\theta \leq 3°$ (Fig 6-7A) and $\theta \leq 10°$ (Fig 6-7B), values of GC_p from Fig. 6-5B shall be used.
6. For buildings sited within Exposure B, calculated pressures shall be multiplied by 0.85.
7. Notation:
   a: 10% of least horizontal dimension or $0.4h$, whichever is smaller, but not less than either 4% of least horizontal dimension or 3 ft (1 m).
   h: Mean roof height in feet (meters), except that eave height shall be used for $\theta \leq 10°$.
   W: Building width, in feet (meters).
   θ: Angle of plane of roof from horizontal, in degrees

28

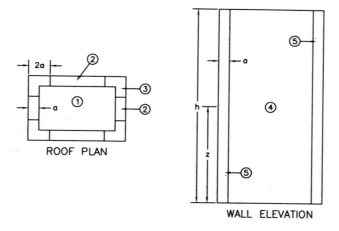

ROOF PLAN

WALL ELEVATION

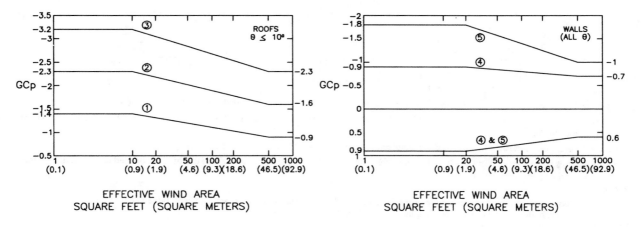

EFFECTIVE WIND AREA
SQUARE FEET (SQUARE METERS)

EFFECTIVE WIND AREA
SQUARE FEET (SQUARE METERS)

NOTES:
1. Vertical scale denotes GC_p to be used with appropriate q_z or q_h.
2. Horizontal scale denotes effective wind area A, in square feet (square meters).
3. Plus and minus signs signify pressures acting toward and away from the surface, respectively.
4. Use q_z with positive values of GC_p and q_h with negative values of GC_p.
5. Each component shall be designed for maximum positive and negative pressures.
6. Coefficients are for roofs with angle $\theta \leq 10°$. For other roof angles and geometry, use GC_p values from Fig. 6-5B and attendant q_h based on Exposure C.
7. If a parapet equal to or higher than 3 ft (1 m) is provided around the perimeter of the roof, Zone 3 shall be treated as Zone 2.
8. Notation:
   a: 10% of least horizontal dimension, but not less than 3 ft (1 m).
   h: mean roof height, in feet (meters).
   z: height above ground, in feet (meters).
   θ: Angle of plane of roof from horizontal, in degrees.

*FIG. 6-8. External Pressure Coefficients, GC_p, for Loads on Building Components and Cladding for Enclosed or Partially Enclosed Buildings with Mean Roof Height h Greater than 60 ft (18 m)

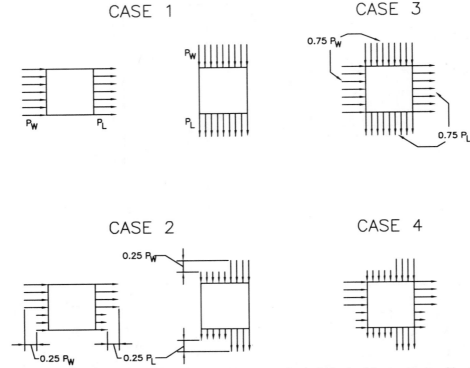

Case 1. Full design wind pressures acting on the projected area perpendicular to each principal axis of the structure considered separately.

Case 2. Wind pressure as defined in Case 1, but with a 25% reduction in pressure acting on 50% of the projected area bounded by the extreme projected edge of the building.

Case 3. Wind pressure as defined in Case 1, but considered to act simultaneously at 75% of the specified value.

Case 4. Wind pressure as defined in Case 3, but with a 25% reduction of these pressures acting on 50% of the projected area bounded by the extreme projected edge of the building.

NOTES:
 1. Design wind pressures for windward and leeward faces obtained in accordance with the provisions of Table 6-1 for main wind-force resisting systems for buildings with mean roof height h greater than 60 ft (18 m).
 2. Diagrams show plan view of building.
 3. Notation:
    p_W: Windward face design pressure.
    p_L: Leeward face design pressure.

FIG. 6-9. Wind Pressure Combinations for Full and Partial Loading of Main Wind-Force Resisting Systems for Buildings with Mean Roof Height _h_ Greater than 60 ft (18 m)

TABLE 6-4
Internal Pressure Coefficients for Buildings, GC_{pi}

Condition	GC_{pi}
Open buildings	0.00
Partially enclosed buildings	+0.80
	−0.30
Buildings satisfying the following conditions:	+0.80
	−0.30
(1) sited in hurricane-prone regions having a basic wind speed greater than or equal to 110 mph (49 m/s) or in Hawaii, and	
(2) having glazed openings in the lower 60 ft (18 m) which are not designed to resist wind-borne debris or are not specifically protected from wind-borne debris impact	
All buildings except those listed above	+0.18
	−0.18

NOTES:

1. Plus and minus signs signify pressures acting toward and away from the internal surfaces.
2. Values of GC_{pi} shall be used with q_z or q_h as specified in Table 6-1.
3. Two cases shall be considered to determine the critical load requirements for the appropriate condition: a positive value of GC_{pi} applied to all internal surfaces, and a negative value of GC_{pi} applied to all internal surfaces.
4. For buildings with mean roof height $h \leq 60$ ft (18 m) and sited within Exposure B, calculated internal pressures shall be multiplied by 0.85.
5. Hurricane-prone regions include areas vulnerable to hurricanes, such as the U.S. Atlantic and Gulf Coasts, Hawaii, Puerto Rico, Guam, Virgin Islands, and American Samoa.
6. If a building by definition complies with both the "Open" and "Partially Enclosed" definitions, it shall be treated as an "Open" building.

constructed features. The exposure in which a specific building or other structure is sited shall be assessed as being one of the following categories:

1. **Exposure A.** Large city centers with at least 50% of the buildings having a height in excess of 70 ft (21.3 m). Use of this exposure category shall be limited to those areas for which terrain representative of Exposure A prevails in the upwind direction for a distance of at least 0.5 mi (0.8 km) or 10 times the height of the building or other structure, whichever is greater. Possible channeling effects or increased velocity pressures due to the building or structure being located in the wake of adjacent buildings shall be taken into account.
2. **Exposure B.** Urban and suburban areas, wooded areas, or other terrain with numerous closely spaced obstructions having the size of single-family dwellings or larger. Use of this exposure category shall be limited to those areas for which terrain representative of Exposure B prevails in the upwind direction for a distance of at least 1,500 ft (460 m) or 10 times the height of the building or other structure, whichever is greater.
3. **Exposure C.** Open terrain with scattered obstructions having heights generally less than 30 ft (9.1 m). This category includes flat open country and grasslands.
4. **Exposure D.** Flat, unobstructed areas exposed to wind flowing over open water for a distance of at least 1 mi (1.61 km). This exposure shall apply only to those buildings and other structures exposed to the wind coming from over the water. Exposure D extends inland from the shoreline a distance of

TABLE 6-5
External Pressure Coefficients for Arched Roofs, C_p

Condition	Rise-to-span ratio, r	C_p		
		Windward quarter	Center half	Leeward quarter
Roof on elevated structure	$0 < r < 0.2$	−0.9	$-0.7 - r$	−0.5
	$0.2 \leq r < 0.3$*	$1.5r - 0.3$	$-0.7 - r$	−0.5
	$0.3 \leq r \leq 0.6$	$2.75r - 0.7$	$-0.7 - r$	−0.5
Roof springing from ground level	$0 < r \leq 0.6$	$1.4r$	$-0.7 - r$	−0.5

*When the rise-to-span ratio is $0.2 \leq r \leq 0.3$, alternate coefficients given by $6r - 2.1$ shall also be used for the windward quarter.

NOTES:

1. Values listed are for the determination of average loads on main windforce resisting systems.
2. Plus and minus signs signify pressures acting toward and away from the surfaces, respectively.
3. For wind directed parallel to the axis of the arch, use pressure coefficients from Fig. 6-3 with wind directed parallel to ridge.
4. For components and cladding: (1) At roof perimeter, use the external pressure coefficients in Fig. 6-5B with θ based on spring-line slope and q_h based on Exposure C; and (2) for remaining roof areas, use external pressure coefficients of this table multiplied by 0.87 and q_h based on Exposure C.

TABLE 6-6
Force Coefficients for Monoslope Roofs over Open Buildings, C_f

Roof angle θ degrees	C_f for L/B Values of:						
	5	3	2	1	1/2	1/3	1/5
10	0.2	0.25	0.3	0.45	0.55	0.7	0.75
15	0.35	0.45	0.5	0.7	0.85	0.9	0.85
20	0.5	0.6	0.75	0.9	1.0	0.95	0.9
25	0.7	0.8	0.95	1.15	1.1	1.05	0.95
30	0.9	1.0	1.2	1.3	1.2	1.1	1.0

Roof angle θ degrees	Location of Center of Pressure, X/L, for L/B Values of:		
	2 to 5	1	1/5 to 1/2
10 to 20	0.35	0.3	0.3
25	0.35	0.35	0.4
30	0.35	0.4	0.45

NOTES:
1. Wind forces act normal to the surface. Two cases shall be considered: (1) wind forces directed inward; and (2) wind forces directed outward.
2. Wind shall be assumed to deviate by ± 10 degrees from horizontal.
3. Notation:
   B: dimension of roof measured normal to wind direction, in feet (meters);
   L: Dimension of roof measured parallel to wind direction, in feet (meters);
   X: Distance to center of pressure from windward edge of roof, in feet (meters); and
   θ: Angle of plane of roof from horizontal, in degrees.

TABLE 6-7
Force Coefficients for Chimneys, Tanks, and Similar Structures, C_f

Cross-Section	Type of surface	C_f for h/D Values of:		
		1	7	25
Square (wind normal to face)	All	1.3	1.4	2.0
Square (wind along diagonal)	All	1.0	1.1	1.5
Hexagonal or octagonal	All	1.0	1.2	1.4
Round ($D\sqrt{q_z} > 2.5$) ($D\sqrt{q_z} > 5.3$, D in m, q_z in N/m^2)	Moderately smooth	0.5	0.6	0.7
	Rough ($D'/D \cong 0.02$)	0.7	0.8	0.9
	Very rough ($D'/D \cong 0.08$)	0.8	1.0	1.2
Round ($D\sqrt{q_z} \le 2.5$) ($D\sqrt{q_z} \le 5.3$, D in m, q_z in N/m^2)	All	0.7	0.8	1.2

NOTES:
1. The design wind force shall be calculated based on the area of the structure projected on a plane normal to the wind direction. The force shall be assumed to act parallel to the wind direction.
2. Linear interpolation is permitted for h/D values other than shown.
3. Notation:
   D: diameter of circular cross-sections and least horizontal dimension of square, hexagonal or octagonal cross-sections at elevation under consideration, in feet (meters);
   D': depth of protruding elements such as ribs and spoilers, in feet (meters); and
   h: height of structure, in feet (meters); and
   q_z: velocity pressure evaluated at height z above ground, in pounds per square foot (N/m^2).

Table 6-8
Force Coefficients for Solid Signs, C_f

At Ground Level		Above Ground Level	
v	C_f	M/N	C_f
≤3	1.2	≤6	1.2
5	1.3	10	1.3
8	1.4	16	1.4
10	1.5	20	1.5
20	1.75	40	1.75
30	1.85	60	1.85
≥40	2.0	≥80	2.0

NOTES:

1. Signs with openings comprising less than 30% of the gross area shall be considered as solid signs.
2. Signs for which the distance from the ground to the bottom edge is less than 0.25 times the vertical dimension shall be considered to be at ground level.
3. To allow for both normal and oblique wind directions, two cases shall be considered:
   a. resultant force acts normal to the face of the sign on a vertical line passing through the geometric center, and
   b. resultant force acts normal to the face of the sign at a distance from a vertical line passing through the geometric center equal to 0.2 times the average width of the sign.
4. Notation:
   v: ratio of height to width;
   M: larger dimension of sign, in feet (meters); and
   N: smaller dimension of sign, in feet (meters).

1,500 ft (460 m) or 10 times the height of the building or structure, whichever is greater.

6.5.3.2 Exposure category for design of main wind-force resisting systems

6.5.3.2.1 Buildings and other structures. Wind loads for the design of the main wind-force resisting system, except as specified in 6.5.3.2.2, shall be based on the exposure categories defined in 6.5.3.1 for any given wind direction.

6.5.3.2.2 Low-rise buildings. Wind loads for the design of the main wind-force resisting systems for low-rise buildings shall use a velocity pressure q_h based on Exposure C when external pressure coefficients GC_{pf} given in Fig. 6-4 are used. However, if the building is sited in Exposure B for all wind directions, the appropriate multipliers as noted in Fig. 6-4 and in Table 6-4 shall be used.

6.5.3.3 Exposure category for design of components and cladding

6.5.3.3.1 Buildings with height h less than or equal to 60 feet (18 m). Components and cladding for buildings with a mean roof height of 60 ft (18 m) or less shall be designed using a velocity pressure q_h based on Exposure C. However, if

TABLE 6-9
Force Coefficients for Open Signs and Lattice Frameworks, C_f

	C_f		
		Rounded Members	
ϵ	Flat-Sided Members	$D\sqrt{q_z} \le 2.5$ $(D\sqrt{q_z} \le 5.3)$	$D\sqrt{q_z} > 2.5$ $(D\sqrt{q_z} > 5.3)$
<0.1	2.0	1.2	0.8
0.1 to 0.29	1.8	1.3	0.9
0.3 to 0.7	1.6	1.5	1.1

NOTES:

1. Signs with openings comprising 30% or more of the gross area are classified as open signs.
2. The calculation of the design wind forces shall be based on the area of all exposed members and elements projected on a plane normal to the wind direction. Forces shall be assumed to act parallel to the wind direction.
3. The area A_f consistent with these force coefficients is the solid area projected normal to the wind direction.
4. Notation:
   ϵ: ratio of solid area to gross area;
   D: diameter of a typical round member, in feet (meters);
   q_z: velocity pressure evaluated at height z above ground, in pounds per square foot (N/m^2).

*TABLE 6-10
Force Coefficients for Trussed Towers, C_f

Tower Cross section	C_f
Square	$4.0\,\epsilon^2 - 5.9\,\epsilon + 4.0$
Triangle	$3.4\,\epsilon^2 - 4.7\,\epsilon + 3.4$

NOTES:

1. For all wind directions considered, the area A_f consistent with the specified force coefficients shall be the solid area of a tower face projected on the plane of that face for the tower segment under consideration.
2. The specified force coefficients are for towers with structural angles or similar flat-sided members.
3. For towers containing rounded members, it is acceptable to multiply the specified force coefficients by the following factor when determining wind forces on such members:
   $0.51\,\epsilon^2 + 0.57$, but not > 1.0
4. Wind forces shall be applied in the directions resulting in maximum member forces and reactions. For towers with square cross-sections, wind forces shall be multiplied by the following factor when the wind is directed along a tower diagonal:
   $1 + 0.75\,\epsilon$, but not > 1.2
5. Wind forces on tower appurtenances such as ladders, conduits, lights, elevators, etc., shall be calculated using appropriate force coefficients for these elements.
6. Loads due to ice accretion as described in Section 11 shall be accounted for.
7. Notation:
   ϵ : ratio of solid area to gross area of one tower face for the segment under consideration.

the building is sited in Exposure B for all wind directions, the appropriate multipliers as noted in Figs. 6-5 through 6-7, and in Table 6-4 shall be used.

6.5.3.3.2 Buildings with height h greater than 60 ft (18 m) and other structures. Components and cladding for buildings with a mean roof height in excess of 60 ft (18 m) and for other structures shall be designed on the basis of the most critical exposure category representative of the site as defined in 6.5.3.1, except that Exposure B shall be used for buildings and other structures sited in terrain representative of Exposure A, and Exposure C for certain roofs indicated in Fig. 6-8.

*6.5.4 Shielding. Where the provisions of 6.4.2 are used there shall be no reductions in velocity pressures due to apparent direct shielding afforded by buildings and other structures or terrain features.

*6.5.5 Wind Speed-up over Hills and Escarpments. The provisions of this section shall apply to isolated hills or escarpments located in Exposure B, C, or D where the upwind terrain is free of such topographic features for a distance equal to $50H$ or 1 mile, whichever is smaller, as measured from the point at which H is determined. Wind speed-up over isolated hills and escarpments that constitute abrupt changes in the general topography shall be considered for buildings and other structures sited on the upper half of hills and ridges or near the edges of escarpments, illustrated in Fig. 6-2, by using factor K_{zt}:

$$K_{zt} = (1 + K_1 K_2 K_3)^2 \qquad \text{(Eq. 6-2)}$$

where K_1, K_2 and K_3 are given in Fig. 6-2. The effect of wind speed-up shall not be required to be considered when $H/L_h < 0.2$, or when $H < 15$ ft (4.5 m) for Exposure D, or < 30 ft (9 m) for Exposure C, or < 60 ft (18 m) for all other exposures.

*6.6 Gust Effect Factors

6.6.1 Values of Gust Effect Factors. For main wind-force resisting systems of buildings and other structures, and for components and cladding of open buildings and other structures, the value of the gust effect factor G shall be 0.8 for exposure A and B, and 0.85 for exposure C and D.

*6.6.2 Flexible Buildings and Other Structures. Gust effect factors G_f for main wind-force resisting systems of flexible buildings and other structures shall be calculated by a rational analysis that incorporates the dynamic properties of the main wind-force resisting system.

6.6.3 Limitations. Where combined gust effect factors and pressure coefficients (GC_p, GC_{pi} and GC_{pf}) are given in the figures and tables, gust effect factors shall not be determined separately.

*6.7 Pressure and Force Coefficients

6.7.1 General. Pressure and force coefficients are given in Figs. 6-3 through 6-8 and Tables 6-4 through 6-10. The values of the coefficients for buildings in Figs. 6-4 through 6-8 and Table 6-4 include the gust effect factors; in these cases the pressure coefficient values and gust effect factors shall not be separated.

6.7.2 Roof Overhangs

6.7.2.1 Main wind-force resisting system. Roof overhangs shall be designed for a positive pressure on the bottom surface of windward roof overhangs corresponding to $C_p = 0.8$ in combination with the pressures indicated in Figs. 6-3 and 6-4.

6.7.2.2 Components and cladding. For all buildings, roof overhangs shall be designed for pressures determined from pressure coefficients given in Fig. 6-5B.

*6.8 Full and Partial Loading

The main wind-force resisting system of buildings with mean roof height greater than 60 ft (18 m) shall be designed for the torsional moments resulting from design wind pressures in Table 6-1 acting in the combinations indicated in Fig. 6-9.

*7. Snow Loads

7.1 Symbols and Notation

C_e = exposure factor as determined from Table 7-2;

C_s = slope factor as determined from Fig. 7-2;

C_t = thermal factor as determined from Table 7-3;

h_b = height of balanced snow load determined by dividing p_f or p_s by γ, in feet (meters);

h_c = clear height from top of balanced snow load to (1) closest point on adjacent upper roof; (2) top of parapet; or (3) top of a projection on the roof, in feet (meters);

h_d = height of snow drift, in feet (meters);

h_o = height of obstruction above the surface of the roof, in feet (meters);

I = importance factor as determined from Table 7-4;

l_u = length of the roof upwind of the drift, in feet (meters);

p_d = maximum intensity of drift surcharge load, in pounds per square foot (kilonewtons per square meter);

p_f = snow load on flat roofs ("flat" = roof slope $\leq 5°$), in pounds per square foot (kilonewtons per square meter);

p_g = ground snow load as determined from Fig. 7-1 and Table 7-1; or a site-specific analysis, in pounds per square foot (kilonewtons per square meter);

p_s = sloped-roof snow load, in pounds per square foot (kilonewtons per square meter);

s = separation distance between buildings, in feet (meters);

w = width of snow drift, in feet (meters);

γ = snow density in pounds per cubic foot (kilograms per cubic meter) as determined from Eq. (7-3);

*7.2 Ground Snow Loads, p_g

Ground snow loads, p_g, to be used in the determination of design snow loads for roofs shall be as set forth in Fig. 7-1 for the contiguous United States and Table 7-1 for Alaska. Site specific case studies shall be made to determine ground snow loads in areas designated CS in Fig. 7-1. Ground snow loads for sites at elevations above the limits indicated in Fig. 7-1 and for all sites within the CS areas shall be approved by the authority having jurisdiction. Ground snow load determination for such sites shall be based on an extreme value statistical analysis of data available in the vicinity of the site using a value with a 2% annual probability of being exceeded (50-year mean recurrence interval).

Snow loads are zero for Hawaii, except in mountainous regions as determined by the authority having jurisdiction.

*7.3 Flat-Roof Snow Loads, p_f

The snow load, p_f, on a roof with a slope equal to or less than 5° (1 in./ft = 4.76°) shall be calculated in pounds per square foot (kilonewtons per square meter) using the following formula:

$$p_f = 0.7\, C_e C_t I p_g \qquad \text{(Eq. 7-1)}$$

*7.3.1 Exposure Factor, C_e. The value for C_e shall be determined from Table 7-2.

*7.3.2 Thermal Factor, C_t. The value for C_t shall be determined from Table 7-3.

*7.3.3 Importance Factor, I. The value for I shall be determined from Table 7-4.

*7.3.4 Minimum Allowable Values of p_f for Low-Slope Roofs. Minimum allowable values of

p_f shall apply to monoslope, hip, and gable roofs with slopes less than 15° and curved roofs where the vertical angle from the eaves to the crown is less than 10°. For locations where the ground snow load, p_g, is 20 lb/sq ft (0.96 kN/m²) or less, the flat-roof snow load, p_f, shall be not less than the ground snow load multiplied by the importance factor [i.e., where $p_g \leq$ 20 lb/sq ft (0.96 kN/m²), $p_f \geq p_g I$ lb/sq ft (kN/m²)]. In locations where the ground snow load, p_g, exceeds 20 lb/sq ft (0.96 kN/m²), the flat-roof snow load, p_f, shall be not less than 20 lb/sq ft (0.96 kN/m²) multiplied by the importance factor [i.e., where $p_g > 20$ lb/sq ft (0.96 kN/m²), $p_f \geq 20\,I$ lb/sq ft (0.96 I kN/m²)].

The live load reductions in 4.8 shall not be applied to snow loads.

*7.4 Sloped-Roof Snow Loads, p_s

Snow loads acting on a sloping surface shall be assumed to act on the horizontal projection of that surface. The sloped-roof snow load, p_s, shall be obtained by multiplying the flat-roof snow load, p_f, by the roof slope factor, C_s:

$$p_s = C_s p_f \qquad \text{(Eq. 7-2)}$$

Values of C_s for warm roofs, cold roofs, curved roofs, and multiple roofs are determined from 7.4.1-7.4.4. The thermal factor, C_t, from Table 7-3 determines if a roof is "cold" or "warm." "Slippery surface" values shall be used only where the roof's surface is unobstructed and sufficient space is available below the eaves to accept all the sliding snow. A roof shall be considered unobstructed if no objects exist on it that prevent snow on it from sliding. Slippery surfaces shall include metal, slate, glass, and bituminous, rubber and plastic membranes with a smooth surface. Membranes with an imbedded aggregate or mineral granule surface shall not be considered smooth. Asphalt shingles, wood shingles, and shakes shall not be considered slippery.

7.4.1 Warm-Roof Slope Factor, C_s. For warm roofs ($C_t = 1.0$ as determined from Table 7-3) with an unobstructed slippery surface that will allow snow to slide off the eaves, the roof slope factor C_s shall be determined using the dashed line in Fig. 7-2a, provided that for nonventilated roofs, their thermal resistance (R-value) equals or exceeds 30 °F·h·sq ft/Btu (5.3 K·m²/W) and for ventilated roofs, their R-value equals or exceeds 20 °F·h·sq ft/Btu (3.5 K·m²/W). Exterior air shall

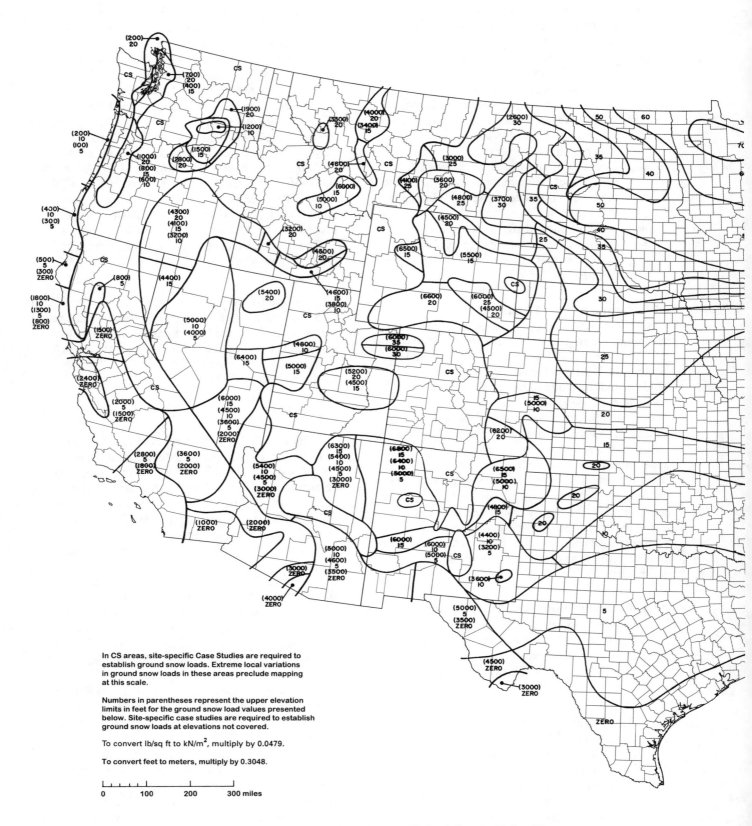

In CS areas, site-specific Case Studies are required to establish ground snow loads. Extreme local variations in ground snow loads in these areas preclude mapping at this scale.

Numbers in parentheses represent the upper elevation limits in feet for the ground snow load values presented below. Site-specific case studies are required to establish ground snow loads at elevations not covered.

To convert lb/sq ft to kN/m², multiply by 0.0479.

To convert feet to meters, multiply by 0.3048.

0   100   200   300 miles

FIG. 7-1. Ground Snow Loads, p_g for the United States (lb/sq ft)

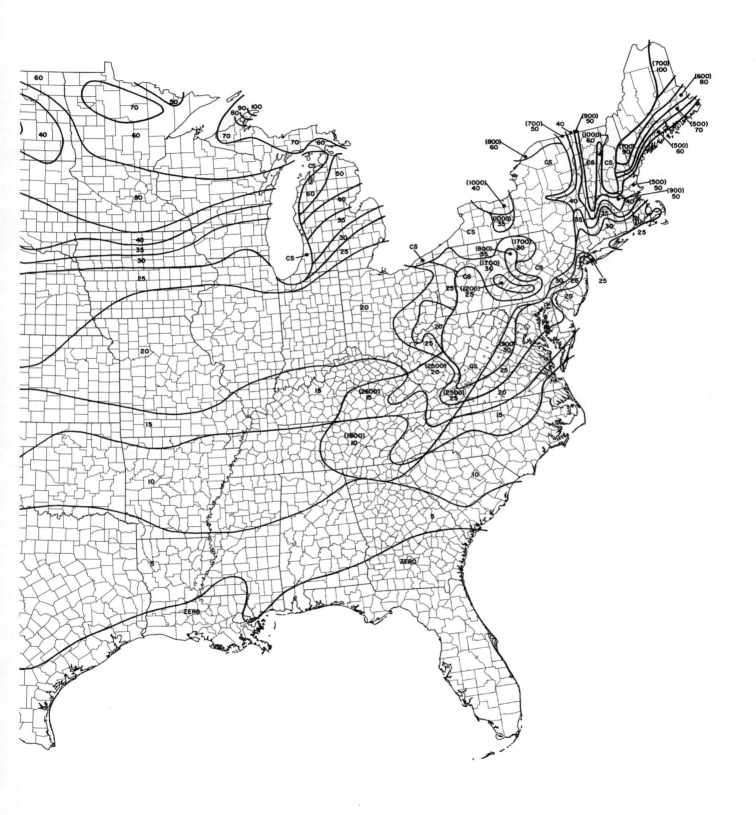

TABLE 7-1
Ground Snow Loads, p_g, for Alaskan Locations

Location	p_g lb/sq ft	(kN/m²)	Location	p_g lb/sq ft	(kN/m²)	Location	p_g lb/sq ft	(kN/m²)
Adak	30	(1.4)	Galena	60	(2.9)	Petersburg	150	(7.2)
Anchorage	50	(2.4)	Gulkana	70	(3.4)	St Paul Islands	40	(1.9)
Angoon	70	(3.4)	Homer	40	(1.9)	Seward	50	(2.4)
Barrow	25	(1.2)	Juneau	60	(2.9)	Shemya	25	(1.2)
Barter Island	35	(1.7)	Kenai	70	(3.4)	Sitka	50	(2.4)
Bethel	40	(1.9)	Kodiak	30	(1.4)	Talkeetna	120	(5.8)
Big Delta	50	(2.4)	Kotzebue	60	(2.9)	Unalakleet	50	(2.4)
Cold Bay	25	(1.2)	McGrath	70	(3.4)	Valdez	160	(7.7)
Cordova	100	(4.8)	Nenana	80	(3.8)	Whittier	300	(14.4)
Fairbanks	60	(2.9)	Nome	70	(3.4)	Wrangell	60	(2.9)
Fort Yukon	60	(2.9)	Palmer	50	(2.4)	Yakutat	150	(7.2)

TABLE 7-2
Exposure Factor, C_e

Terrain Category	Exposure of roof*		
	Fully Exposed	Partially Exposed	Sheltered
A (see Section 6.5.3)	N/A	1.1	1.3
B (see Section 6.5.3)	0.9	1.0	1.2
C (see Section 6.5.3)	0.9	1.0	1.1
D (see Section 6.5.3)	0.8	0.9	1.0
Above the treeline in windswept mountainous areas.	0.7	0.8	N/A
In Alaska, in areas where trees do not exist within a 2-mile (3 km) radius of the site.	0.7	0.8	N/A

The terrain category and roof exposure condition chosen shall be representative of the anticipated conditions during the life of the structure.

*Definitions

Partially Exposed: All roofs except as indicated below.

Fully Exposed: Roofs exposed on all sides with no shelter** afforded by terrain, higher structures or trees. Roofs that contain several large pieces of mechanical equipment or other obstructions are not in this category.

Sheltered: Roofs located tight in among conifers that qualify as obstructions.

**Obstructions within a distance of 10 h_o provide "shelter," where h_o is the height of the obstruction above the roof level. If the only obstructions are a few deciduous trees that are leafless in winter, the "fully exposed" category shall be used except for terrain category "A." Note that these are heights above the roof. Heights used to establish the Terrain Category in Section 6.5.3 are heights above the ground.

TABLE 7-3
Thermal Factor, C_t

Thermal Condition*	C_t
All structures except as indicated below	1.0
Structures kept just above freezing and others with cold, ventilated roofs having a thermal resistance (R-value) greater than 25 °F·h·sq ft/Btu (4.4 $K \cdot m^2/W$)	1.1
Unheated structures	1.2

*These conditions shall be representative of the anticipated conditions during winters for the life of the structure.

TABLE 7-4
Importance Factor, I (Snow Loads)

Category*	I
I	0.8
II	1.0
III	1.1
IV	1.2

*See Section 1.5 and Table 1-1.

be able to circulate freely under a ventilated roof from its eaves to its ridge. For warm roofs that do not meet the aforementioned conditions, the solid line in Fig. 7-2a shall be used to determine the roof slope factor C_s.

7.4.2 Cold Roof Slope Factor, C_s. For cold roofs ($C_t > 1.0$ as determined from Table 7-3) with an unobstructed slippery surface that will allow snow to slide off the eaves, the roof slope factor C_s shall be determined using the dashed line in Fig. 7-2b. For all other cold roofs the solid line in Fig. 7-2b shall be used to determine the roof slope factor C_s.

***7.4.3 Roof Slope Factor for Curved Roofs.** Portions of curved roofs having a slope exceeding 70° shall be considered free of snow load, (i.e., $C_s = 0$). Balanced loads shall be determined from the balanced load diagrams in Fig. 7-3 with C_s determined from the appropriate curve in Fig. 7-2.

***7.4.4 Roof Slope Factor for Multiple Folded Plate, Sawtooth, and Barrel Vault Roofs.** Multiple folded plate, sawtooth, or barrel vault roofs shall have a $C_s = 1.0$, with no reduction in snow load because of slope (i.e., $p_s = p_f$).

***7.4.5 Ice Dams and Icicles Along Eaves.** Two types of warm roofs that drain water over their eaves shall be capable of sustaining a uniformly distributed load of $2 p_f$ on all overhanging portions there:

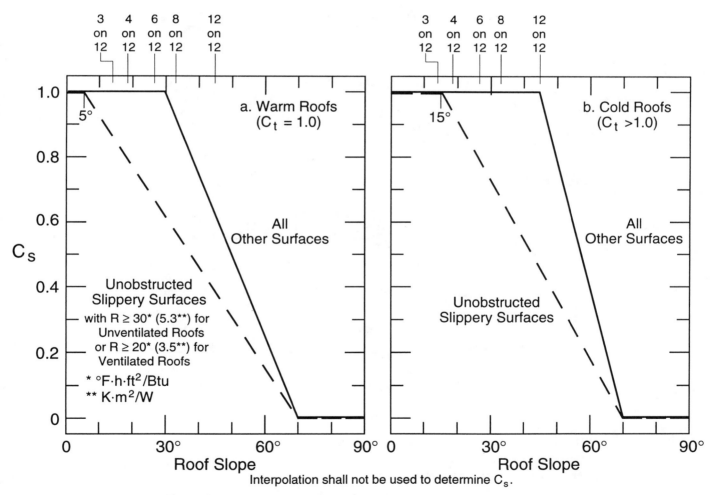

FIG. 7-2. Graphs for Determining Roof Slope Factor C_s for Warm and Cold Roofs.

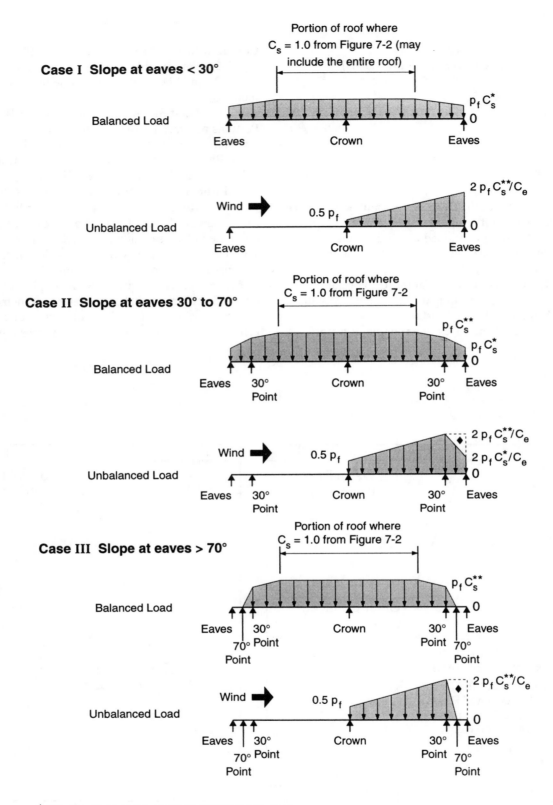

* Use the slope at the eaves to determine C_s here.

** Use 30° slope to determine C_s here.

♦ Alternate distribution if another roof abuts.

FIG. 7-3. Balanced and Unbalanced Loads for Curved Roofs

Those that are unventilated and have an R-value less than 30 °F·h·sq ft/Btu (5.3 K·m²/W) and those that are ventilated and have an R-value less than 20 °F·h·sq ft/Btu (3.5 K·m²/W). No other loads except dead loads shall be present on the roof when this uniformly distributed load is applied.

*7.5 Partial Loading

The effect of (1) having the full balanced snow load over any one portion of the loaded area and half the balanced snow load everywhere else; and (2) having half the balanced snow load over any one portion of the loaded area and the full balanced snow load everywhere else shall be determined as follows:

7.5.1 Continuous Beam Systems.
Four loadings shall be investigated. First, the full balanced load shall remain only on any individual span. Second, the full balanced load shall remain only on any two adjacent spans. Third, half the balanced load shall be only on any individual span. Fourth, half the balanced load shall be only on any two adjacent spans. These four loading diagrams are shown in Fig. 7-4. If a cantilever is present, it shall be considered to be a span.

7.5.2 Other Structural Systems.
Areas sustaining only half the balanced snow load shall be chosen so as to produce the greatest effects on members being analyzed.

*7.6 Unbalanced Roof Snow Loads

Balanced and unbalanced loads shall be analyzed separately. Winds from all directions shall be accounted for when establishing unbalanced loads.

*7.6.1 Unbalanced Snow Loads for Hip and Gable Roofs.
For hip and gable roofs with a slope less than 15° or exceeding 70°, unbalanced snow loads are not required to be applied. For slopes between 15° and 70°, the structure shall be designed to resist an unbalanced uniform snow load on the leeward side equal to 1.3 times the sloped roof snow load, p_s, divided by C_e (i.e., 1.3 p_s/C_e). In the unbalanced situation, the windward side shall be considered free of snow. Balanced and unbalanced loading diagrams are presented in Fig. 7-5.

*7.6.2 Unbalanced Snow Loads for Curved Roofs.
Portions of curved roofs having a slope exceeding 70 degrees shall be considered free of snow load. If the slope of a straight line from the eaves (or the 70° point, if present) to the crown is less than 10° or greater than 60°, unbalanced snow loads shall not be taken into account.

Unbalanced loads shall be determined according to the loading diagrams in Fig. 7-3. In all cases the windward side shall be considered free of snow. If the ground or another roof abuts a Case II or Case III (see Fig. 7-3) curved roof at or within 3 ft (0.9 m) of its eaves, the snow load shall not be decreased between the 30° point and the eaves but shall remain constant at the 30° point value. This distribution is shown as a dashed line in Fig. 7-3.

*7.6.3 Unbalanced Snow Loads for Multiple Folded Plate, Sawtooth, and Barrel Vault Roofs.
Unbalanced loads shall be applied to folded plate, sawtooth, and barrel vaulted multiple roofs with a slope exceeding 3/8 in./ft (1.79°). According to 7.4.4, $C_s = 1.0$ for such roofs, and the balanced snow load equals p_f. The unbalanced snow load shall increase from one-half the balanced load at the ridge or crown (i.e., 0.5 p_f) to two times the balanced load given in 7.4.4 divided by C_e at the valley (i.e., $2p_f/C_e$). Balanced and unbalanced loading diagrams for a sawtooth roof are presented in Fig. 7-6. However, the snow surface above the valley shall not be at an elevation higher than the snow above the ridge. Snow depths shall be determined by dividing the snow load by the density of that snow from Eq. (7-3), which is in 7.7.2.

*7.6.4 Unbalanced Snow Loads for Dome Roofs.
Unbalanced snow loads shall be applied to domes and similar rounded structures. Snow loads, determined in the same manner as for curved roofs in 7.6.2, shall be applied to the downwind 90° sector in plan view. At both edges of this sector, the load shall decrease linearly to zero over sectors of 22.5° each. There shall be no snow load on the remaining 225° upwind sector.

*7.7 Drifts on Lower Roofs (Aerodynamic Shade)

Roofs shall be designed to sustain localized loads from snow drifts that form in the wind shadow of (1) higher portions of the same structure; and (2) adjacent structures and terrain features.

7.7.1 Regions with Light Snow Loads.
In areas where the ground snow load p_g is less than 5 lb/sq ft (0.24 kN/m²), drift loads are not required to be applied.

7.7.2 Lower Roof of a Structure.
Snow that forms drifts comes from a higher roof or, with the wind from the opposite direction, from the roof on which the drift is located. These two kinds of drifts ("leeward" and "windward" respectively) are shown in Fig. 7-7. The geometry of the surcharge

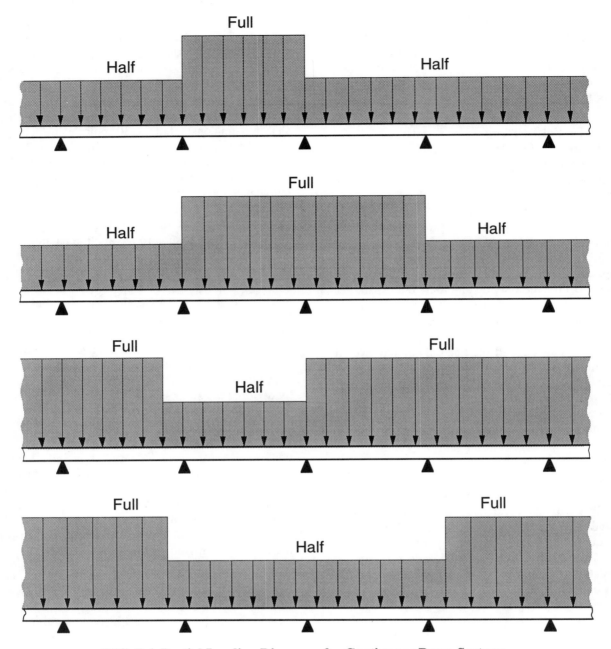

FIG. 7-4. Partial Loading Diagrams for Continuous Beam Systems

load due to snow drifting shall be approximated by a triangle as shown in Fig. 7-8. Drift loads shall be superimposed on the balanced snow load. If h_c/h_b is less than 0.2, drift loads are not required to be applied.

For leeward drifts the drift height h_d shall be determined directly from Fig. 7-9 using the length of the upper roof. For windward drifts the drift height shall be determined by substituting the length of the lower roof for l_u in Fig. 7-9 and using half of h_d as determined from Fig. 7-9 as the drift height. The larger of these two heights shall be used in design. If this height is equal to or less than h_c, the drift width, w, shall equal 4 h_d and the drift height shall equal h_d. If this height exceeds h_c, the drift width, w, shall equal 4 h_d^2/h_c and the drift height shall equal h_c. However, the drift width w shall not be greater than 8 h_c. If the drift width, w, exceeds the width of the lower roof, the drift shall be truncated at the far edge of the roof, not reduced to

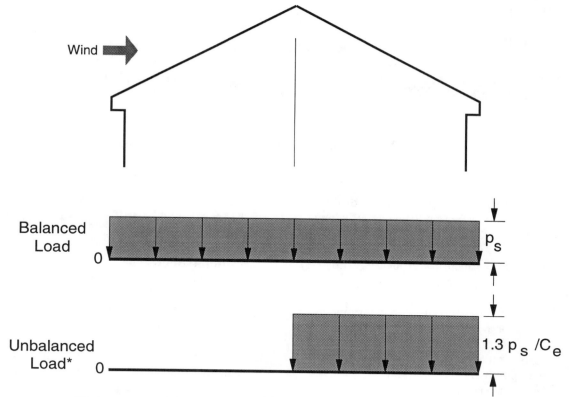

*If slope < 15° or >70°, unbalanced loads need not be considered.

FIG. 7-5. Balanced and Unbalanced Snow Loads for Hip and Gable Roofs

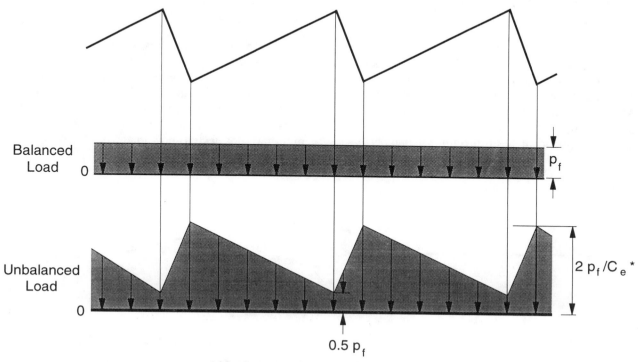

* May be somewhat less; see Section 7.6.3

FIG. 7-6. Balanced and Unbalanced Snow Loads for a Sawtooth Roof

FIG. 7-7. Drifts Formed at Windward and Leeward Steps

zero there. The maximum intensity of the drift surcharge load, p_d, equals $h_d\gamma$ (in SI: $h_d\gamma/102$) where snow density, γ, is defined in Eq. (7-3):

$$\gamma = 0.13\,p_g + 14 \text{ but not more than } 30 \text{ lb/cu ft} \quad \text{(Eq. 7-3)}$$
$$(\text{in SI: } \gamma = 43.5\,p_g + 224 \text{ but not more than } 48 \text{ kg/m}^3)$$

This density shall also be used to determine h_b by dividing p_f (or p_s) by γ (in SI: also multiply by 102 to get the depth in meters).

7.7.3 Adjacent Structures and Terrain Features. The requirements in 7.7.1 and 7.7.2 shall also be used to determine drift loads caused by a higher structure or terrain feature within 20 ft (6.1 m) of a roof. The separation distance, s, between the roof and adjacent structure or terrain feature shall reduce applied drift loads on the lower roof by the factor $(20 - s)/20$ where s is in feet $[(6.1 - s)/6.1$ where s is in meters].

*7.8 Roof Projections

The method in 7.7.2 shall be used to calculate drift loads on all sides of roof projections and at parapet walls. The height of such drifts shall be taken as half the drift height from Fig. 7-8 (i.e., 0.5 h_d) with l_u equal to the length of the roof upwind of the projection or parapet

wall. If the side of a roof projection is less than 15 ft (4.6 m) long, a drift load is not required to be applied to that side.

*7.9 Sliding Snow

The extra load caused by snow sliding off a sloped roof onto a lower roof shall be determined assuming that all the snow that accumulates on the upper roof under the balanced loading condition slides onto the lower roof. The solid lines in Fig. 7-2 shall be used to determine the total extra load available from the upper roof, regardless of the surface of the upper roof.

The sliding snow load shall not be reduced unless a portion of the snow on the upper roof is blocked from sliding onto the lower roof by snow already on the lower roof or is expected to slide clear of the lower roof.

Sliding loads shall be superimposed on the balanced snow load.

*7.10 Rain-on-Snow Surcharge Load

For locations where p_g is 20 lb/sq ft (0.96 kN/m²) or less but not zero, all roofs with a slope less than 1/2 in./ft (2.38°), shall have a 5 lb/sq ft (0.24 kN/m²) rain-on-snow surcharge load applied to establish the design snow load. Where the minimum flat roof design snow load from 7.3.4 ex-

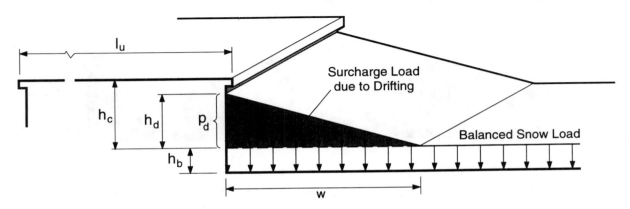

FIG. 7-8. Configuration of Snow Drifts on Lower Roofs

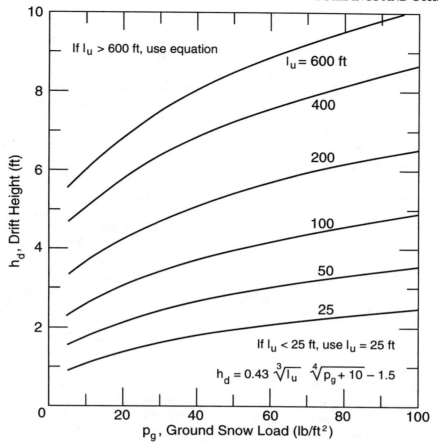

FIG. 7-9. Graph and Equation for Determining Drift Height h_d

---

ceeds p_f as determined by Eq. (7-1), the rain-on-snow surcharge load shall be reduced by the difference between these two values, with a maximum reduction of 5 lb/sq ft (0.24 kN/m²).

*7.11 Ponding Instability

Roofs shall be designed to preclude ponding instability. For roofs with a slope less than 1/4 in./ft (1.19°), roof deflections caused by full snow loads shall be investigated when determining the likelihood of ponding instability from rain-on-snow or from snow meltwater (see Section 8.4).

*7.12 Existing Roofs

Existing roofs shall be evaluated for increased snow loads caused by additions, alterations, and new structures located nearby (see footnote to Table 7-2 and Section 7.7.3) and strengthened as necessary.

*8. Rain Loads

*8.1 Symbols and Notations

R = rain load on the undeflected roof, in pounds per square foot (kilonewtons per square meter). When the phrase "undeflected roof" is used, deflections from loads (including dead loads) shall not be considered when determining the amount of rain on the roof.

d_s = depth of water on the undeflected roof up to the inlet of the secondary drainage system when the primary drainage system is blocked (i.e., the static head), in inches (millimeters).

d_h = additional depth of water on the undeflected roof above the inlet of the secondary drainage system at its design flow (i.e., the hydraulic head), in inches (millimeters).

*8.2 Roof Drainage

Roof drainage systems shall be designed in accordance with the provisions of the code having jurisdiction. The flow capacity of secondary (overflow) drains or scuppers shall not be less than that of the primary drains or scuppers.

*8.3 Design Rain Loads

Each portion of a roof shall be designed to sustain the load of all rainwater that will accumulate on it if the primary drainage system for that portion is blocked plus the uniform load caused by water that rises above the inlet of the secondary drainage system at its design flow.

$$R = 5.2 \, (d_s + d_h)$$
$$[\text{In SI: } R = 0.0098 \, (d_s + d_h)] \qquad \text{(Eq. 8-1)}$$

If the secondary drainage system contains drain lines, such lines shall be independent of the primary drain lines.

*8.4 Ponding Instability

"Ponding" refers to the retention of water due solely to the deflection of relatively flat roofs. Roofs with a slope less than 1/4 in./ft (1.19°) shall be investigated by structural analysis to assure that they possess adequate stiffness to preclude progressive deflection (i.e., instability) as rain falls on them or meltwater is created from snow on them. The larger of snow load or rain load shall be used in this analysis. The primary drainage system within an area subjected to ponding shall be considered to be blocked in this analysis.

*8.5 Controlled Drainage

Roofs equipped with hardware to control the rate of drainage shall be equipped with a secondary drainage system at a higher elevation that limits accumulation of water on the roof above that elevation. Such roofs shall be designed to sustain the load of all rainwater that will accumulate on them to the elevation of the secondary drainage system plus the uniform load caused by water that rises above the inlet of the secondary drainage system at its design flow (determined from Section 8.3).

Such roofs shall also be checked for ponding instability (determined from Section 8.4).

9. Earthquake Loads

[Note to user: This Section is based on the 1994 *NEHRP Recommended Provisions for the Development of Seismic Regulations for New Buildings*. Differences are shown in italic, and deletions are marked by an asterisk (*).]

9.1 General Provisions

9.1.1 Purpose. *Section* 9 presents criteria for the design and construction of buildings and *similar* structures subject to earthquake ground motions. *The specified earthquake loads are based upon postelastic energy dissipation in the structure, and because of this fact, the provisions for design, detailing, and construction shall be satisfied even for structures and members for which load combinations that do not contain the earthquake effect indicate larger demands than combinations including earthquake.* *

9.1.2 Scope. Every building, * and portion thereof, shall be designed and constructed to resist the effects of earthquake motions * as prescribed by these provisions. *Certain nonbuilding structures, as described in Section 9.2.6, are within the scope and shall be designed and constructed as required for buildings.* Additions to existing structures also shall be designed and constructed to resist the effects of earthquake motions * as prescribed by these provisions. Existing * structures and alterations to existing *structures* need only comply with these provisions when required by Sections 9.1.3.2 and 9.1.3.3.

Exceptions:

1. Buildings located *where the* effective peak velocity-related acceleration (A_v) value *read from Map 9-2* is less than 0.05 shall only be required to comply with Section 9.2.2.5.1

2. Detached one- and two-family dwellings that are located *in seismic map areas having an effective peak velocity-related acceleration (A_v) value less than 0.10 or* at sites where the seismic coefficient C_a is less than 0.15 are exempt from *the* requirements of these provisions.

3. Detached one- and two-family wood frame dwellings *not included in exception 2* with not more than two stories and *satisfying* the limitations of Section A.9.9.10 *are only required to be constructed in accordance with Section A.9.9.10.*

4. Agricultural storage buildings that are intended only for incidental human occupancy are exempt from *the* requirements of these provisions.

Special structures including, but not limited to, *vehicular* bridges, transmission towers, * piers and wharves, hydraulic structures, and nuclear reactors require special consideration of their response characteristics and environment that is beyond the scope of these provisions.

9.1.3 Application of Provisions. Buildings *and structures* within the scope of these provisions shall be designed and constructed as required by this section. *When required by the authority having jurisdiction*, design documents shall be submitted to determine compliance with these provisions. *

9.1.3.1 New Buildings. New buildings *and structures* shall be designed and constructed in accordance with the quality assurance requirements of Sec. 9.1.6. The analysis and design of structural systems and components, including foundations, frames, walls, floors, and roofs, shall be in accordance with the applicable requirements of Sec. 9.2 and 9.4. Materials used in construction and components made of these materials shall be designed and constructed to meet the requirements of Sections 9.5–9.9. Architectural, electrical, and mechanical systems and components including tenant * improvements shall be designed in accordance with Section 9.3.

9.1.3.2 Additions to Existing Structures. Additions shall be made to existing *structures* only as follows:

9.1.3.2.1. An addition that is structurally independent from an existing *structure* shall be designed and constructed in accordance with the seismic requirements *for new structures*.

9.1.3.2.2. An addition that is not structurally independent from an existing *structure* shall be designed and constructed such that the entire *structure* conforms to the seismic force resistance requirements for new *structures* unless the following three conditions are complied with:

1. The addition shall comply with the requirements for new *structures*,
2. The addition shall not increase the seismic forces in any structural element of the existing *structure* by more than 5% unless the capacity of the element subject to the increased forces is still in compliance with these provisions, and
3. The addition shall not decrease the seismic resistance of any structural element of the existing *structure* unless the reduced resistance is equal to or greater than that required for new *structures*.

9.1.3.3 Change of Use. When a change of use results in a *structure* being reclassified to a higher *category per Table 1-1*, the *structure* shall conform to the seismic requirements for new construction.

Exception: When a change of use results in a structure being reclassified from Category II to Category III, and the structure is located in a seismic map area having an effective peak velocity-related acceleration (A_v) value of less than 0.15, compliance with these provisions is not required.

9.1.4 Seismic Performance. Seismic performance is a measure of the degree of protection provided for the public and building occupants against the potential hazards resulting from the effects of earthquake motions on *structures*. The level of seismicity and the *category per Table 1-1* are used in assigning structures to Seismic Performance Categories. *Category* IV is associated with the uses requiring the highest level of protection; Seismic Performance Category E is assigned to provide the highest level of design performance criteria.

9.1.4.1 Seismic Ground Acceleration Maps. The effective peak acceleration (A_a) and the effective peak velocity-related acceleration (A_v) shall be determined from Maps 9-1 and 9-2, respectively. *When reading Maps 9-1 and 9-2 use interpolation or the higher adjacent value.* Where site-specific ground motions are used or required, they shall be developed on the same basis, with 90% probability of the ground motions not being exceeded in 50 years.
*

9.1.4.2 Seismic Coefficients: The values of seismic coefficients (C_a and C_v) shall be determined from Section 9.1.4.2.3 or Tables 9.1.4.2.4A and 9.1.4.2.4B (shown herein) based on Soil Profile Types defined as follows:

A. Hard rock with measured shear wave velocity, $\bar{v}_s > 5{,}000$ ft/sec (1,500 m/s)
B. Rock with 2,500 ft/sec $< \bar{v}_s \leq 5{,}000$ ft/sec (760 m/sec $< \bar{v}_s \leq 1500$ m/s)
C. Very dense soil and soft rock with 1,200 ft/sec $\leq \bar{v}_s \leq 2{,}500$ ft/sec (*370 m/s $\leq \bar{v}_s \leq$ 760 m/s*) *or* * $\bar{N}$ or $\bar{N}_{ch} > 50$ or $\bar{s}_u \geq 2{,}000$ psf (100 kPa)
D. Stiff soil with 600 ft/sec $\leq \bar{v}_s \leq 1{,}200$ ft/sec (180 m/s $\leq \bar{v}_s \leq$ *370* m/s) or with $15 \leq \bar{N}$ or $\bar{N}_{ch} \leq 50$ or 1,000 psf $\leq \bar{s}_u \leq 2{,}000$ psf (50 kPa $\leq \bar{s}_u \leq 100$ kPa)
E. A soil profile with $\bar{v}_s < 600$ ft/sec (180 m/s) or any profile with more than 10 ft (3 m) of soft clay. Soft clay is defined as soil with *PI* > 20, $w \geq 40$%, and $\bar{s}_u < 500$ psf (25 kPa)

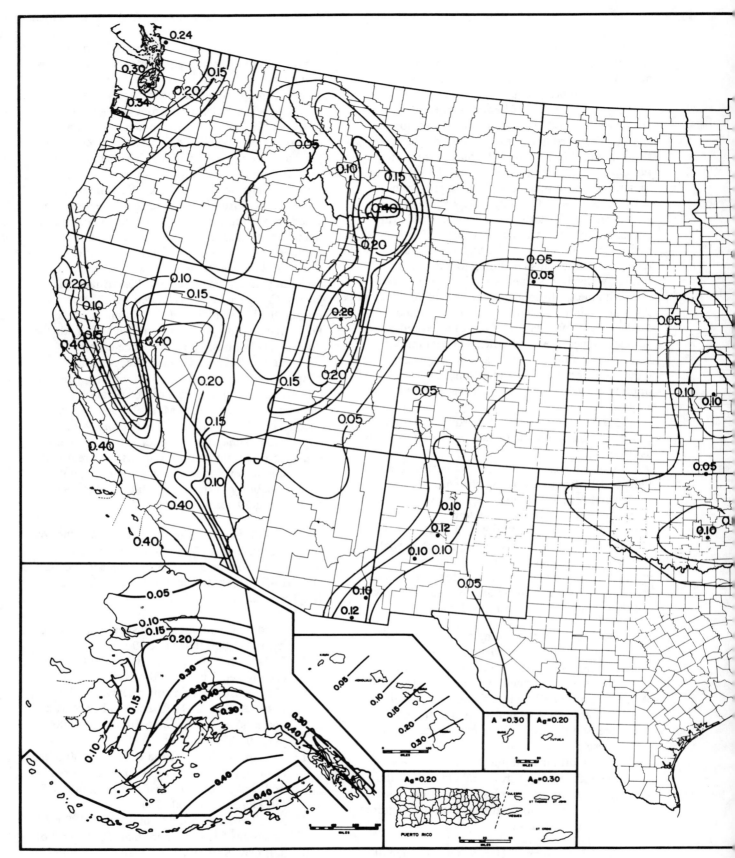

MAP 9-1. *Contour Map for Coefficient A_a*

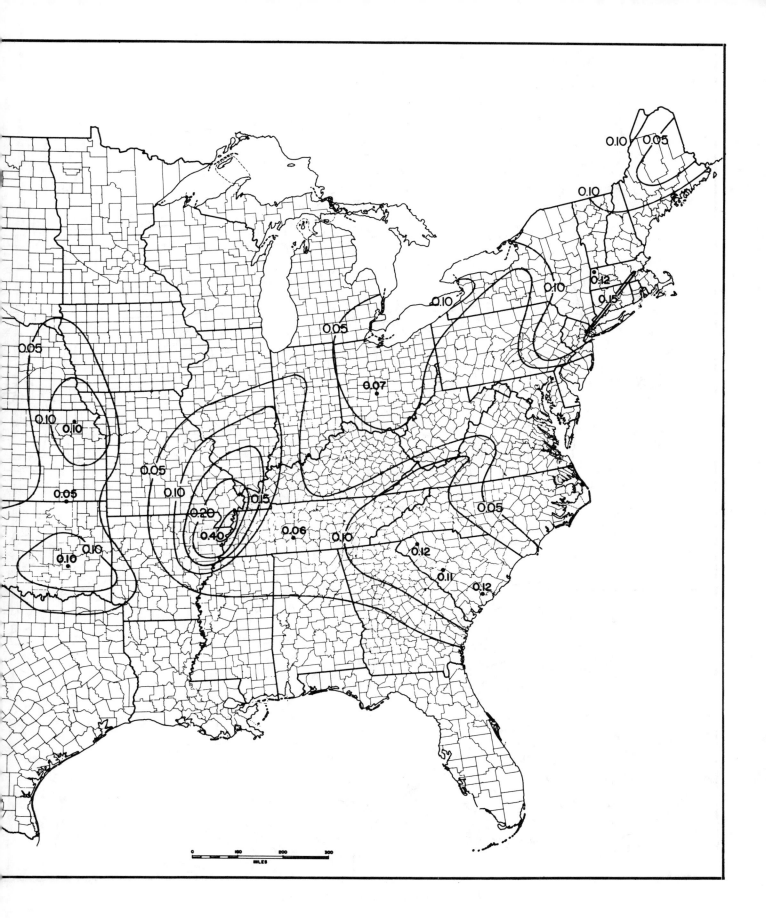

49

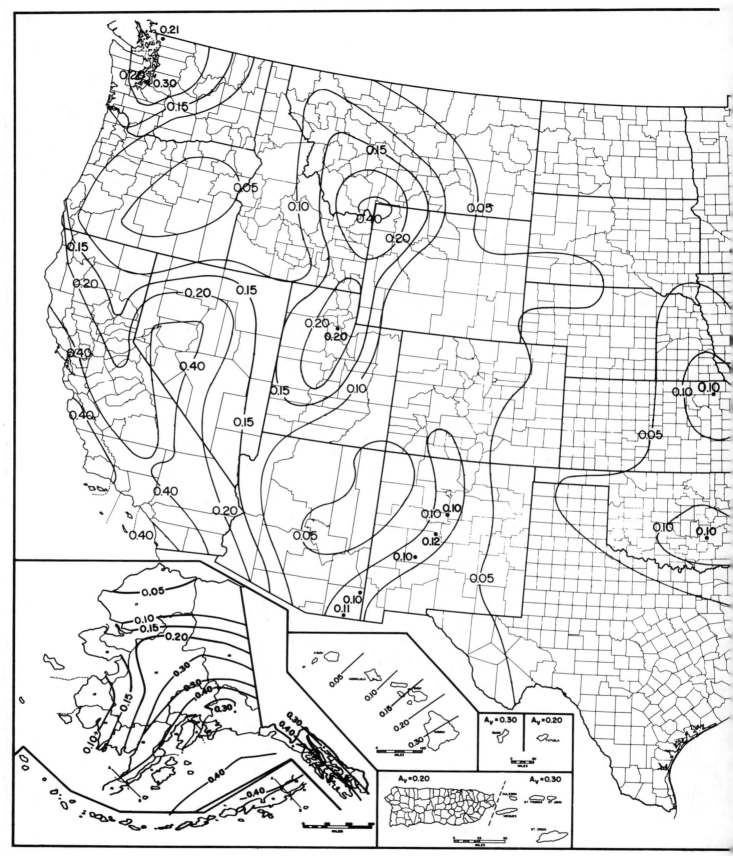

MAP 9-2. *Contour Map for* Coefficient A_v

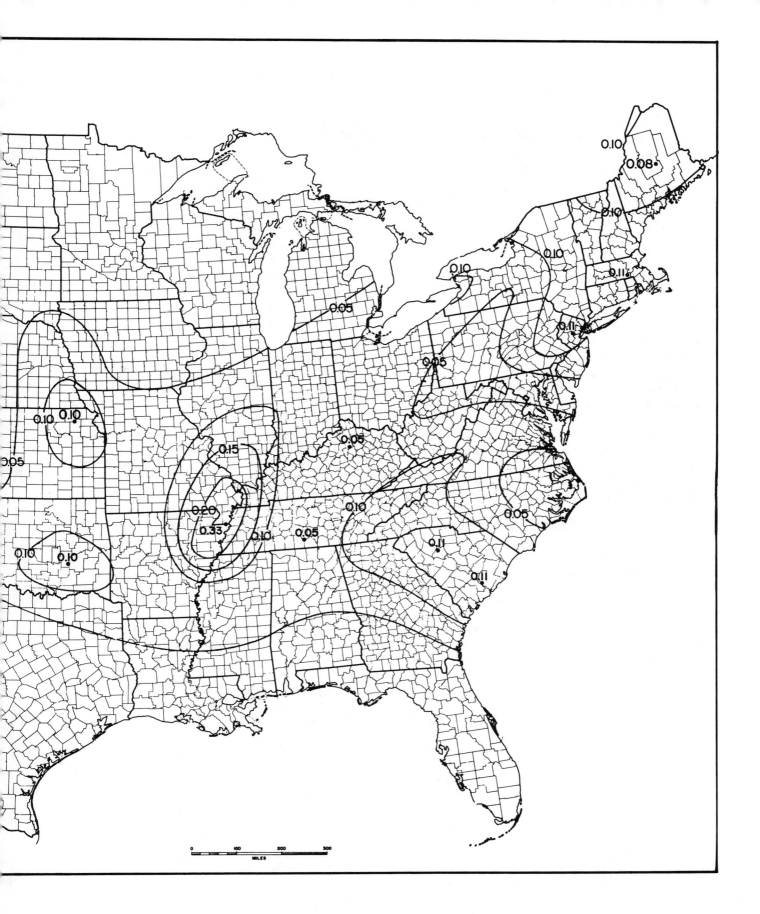

51

F. Soils requiring site-specific evaluations:
1. Soils vulnerable to potential failure or collapse under seismic loading such as liquefiable soils, quick and highly sensitive clays, collapsible weakly cemented soils.
2. Peats and/or highly organic clays [$H > 10$ ft (3 m) of peat and/or highly organic clay, where H = thickness of soil]
3. Very high plasticity clays [$H > 25$ ft (7.6 m) with $PI > 75$]
4. Very thick soft/medium stiff clays [$H > 120$ ft (37 m)]

Exception: When the soil properties are not known in sufficient detail to determine the Soil Profile Type, Type D shall be used. Soil Profile *Type E* shall *be used when the authority having jurisdiction* determines that Soil Profile *Type E* is present at the site or in the event that *Type E* is established by geotechnical data.

The following standards are referenced in the provisions for determining the seismic coefficients:

[9.1.4.2-1] ASTM D1586-84, Test Method for Penetration Test and Split-Barrell Sampling of Soils, 1984.

[9.1.4.2-2] ASTM D4318-93, Test Method for Liquid Limit, Plastic Limit, and Plasticity Index of Soils, 1993.

[9.1.4.2-3] ASTM D2216-92, Test Method for Laboratory Determination of Water (Moisture) Content of Soil and Rock, 1992.

[9.1.4.2-4] ASTM D2166-91, Test Method for

Unconfined Compressive Strength of Cohesive Soil, 1991.

[9.1.4.2-5] ASTM D2850-87, Test Method for Unconsolidated, Undrained Compressive Strength of Cohesive Soils in Triaxial Compression.
*

9.1.4.2.1 Steps for Classifying a Site: The Soil Profile Type of a site shall be determined using the following steps:

Step 1: Check for the four categories of Soil Profile Type F requiring site-specific evaluation. If the site corresponds to any of these categories, classify the site as Soil Profile Type F and conduct a site-specific evaluation.

Step 2: Check for the existence of a total thickness of soft clay > 10 ft (3 m). * If this criterion is satisfied, classify the site as Soil Profile Type E.

Step 3: Categorize the site using one of the following three methods with $\bar{v}_s$, $\bar{N}$, and $\bar{s}_u$ computed in all cases as specified by the definitions in Section 9.1.4.2.2:

a. The $\bar{v}_s$ method: Determine $\bar{v}_s$ for the top 100 ft (30.5 m) *of soil. Compare the value of $\bar{v}_s$ with those given in Section 9.1.4.2 and Table 9.1.4.2 and assign the corresponding Soil Profile Type.*

$\bar{v}_s$ for rock * shall be measured on site or estimated by a geotechnical engineer or engineering geologist/seismologist for competent rock with moderate fracturing and weathering.

TABLE 9.1.4.2
Soil Profile Type Classification

Soil Profile Type	$\bar{v}_s$	$\bar{N}$ or $\bar{N}_{ch}$	$\bar{s}_u$
A *Hard rock*	> 5,000 fps (> 1500 m/s)	Not applicable	Not applicable
B *Rock*	2,500 to 5,000 fps (760 to 1500 m/s)	Not applicable	Not applicable
C *Very dense soil and soft rock*	1,200 to 2,500 fps (370 to 760 m/s)	>50	>2,000 psf (>100 kPa)
D *Stiff soil*	600 to 1,200 fps (180 to 370 m/s)	15 to 50	1,000 to 2,000 psf (50 to 100 kPa)
E *Soil*	<600 fps (<180 m/s)	<15	<1000 psf (<50 kPa)
F *Soils requiring site specific evaluation*		1. Soils vulnerable to potential failure or collapse 2. Peats and/or highly organic clays 3. Very high plasticity clays 4. Very thick soft/medium clays	

$\overline{v}_s$ for softer and more highly fractured and weathered rock shall be measured on site or shall be classified as Soil Profile Type C.

The classification of hard rock, Soil Profile Type A, shall be supported by on-site measurements of $\overline{v}_s$ or on profiles of the same rock type in the same formation with an equal or greater degree of weathering and fracturing. Where hard rock conditions are known to be continuous to a depth of at least 100 ft (30 m), surficial measurements of $\overline{v}_s$ *are not prohibited from being* extrapolated to assess $\overline{v}_s$.

The rock categories, Soil Profile Types A and B, shall not be assigned to a site if there is more than 10 ft (3 m) of soil between the rock surface and the bottom of the spread footing or mat foundation.

b. The $\overline{N}$ method: Determine $\overline{N}$ for the top 100 ft (30.5 m) *of soil. Compare the value of* $\overline{N}$ *with those given in Section 9.1.4.2 and Table 9.1.4.2 and assign the corresponding Soil Profile Type.*

c. The $\overline{s}_u$ method: For cohesive soil layers, determine $\overline{s}_u$ for the top 100 ft (30 m) of soil. For cohesionless soil layers determine $\overline{N}_{ch}$ for the top 100 ft (30 m) of soil. Cohesionless soil is defined by a *PI* < 20, where cohesive soil is defined by a *PI* > 20. *Compare the values of* $\overline{s}_u$ *and* $\overline{N}_{ch}$ *with those given in Section 9.1.4.2 and Table 9.1.4.2 and assign the corresponding Soil Profile Type. When the* $\overline{N}_{ch}$ *and* $\overline{s}_u$ *criteria differ, assign the category with the softer soil (Soil Profile Type E soil is softer than D).*

9.1.4.2.2 Definitions: The definitions presented below apply to the upper 100 ft (30 m) of the site profile. Profiles containing distinctly different soil layers shall be subdivided into those layers designated by a number that ranges from 1 to *n* at the bottom where there are a total of *n* distinct layers in the upper 100 ft (30 m). *Where some of the n layers are cohesive and others are not, k is the number of cohesive layers and m is the number of cohesionless layers.* The symbol *i* refers to any one of the layers between 1 and *n*.

v_{si} is the shear wave velocity in ft/sec (m/s).

d_i is the thickness of any layer between 0 and 100 ft (30 m).

$\overline{v}_s$ is:

$$\overline{v}_s = \frac{\sum\limits_{i=1}^{n} d_i}{\sum\limits_{i=1}^{n} \dfrac{d_i}{v_{si}}}$$ (9.1.4.2-1)

whereby $\sum\limits_{i=1}^{n} d_i = 100$ ft (30 m)

N_i is the Standard Penetration Resistance [9.1.4.-1] not to exceed 100 blows/ft as directly measured in the field without corrections.

$\overline{N}$ is:

$$\overline{N} = \frac{\sum\limits_{i=1}^{n} d_i}{\sum\limits_{i=1}^{n} \dfrac{d_i}{N_i}}$$ (9.1.4.2-2)

$\overline{N}_{ch}$ is:

$$\overline{N}_{ch} = \frac{d_s}{\sum\limits_{i=1}^{} \dfrac{d_i}{N_i}}$$ (9.1.4.2-3)

whereby $\sum\limits_{i=1}^{m} d_i = d_s$.

(Use only d_i and N_i for cohesionless soils.)

d_s is the total thickness of cohesionless soil layers in the top 100 ft (30 m).

s_{ui} is the undrained shear strength in psf (kPa), not to exceed 5,000 psf (*240 kPa*), [9.1.4.2-4] or [9.1.4.2-5].

$\overline{s}_u$ is

$$\overline{s}_u = \frac{d_c}{\sum\limits_{i=1}^{k} \dfrac{d_i}{S_{ui}}}$$ (9.1.4.2-4)

whereby $\sum\limits_{i=1}^{k} d_i = d_c$.

d_c is the total thickness $(100 - d_s)$ of cohesive soil layers in the top 100 ft (30 m).

TABLE 9.1.4.2.3A
Values of F_a as a Function of Site Conditions and Shaking Intensity

Soil Profile Type	Shaking Intensity				
	$A_a \leq 0.1g$	$A_a = 0.2g$	$A_a = 0.3g$	$A_a = 0.4g$	$A_a \geq 0.5g^b$
A	0.8	0.8	0.8	0.8	0.8
B	1.0	1.0	1.0	1.0	1.0
C	1.2	1.2	1.1	1.0	1.0
D	1.6	1.4	1.2	1.1	1.0
E	2.5	1.7	1.2	0.9	a
F	a	a	a	a	a

Note: Use straight line interpolation for intermediate values of A_a.

[a]Site-specific geotechnical investigation and dynamic site response analyses shall be performed.

[b]*Site-specific studies required per Section 9.1.4.2.3 may result in higher values of A_a than included on the hazard maps, as may the provisions of Section 9.2.6.*

PI is the plasticity index, [9.1.4.2-2].

w is the moisture content in percent, [9.1.4.2-3].

9.1.4.2.3 Site Coefficients: When the values for site coefficients F_a and F_v are required for other provisions, such as Section 9.2.6, they shall be determined from Tables 9.1.4.2.3A and 9.1.4.2.3B respectively.

9.1.4.2.4 Seismic Coefficient C_a and C_v: Seismic coefficient C_a based on Soil Profile Type and A_a is determined from Table 9.1.4.2.4A.

Seismic coefficient C_v based on Soil Profile Type and A_v is determined from Table 9.1.4.2.4B.

*

Alternately, determine seismic coefficients C_a and C_v from the site coefficients as follows:

$$C_a = F_a A_a \qquad (9.1.4.2.4\text{-}1)$$

$$C_v = F_v A_v \qquad (9.1.4.2.4\text{-}2)$$

9.1.4.3 High Hazard Exposure Structures: All buildings and structures assigned to Category IV per Table 1-1 shall meet the following requirements:

9.1.4.3.1 *Category IV* Building Protected Access Where operational access to a *Category IV* building is required through an adjacent building, the adjacent building shall conform to the requirements for *Category IV* buildings. Where operational access is less than 10 ft (3 m) from the interior lot line or another building on the same lot, protection from potential falling debris from adjacent buildings shall be provided by the owner of the *Category IV* building.

9.1.4.3.2 *Category IV* Function Designated seismic systems in *Category IV* buildings shall be provided with the capacity to function, in so far as practical, during and after an earthquake. Site-specific conditions as specified in Section 9.3.3.8 that could result in the interruption of util-

TABLE 9.1.4.2.3B
Values of F_v as Function of Site Conditions and Shaking Intensity

Soil Profile Type	Shaking Intensity				
	$A_a \leq 0.1g$	$A_a = 0.2g$	$A_a = 0.3g$	$A_a = 0.4g$	$A_a \geq 0.5g^b$
A	0.8	0.8	0.8	0.8	0.8
B	1.0	1.0	1.0	1.0	1.0
C	1.7	1.6	1.5	1.4	1.3
D	2.4	2.0	1.8	1.6	1.5
E	3.5	3.2	2.8	2.4	a
F	a	a	a	a	a

Note: Use straight line interpolation for intermediate values of A_v.

[a]Site-specific geotechnical investigation and dynamic site response analyses shall be performed.

[b]*Site-specific studies required per Section 9.2.2.4.3 may result in higher values of A_v than included on the hazard maps, as may the provisions of Section 9.2.6.*

TABLE 9.1.4.2.4A
Seismic Coefficient C_a

Soil Profile Type	Shaking Intensity						
	$A_a < 0.05g$	$A_a = 0.05g$	$A_a = 0.10g$	$A_a = 0.20g$	$A_a = 0.30g$	$A_a = 0.40g$	$A_a \geq 0.5g^b$
A	A_a	0.04	0.08	0.16	0.24	0.32	0.40
B	A_a	0.05	0.1	0.2	0.3	0.40	0.50
C	A_a	0.06	0.12	0.24	0.33	0.40	0.50
D	A_a	0.08	0.16	0.28	0.36	0.44	0.50
E	A_a	0.13	0.25	0.34	0.36	0.36	a

NOTE: For intermediate values, the higher value or straight-line interpolation shall be used to determine the value of C_a.

aSite specific geotechnical investigation and dynamic site response analyses shall be performed.

bSite specific studies required per Section 9.2.2.4.3 may result in higher values of A_a than included on the hazard maps, as may the provisions of Section 9.2.6.

TABLE 9.1.4.2.4B
Seismic Coefficient C_v

Soil Profile Type	Shaking Intensity						
	$A_a < 0.05g$	$A_a = 0.05g$	$A_a = 0.10g$	$A_a = 0.20g$	$A_a = 0.30g$	$A_a = 0.40g$	$A_a \geq 0.5g^b$
A	A_v	0.04	0.08	0.16	0.24	0.32	0.40
B	A_v	0.05	0.10	0.20	0.30	0.40	0.50
C	A_v	0.09	0.17	0.32	0.45	0.56	0.65
D	A_v	0.12	0.24	0.40	0.54	0.64	0.75
E	A_v	0.18	0.35	0.64	0.84	0.96	a

NOTE: For intermediate values, the higher value or straight-line interpolation shall be used to determine the value of C_v.

aSite specific geotechnical investigation and dynamic site response analyses shall be performed.

bSite specific studies required per Section 9.2.2.4.3 may result in higher values of A_v than included on the hazard maps, as may the provisions of Section 9.2.6.

ity services shall be considered when providing the capacity to continue to function.

9.1.4.4 Seismic Performance Category Buildings shall be assigned a Seismic Performance Category in accordance with Table 9.1.4.4.

9.1.4.5 Site Limitation for Seismic Performance Category E A building assigned to category E shall not be sited where there is a *known* potential for an active fault to cause rupture of the ground surface at the building.

9.1.5 Alternate Materials and Methods of Construction Alternate materials and methods of

TABLE 9.1.4.4
Seismic Performance Category

Value of A_v	Category per Table 1-1		
	I or II	III	IV
$A_v < 0.05$	A	A	A
$0.05 \leq A_v < 0.10$	B	B	C
$0.10 \leq A_v < 0.15$	C	C	D
$0.15 \leq A_v < 0.20$	C	D	D
$0.20 \leq A_v$	D	D	E

construction to those prescribed in these provisions shall not be used unless approved by the *authority having jurisdiction*. Substantiating evidence shall be submitted demonstrating that the proposed alternate, for the purpose intended, will be at least equal in strength, durability, and seismic resistance.

9.1.6 Quality Assurance *The performance required of buildings in Seismic Performance Categories C, D, or E requires that special attention be paid to quality assurance during construction. Refer to A.9.1.6 for supplementary provisions.*

9.1.7 Definitions *The definitions presented in this section provide the meaning of the terms used in these provisions. Definitions of terms that have a specific meaning relative to the use of wood, steel, concrete, or masonry are presented in the section devoted to the material (Sections A.9.5–A.9.9, respectively).*

Acceleration:

Effective Peak Acceleration: A coefficient representing ground motion at a period of about 0.1–0.5 sec (A_a) as determined from Section 9.1.4.1.

Effective Peak Velocity-Related Acceleration: A coefficient representing ground motion at a period of about 1.0 sec (A_v) as determined from Section 9.1.4.1.

Active Fault: A fault determined to be active by the authority having jurisdiction, from properly substantiated geotechnical data (e.g., most recent mapping of active faults by the U.S. Geological Survey).

Appendage: An architectural component such as a canopy, marquee, ornamental balcony, or statuary.

Approval: The written acceptance by the *authority having jurisdiction* of documentation that establishes the qualification of a material, system, component, procedure, or person to fulfill the requirements of these provisions for the intended use.

Architectural Component Support: Those structural members or assemblies of members, including braces, frames, struts and attachments, that transmit all loads and forces between architectural systems, components, or elements and the building structure.

Attachments: Means by which components and their supports are secured or connected to the seismic-force-resisting system of the structure. Such attachments include anchor bolts, welded connections, and mechanical fasteners.

Base: The level at which the horizontal seismic ground motions are considered to be imparted to the building.

Base Shear: Total design lateral force or shear at the base.

Brittle: Systems, members, materials, and connections that do not exhibit significant energy dissipation capacity in the inelastic range.

*

Component: A part of an architectural, electrical, mechanical, or structural system.

Component, Equipment: A mechanical or electrical component or element that is part of a mechanical and/or electrical system within or without a building system.

Component, Flexible: Component, including its attachments, having a fundamental period greater than 0.06 sec.

Component, Rigid: Component, including its attachments, having a fundamental period less than or equal to 0.06 sec.

*

Concrete, Plain: Concrete that is either unreinforced or contains less reinforcement than the minimum amount specified in Ref. 9.6-1 for reinforced concrete.

Concrete, Reinforced: Concrete reinforced

with no less than the minimum amount required by [9.6-1], prestressed or nonprestressed, and designed on the assumption that the two materials act together in resisting forces.

*

Container: A large-scale independent component used as a receptacle or vessel to accommodate plants, refuse, or similar uses, *not including liquids.*

*

Design Documents: The drawings, specifications, computations, reports, certifications, or other substantiation required by *the authority having jurisdiction* to verify compliance with these provisions.

Design Earthquake: The earthquake that produces ground motions at the site under consideration that have a 90% probability of not being exceeded in 50 years.

Designated Seismic Systems: The seismic force resisting system and those architectural, electrical, and mechanical systems or their components *for which the component importance factor, I_p, is 1.5.*

Diaphragm: A horizontal, or nearly horizontal, portion of the seismic resisting system designed to transmit seismic forces to the vertical elements of the seismic force resisting system.

Displacement

Design Displacement: The design earthquake lateral displacement, excluding additional displacement due to actual and accidental torsion, required for design of the isolation system.

Total Design Displacement: The design earthquake lateral displacement, including additional displacement due to actual and accidental torsion, required for design of the isolation system or an element thereof.

Total Maximum Displacement: The maximum capable earthquake lateral displacement, including additional displacement due to actual and accidental torsion, required for verification of the stability of the isolation system or elements thereof, design of building separations, and vertical load testing of isolator unit prototypes.

Displacement Restraint System: A collection of structural elements that limits lateral displacement due to the maximum capable earthquake.

Effective Stiffness: The value of the lateral force in the isolation system, or an element thereof, divided by the corresponding lateral displacement.

Effective Damping: The value of equivalent viscous damping corresponding to energy dissipated during cyclic response of the isolation system.

Enclosure: An interior space surrounded by walls

Equipment Support: Those structural members, assemblies of members, or manufactured elements, including braces, frames, legs, lugs, snuggers, hangers, or saddles, that transmit gravity and operating loads between the equipment and the structure.

*

Frame:

Braced Frame: An essentially vertical truss, or its equivalent, of the concentric or eccentric type that is provided in a bearing wall, building frame, or dual system to resist seismic forces.

Concentrically Braced Frame (CBF): A braced frame in which the members are subjected primarily to axial forces.

Eccentrically Braced Frame (EBF): A diagonally braced frame in which at least one end of each brace frames into a beam a short distance from a beam-column joint or from another diagonal brace.

Ordinary Concentrically Braced Frame (OCBF): A steel concentrically braced frame in which members and connections are designed in accordance with the provisions of [9.5-3] without modification.

Special Concentrically Braced Frame (SCBF): A steel concentrically braced frame in which members and connections are designed for ductile behavior. Special concentrically braced frames shall conform to Section A.9.5.2.1.

Moment Frame:

Intermediate Moment Frame (IMF): A moment frame in which members and joints are capable of resisting forces by flexure as well as along the axis of the members. Intermediate moment frames of reinforced concrete shall conform to Section A.9.6.3.2.

Ordinary Moment Frame (OMF): A moment frame in which members and joints are capable of resisting forces by flexure as well as along the axis of the members. Ordinary moment frames shall conform to [9.5-3] or Section A.9.6.3.1.

Special Moment Frame (SMF): A moment frame in which members and joints are capable of resisting forces by flexure as well as along the axis of the members. Special moment frames shall conform to [9.5-3] or Section A.9.6.3.3.

Frame System:

Building Frame System: A structural system with an essentially complete space frame providing support for vertical loads. Seismic force resistance is provided by shear walls or braced frames.

Dual Frame System: A structural system with an essentially complete space frame providing support for vertical loads. Seismic force resistance is provided by moment resisting frames and shear walls or braced frames as prescribed in Section 9.2.1.2.1.

Space Frame System: A structural system composed of interconnected members, other than bearing walls, that is capable of supporting vertical loads and that also may provide resistance to seismic forces.

Gravity Load (W): The total dead load and applicable portions of other loads as defined in Section 9.2.3.2

*

High Temperature Energy Source: A fluid, gas, or vapor whose temperature exceeds 220°F.

Inspection, Special: The observation of the work by the special inspector to determine compliance with the approved design documents and these provisions.

Continuous Special Inspection: The full-time observation of the work by an approved special inspector who is present in the area where work is being performed.

Periodic Special Inspection: The part-time or intermittent observation of the work by an approved special inspector who is present in the area where work has been or is being performed.

Inspector, Special (who shall be identified as the Owner's Inspector): A person approved by the *authority having jurisdiction* to perform special inspection. *The authority having jurisdiction* shall have the option to approve the quality assurance personnel of a fabricator as a special inspector.

Inverted Pendulum Type Structures: Structures that have a large portion of their mass concentrated near the top and, thus, have essentially one degree of freedom in horizontal translation. The structures are usually *T*-shaped with a single column supporting the beams or slab at the top.

Isolation Interface: The boundary between the upper portion of the structure, which is isolated, and the lower portion of the structure, which moves rigidly with the ground.

Isolation System: The collection of structural elements that includes all individual isolator units, all structural elements that transfer force between elements of the isolation system, and all connections to other structural elements. The isolation system also includes the wind-restraint system if such a system is used to meet the design requirements of this section.

Isolator Unit: A horizontally flexible and vertically stiff structural element of the isolation system that permits large lateral deformations under design seismic load. An isolator unit may be used either as part of or in addition to the weight-supporting system of the building.

*

Maximum Capable Earthquake: The maximum level of earthquake ground shaking that may ever be expected at the building site within the known geological framework. In map areas with an A_a value of 0.3 or greater, this intensity may be taken as the level of earthquake ground motion that has a 10% probability of being exceed in a 100-year time period.

*

P-Delta Effect: The secondary effect on shears and moments of frame members due to the action of the vertical loads induced by displacement of the building frame resulting from seismic forces.

Quality Assurance Plan: A detailed written procedure that establishes the systems and components subject to special inspection and testing. The type and frequency of testing and the extent and duration of special inspection are given in the quality-assurance plan.

Roofing Unit: A unit of roofing *tile or similar* material weighing more than 1 lb.

Seismic Coefficients: Coefficients C_a and C_v determined from Section 9.1.4.2.4 or Tables 9.1.4.2.4A or 9.1.4.2.4B based on Soil Profile Type and A_a and A_v, respectively.

Seismic Force Resisting System: That part of the structural system that has been considered in the design to provide the required resistance to the seismic forces prescribed herein.

Seismic Forces: The assumed forces prescribed herein, related to the response of the building to earthquake motions, to be used in the design of the building and its components.

*

Seismic Performance Category: A classification assigned to a building as defined in Section 9.1.4.4.

*

Shear Panel: A floor, roof, or wall component sheathed to act as a shear wall or diaphragm.

*

Storage Racks: Include industrial pallet racks, moveable shelf racks, and stacker racks made of cold-formed or hot-rolled structural members. Does not include other types of racks such as drive-in and drive-through racks, cantilever racks, portable racks, or racks made of materials other than steel.

Story Drift: The difference of horizontal deflections at the top and bottom of the story as determined in Section 9.2.3.7.1.

Story Drift Ratio: The story drift, as determined in Section 9.2.3.7.1, divided by the story height.

Story Shear: The summation of design lateral seismic forces at levels above the story under consideration.

*

Testing Agency: A company or corporation that provides testing and/or inspection services. The person in charge of the special inspector(s) and the testing services shall be an engineer licensed by the state to practice as such in the applicable discipline.

Toughness: The ability of a material to absorb energy without losing significant strength.

*

Utility or Service Interface: The connection of the building's mechanical and electrical distribution systems to the utility or service company's distribution system.

Veneers: Facings or ornamentation of brick, concrete, stone, tile, or similar materials attached to a backing.

Wall: A component, *usually placed vertically,* used to enclose or divide space.

Bearing Wall: An exterior or interior wall providing support for vertical loads.

Cripple Wall: Short stud wall between the foundation and the lowest framed floors with studs not less than 14 in. long—also known as a knee wall.

Light Framed Wall: A wall with wood or steel studs.

Nonbearing Wall: An exterior or interior wall that does not provide support for vertical loads other than its own weight.

Shear Wall: A wall, bearing or nonbearing, designed to resist seismic forces acting in the plane of the wall.

Wall System, Bearing: A structural system with bearing walls providing support for all or major portions of the vertical loads. Shear walls or braced frames provide seismic force resistance.

*

9.1.8 Symbols. The unit dimensions used with the items covered by the symbols shall be consistent throughout except where specifically noted. The symbols and definitions presented in this section apply to these provisions as indicated.

A_a = The seismic coefficient representing the effective peak acceleration as determined in Section 9.1.4.1.

A,B,C,D,E = *The Seismic Performace Category as defined in Table 9.1.4.4*

A,B,C,D,E,F = The Soil Profile Types as defined in Section 9.1.4.2

A_o = The area of the load-carrying foundation, Section 9.2.5.2.1.

A_p = Component acceleration coefficient (expressed as a percentage of gravity) at point of attachment to structure, Eq. (9.3.1.3-3).

A_r = Component acceleration coefficient (expressed as a percentage of gravity) at structure roof level, Eq. (9.3.1.3-4).

A_s = Structure response accleration coefficient (expressed as a percentage of gravity), Section 9.3.1.3.

A_v = The seismic coefficient representing the effective peak velocity-related acceleration as determined in Section 9.1.4.1.

A_x = The torsional amplification factor, Section 9.2.3.5.2

a_d = The incremental factor related to P-delta effects in Section 9.2.3.7.2.

a_p = The amplification factor related to the response of a system or component as affected by the type of seismic attachment, determined in Section 9.3.1.3.

C_a = The seismic coefficient based upon the Soil Profile Type and the Value A_a as determined in Section 9.1.4.2.3 or Table 9.1.4.2.4A.

C_d = The deflection amplification factor as given in Table 9.2.2.2.

C_s = The seismic design coefficient determined in Section 9.2.3.2 (dimensionless).

$\tilde{C}_s$ = the value of C_s computed from Eq. (9.2.3.2.1-1) using the fundamental natural period of the flex-

ibly supported (T) defined in Section 9.2.5.2.1.1.

C_{sm} = The modal seismic design coefficient determined in Section 9.2.4.5 (dimensionless).

C_T = The building period coefficient in Section 9.2.3.3.

C_u = Coefficient for upper limit on calculated period; see Section 9.2.3.3

C_v = The seismic coefficient based upon the Soil Profile Type and the value A_v as determined in Section 9.1.4.2.3 or Table 9.1.4.2.4B.

C_{vx} = The vertical distribution factor as determined in Section 9.2.3.4.

C_{vxm} = The vertical distribution factor in the mth mode, Section 9.2.4.6

D = The effect of dead load.

Dp = Relative seismic displacement that the component must be designed to accomodate, Section 9.3.1.4.

F_a = Acceleration-based site factor (at 0.3-sec period).

F_i, F_n, F_x = The portion of the seismic base shear, V, induced at Level i, n, or x, respectively, as determined in Section 9.2.3.4.

F_p = The seismic force acting on a component of a building as determined in 9.2.2.5.1.1, 9.2.2.5.1.2, 9.2.2.5.1.3, or 9.3.1.3.

F_v = Velocity-based site factor (at 1.0-sec period).

F_{xm} = The portion of the seismic base shear, V_m, induced at Level x as determined in Section 9.2.4.6.

G_o = The average shear modulus for the soils beneath the foundation at small strain levels, Section 9.2.5.2.1.1.

g = The acceleration due to gravity.

h = Average Roof elevation of structure relative to grade elevation, Section 9.3.1.3.

H = Thickness of soil.

h_i, h_n, h_x = The height above the base Level i, n, or x, respectively.

h_{sx} = The story height below Level x = $(h_x - h_{x-1})$.

$\bar{h}$ = The effective height of the building as determined in Section 9.2.5.2.1.1.

I_o = The static moment of inertia of the

load carrying foundation about a horizontal centroidal axis normal to the direction in which the structure is analyzed, Section 9.2.5.2.1.

I_p = Component importance factor that varies from 1.00 to 1.50, Section 9.3.1.5.

i = The building level referred to by the subscript i; $i = 1$ designates the first level above the base.

K_p = The stiffness of the equipment support attachment, Section 9.3.3.3.

K_y = The lateral stiffness of the foundation as determined in Section 9.2.5.2.1.1.

K_θ = The rocking stiffness of the foundation as determined in Section 9.2.5.2.1.1.

k = The distribution exponent given in Section 9.2.3.4.

$\bar{k}$ = The stiffness of the building when fixed at the base, determined in Section 9.2.5.2.1.1.

L_o = The overall length of the side of the foundation in the direction being analyzed, Section 9.2.5.2.1.2.

M_f = The foundation overturning design moment as defined in Section 9.2.3.6.

M_t = The torsional moment resulting from the location of the building masses, Section 9.2.3.5.2.

M_{ta} = The accidental torsional moment as determined in Section 9.2.3.5.2.

M_x = The building overturning design moment at Level x as defined in Section 9.2.3.6 or Section 9.2.4.7.

M_o = The overturning moment at the base determined in accordance with Section 9.2.3.6 using the unmodified seismic forces and not including the reduction permitted in the design of the foundation, Section 9.2.5.2.3.

M_{ol} = The overturning base moment for the fundamental mode of the fixed-base building, as determined in Sec. 9.2.4.7. using the unmodified modal base shear V_1, Section 9.2.5.2.3.2.

m = A subscript denoting the mode of vibration under consideration; i.e., $m = 1$ for the fundamental mode.

N = Number of stories, Section 9.2.3.3.

N = Standard penetration resistance, [9.1.4.2-1].

$\bar{N}$ = Average field standard penetration resistance for the top 100 ft (30 m); see Section 9.1.4.2.

N_{ch} = Average standard penetration resistance for cohesionless soil layers for the top 100 ft (30 m); see Section 9.1.4.2.

n = Designates the level that is uppermost in the main portion of the building.

PI = Plasticity index, [9.1.4.2-2].

P_x = The total unfactored vertical design load at and above Level x, for use in Section 9.2.3.7.2.

Q_E = The effect of horizontal seismic (earthquake-induced) forces, Sec 9.2.2.6

R = The response modification coefficient as given in Table 9.2.2.2.

R_p = Component response modification factor that varies from 1.50 to 6.00, Table 9.3.2.2 and Table 9.3.3.2.

r_a, r_m = Characteristic foundation lengths as determined in Section 9.2.5.2.1.1

$\bar{s}_u$ = Average undrained shear strength in top 100 ft (30 m); see Section 9.1.4.2, [9.1.4.2-4] or [9.1.4.2-5].

T = The fundamental period of the building as determined in Section 9.2.3.2.1

T_a = The approximate fundamental period of the building as determined in Section 9.2.3.3

T_m = The modal period of vibration of the mth mode of the building as determined in Section 9.2.4.5.

T_p = The fundamental period of the component and its attachment, Section 9.3.3.3.

V = The total design lateral force or shear at the base, Section 9.2.3.2.

V_t = The design value of the seismic base shear as determined in Section 9.2.4.8.

V_x = The seismic design shear in Story x as determined in Section 9.2.3.5 or 9.2.4.8.

w = Moisture content (in percent), [9.1.4.2-3].

W = The total gravity load of the building as defined in Section 9.2.3.2.

W_c = The gravity load of a component of the building.

W_m = The effective modal gravity load determined in accordance with Eq. (9.2.4.5).

W_p = Component operating weight, Section 9.3.1.3.

w_i, w_n, w_x = The portion of W that is located at or assigned to Level i, n, or x, respectively.

$\overline{W}$ = The effective gravity load of the building as determined in Section 9.2.5.2.1.

X = Height of upper support attachment at level as measured fgrom grade, Section 9.3.1.4.

x = The level under consideration;

x = 1 designates the first level above the base.

Y = Height of lower support attachement at level y as measured from grade, Section 9.3.1.4.

α = The relative weight density of the structure as determined in Section 9.2.5.2.1.1.

$\tilde{\beta}$ = The fraction of critical damping for the structure-foundation system determined in Section 9.2.5.2.1.2.

β_o = The foundation damping factor as specified in Fig. 9.2.5.2.1.2.

γ = The average unit weight of the soils, Section 9.2.5.2.1.1.

Δ = The design story drift as determined in Section 9.2.3.7.1.

Δ_{aA} = Allowable story drift for Building A, Section 9.3.1.4.

Δ_{aB} = Allowable story drift for Building, Section 9.3.1.4.

Δ_a = The allowable story drift as specified in Section 9.2.2.7.

Δ_m = The design modal story drift determined in Section 9.2.4.6.

δ_{max} = The maximum displacement at Level x, considering torsion, Section 9.2.3.5.2

δ_{avg} = The average of the displacements at the extreme points of the structure at Level x, Sec 9.2.3.5.2.

δ_x = The deflection of Level x at the center of the mass at and above Level x, Eq. 9.2.3.7.1

δ_{xA} = Deflection at building level x of Building A, Section 9.3.1.4.

δ_{xe} = The deflection of Level x at the center of the mass at and above Level x determined by an elastic analysis, Section 9.2.3.7.1.

δ_{xem} = The modal deflection of Level x at the center of the mass at and above Level x determined by an elastic analysis, Section 9.2.4.6.

δ_{xm} = The modal deflection of Level x at the center of the mass at and above Level x as determined by Eq. (9.2.4.6-3).

δ_{yA} = Deflection at building level y of Building A, Section 9.3.1.4.

δ_{xB} = Deflection at building level x of Building B, Section 9.3.1.4.

δ_{yB} = Deflection at building level y of Building B, Section 9.3.1.4.

θ = The stability coefficient for P-delta effects as determined in Section 9.2.3.7.2.

τ = The overturning moment reduction factor, Eq. 9.2.3.4.

ϕ = The strength reduction factor or resistance factor.

ϕ_{im} = The displacement amplitude at the ith level of the building for the fixed base condition when vibratingin its mth mode, Section 9.2.4.5.

$\overline{v}_s$ = Average shear wave velocity in top 100 ft (30 m); see Section 9.1.4.2.

v_{so} = The average shear wave velocity for the soils beneath the foundation at small strain levels (10^{-3} % or less), Section 9.2.5.2.1.1.

9.2 Structural Design Criteria, Analysis & Procedures

9.2.1 This section has been intentionally left blank *

9.2.2 Structural Design Requirements

9.2.2.1 **Design Basis.** The seismic analysis and design procedures to be used in the design of buildings and their components shall be as prescribed in this chapter. The design ground motions can occur along any *horizontal* direction of a building. The design seismic forces, and their distribution over the height of the building, shall be established in accordance with the procedures in Sections 9.2.3 *and* 9.2.4 and the corresponding internal forces in the members of the building shall be determined using a linearly elastic model. An approved alternate procedure *shall not* be used to establish the seismic forces and their distribution *unless* the corresponding internal forces and deformations in the members *are* determined using a model consistent with the procedure adopted.

Individual members shall be sized for the shears, axial forces, and moments determined in accordance with these provisions, and connections shall develop the strength of the connected members or the forces indicated previously. The deformation of the building shall not exceed the prescribed limits when the building is subjected to the design seismic forces.

A continuous load path, or paths, with adequate strength and stiffness shall be provided to transfer all forces from the point of application to the final point of resistance. The foundation shall be designed to *resist* the forces developed *and accommodate* the movements imparted to the building by the design ground motions. In the determination of the foundation design criteria, *special recognition shall be given* to the dynamic nature of the forces, the expected ground motions, and the design basis for strength and ductility of the structure.

9.2.2.2 Structural Framing Systems. The basic structural framing systems to be used are indicated in Table 9.2.2.2. Each type is subdivided by the types of vertical element used to resist lateral seismic forces. The structural system used shall be in accordance with the seismic performance category and height limitations indicated in Table 9.2.2.2 The appropriate response modification factor (R) and the deflection amplification factor (C_d) indicated in Table 9.2.2.2 shall be used in determining the base shear and design story drift. Structural framing and resisting systems that are not contained in Table 9.2.2.2 shall *not* be permitted *unless* analytical and test data are submitted that establish the dynamic characteristics and demonstrate the lateral force resistance and energy dissipation capacity to be equivalent to the structural systems listed in Table 9.2.2.2 for equivalent response modification factor (R) values. Special framing requirements are indicated in Sections 9.2.2.5, 9.5, 9.6, 9.7, 9.8, and 9.9 for buildings assigned to the various seismic performance categories.

9.2.2.2.1 Dual System. For a dual system, the moment frame shall be capable of resisting at least 25% of the design seismic forces. The total seismic force resistance is to be provided by the combination of the moment frame and the shear walls or braced frames in proportion to their rigidities.

9.2.2.2.2 Combinations of Framing Systems. Different structural framing systems are permitted along the two orthogonal axes of the building. Combinations of framing systems shall comply with the requirements of this section.

9.2.2.2.2.1 Combination Framing Factor. The response modification factor, R, in the direction under consideration at any story shall not exceed the lowest response modification factor (R) for the seismic force resisting system in the same direction considered above that story.

Exception: *The limit does not apply to* supported structural systems with a weight equal to or less than 10 percent of the weight of the building.

9.2.2.2.2.2 Combination Framing Detailing Requirements. The detailing requirements of Section 9.2.2.5 required by the higher response modification factor (R) shall be used for structural components common to systems having different response modification factors.

9.2.2.2.3 Seismic Performance Categories A, B, and C. The structural framing system for buildings assigned to Seismic Performance Categories A, B, and C shall comply with the building height and structural limitations in Table 9.2.2.2

9.2.2.2.4 Seismic Performance Category D. The structural framing system for a building assigned to Seismic Performance Category D shall comply with Section 9.2.2.2.3 and the additional provisions of this section.

9.2.2.2.4.1 *Increased* Building Height Limit. The height limits in Table 9.2.2.2 *shall* be increased to 240 ft (75 m) in buildings that have steel braced frames or concrete cast-in-place shear walls *and that meet the requirements of this section. In such buildings* the braced frames or shear walls in any one plane shall resist no more than the following portion of the seismic forces in each direction including torsional effects: 60% when the braced frame or shear walls are arranged only on the perimeter; 40% when some of the braced frames or shear walls are arranged on the perimeter; 30% for other arrangements.

9.2.2.2.4.2 Interaction Effects. Moment resisting frames that are enclosed or adjoined by more rigid elements not considered to be part of the seismic force-resisting system shall be designed so that the action or failure of those ele-

TABLE 9.2.2.2
Structural Systems *

Basic Structural System and Seismic Force Resisting System	Response Modification Coefficient, R^a	Deflection Amplification Factor, $C_d{}^b$	Structural System Limitations and Building Height (ft) Limitations^c			
			Seismic Performance Category			
			A&B	C	D^d	E^e
Bearing Wall System						
Light Frame walls with shear panels	6½	4	NL	NL	160	100
Reinforced concrete shear walls	4½	4	NL	NL	160	100
Reinforced masonry shear walls	3½	3	NL	NL	160	100
Concentrically-braced frames	4	3½	NL	NL	160	100
Plain (unreinforced) masonry shear walls	1¼	1¼	NL	f	NP	NP
Plain concrete shear walls	1½	1½	NL	g	NP	NP
Building Frame System						
Eccentrically-braced frames, moment resisting connections at columns away from link	8	4	NL	NL	160	100
Eccentrically-braced frames, non-moment resisting connections at columns away from link	7	4	NL	NL	160	100
Light frame walls with shear panels	7	4½	NL	NL	160	100
Concentrically-braced frames	5	4½	NL	NL	160	100
Special concentrically braced frame of steel	6	5	NL	NL	160	100
Reinforced concrete shear walls	5½	5	NL	NL	160	100
Reinforced masonry shear walls	4½	4	NL	NL	160	100
Plain (unreinforced) masonry shear walls	1½	1½	NL	f	NP	NP
Plain concrete shear walls	2	2	NL	g	NP	NP
Moment Resisting Frame System						
Special moment frames of steel	8	5½	NL	NL	NL	NL
Special moment frames of reinforced concrete	8	5½	NL	NL	NL	NL
Intermediate moment frames of reinforced concrete	5	4½	NL	NL	NL	NL
Ordinary moment frames of steel	4½	4	NL	NL	160	100
Ordinary moment frames of reinforced concrete	3	2½	NL^h	NP	NP	NP
Dual System with a Special Moment Frame Capable of Resisting at Least 25% of Prescribed Seismic Forces						
Eccentrically-braced frames, moment resisting connections at columns away from link	8	4	NL	NL	NL	NL
Eccentrically-braced frames, non-moment resisting connections at columns away from link	7	4	NL	NL	NL	NL
Concentrically-braced frames	6	5	NL	NL	NL	NL
Special concentrically-braced frames of steel	8	6½	NL	NL	NL	NL
Reinforced concrete shear walls	8	6½	NL	NL	NL	NL
Reinforced masonry shear walls	6½	5½	NL	NL	NL	NL
Wood sheathed shear panels	8	5	NL	NL	NL	NL
Dual System with an Intermediate Moment Frame of Reinforced Concrete or an Ordinary Moment Frame of Steel Capable of Resisting at Least 25% of Prescribed Seismic Forces						
Special concentrically braced frames	6	5	NL	NL	160	100
Concentrically-braced frames	5	4½	NL	NL	160	100
Reinforced concrete shear walls	6	5	NL	NL	160	100
Reinforced masonry shear walls	5	4½	NL	NL	160	100
Wood-sheathed shear panels	7	4½	NL	NL	160	100
Inverted Pendulum Structures-Seismic Force Resisting System						
Special moment frames of structural steel	2½	2½	NL	NL	NL	NL
Special moment frames of reinforced concrete	2½	2½	NL	NL	NL	NL
Ordinary moment frames of structural steel	1¼	1¼	NL	NL	NP	NP

^{a}Response modification coefficient, R, for use throughout the *Standard. Note R reduces forces to a strength level, not an allowable stress level.*

^{b}Deflection amplification factor, C_d, for use in Sections 9.2.3.7.1 and 9.2.3.7.2.

^{c}NL = Not Limited and NP = Not Permitted. For metric units *use* 30 m for 100 ft and use 50 m for 160 ft.

^{d}See Section 9.2.2.2.4.1 for a descriptions of building systems limited to buildings with a height of 240 ft (75 m) or less.

^{e}See Sec. 9.2.2.2.4.5 for building systems limited to buildings with a height of 160 ft (50 m) or less.

^{f}The masonry shear walls shall have nominal reinforcement as required by [9.8-1], Section 10.5.3.2 (ACI 530/ASCE 5).

^{g}Plain concrete shear walls have nominal reinforcement in accordance with Section 10.5.3.2 of [9.8-1].

^{h}See Section A9.6.5.2 *for limitations on use of* ordinary moment concrete frames in buildings of Seismic Performance Category B on Soil Profile Types E or F.

ments will not impair the vertical load and seismic force-resisting capability of the frame. The design shall consider and provide for the effect of these rigid elements on the structural system at building deformations corresponding to the design story drift (Δ) as determined in Section 9.2.3.7

9.2.2.2.4.3 Deformational Compatibility. Every structural component not included in the seismic force-resisting system in the direction under consideration shall be designed to be adequate for the vertical load-carrying capacity and the induced moments resulting from the design story drift (Δ) as determined in accordance with Section 9.2.3.7 (also see Section 9.2.2.7).

9.2.2.2.4.4 Special Moment Frames. A special moment frame that is used but not required by Table 9.2.2.2 *shall not* be discontinued and supported by a more rigid system with a lower response modification factor (R) *unless* the requirements of Sections 9.2.2.5.2.4 and 9.2.2.5.4.2 are met. Where a special moment frame is required by Table 9.2.2.2, the frame shall be continuous to the foundation.

9.2.2.2.4.5 Seismic Performance Category E. The framing systems of buildings assigned to Category E shall conform to the requirements of Section 9.2.2.2.4 for Category D and to the additional requirements and limitations of this section. The *increased* height limit of Section 9.2.2.2.4.1 for braced frame or shear wall systems shall be reduced from 240 ft (75 m) to 160 ft (50 m).

9.2.2.3 Building Configuration. Buildings shall be classified as regular or irregular based upon the criteria in this section. Such classification shall be based on the plan and vertical configuration.

9.2.2.3.1 Plan Irregularity. Buildings having one or more of the irregularity types listed in Table 9.2.2.3.1 shall be designated as having plan structural irregularity. *Such buildings assigned to the Seismic Performance Categories listed in Table 9.2.2.3.1* shall comply with the requirements in the sections referenced in *that* table.

9.2.2.3.2 Vertical Irregularity. Buildings having one or more of the irregularity types listed in Table 9.2.2.3.2 shall be designated as having vertical irregularity. *Such buildings assigned to the Seismic Performance Categories listed in Table 9.2.2.3.2* shall comply with the requirements in the sections referenced in that table.

Exceptions:

1. Vertical Structural irregularities of Types 1 or 2 in Table 9.2.2.3.2 do not apply where no story drift ratio under design lateral seismic force is less than or equal to 130% of the story drift ratio of the next story above. Torsional effects need not be considered in the calculation of story drifts. The story drift ratio relationship for the top two stories of the building are not required to be evaluated.

TABLE 9.2.2.3.1
Plan Structural Irregularities

Irregularity Type and Description	Reference Section	Seismic Performance Category Application
1. Torsional Irregularity	9.2.2.5.4.2	D and E
Torsional irregularity *is defined to exist* where the maximum story drift, computed including accidental torsion, at one end of the structure transverse to an axis is more than 1.2 times the average of the story drifts at the two ends of the structure. *Torsional irregularity requirements in the reference sections apply only* to buildings in which the diaphragms are rigid in relation to the vertical structural elements that resist seismic forces.	9.2.3.5.1	C, D, and E
2. Re-entrant Corners	9.2.2.5.4.2	D and E
Plan configurations of a structure and its lateral force-resisting system contain re-entrant corners, where both projections of the structure beyond a re-entrant corner are greater than 15 percent of the plan dimension of the structure in the given direction.		
3. Diaphragm Discontinuity	9.2.2.5.4.2	D and E
Diaphragms with abrupt discontinuities or variations in stiffness, including those having cutout or open areas greater than 50 percent of the gross enclosed diaphragm area, or changes in effective diaphragm stiffness of more than 50 percent from one story to the next.		
4. Out-of-Plane Offsets	9.2.2.5.4.2	D and E
Discontinuities in a lateral force resistance path, such as out-of-plane offsets of the vertical elements.		
5. Nonparallel Systems	9.2.2.5.3.1	C, D, and E
The vertical lateral force-resisting elements are not parallel to or symmetric about the major orthogonal axes of the lateral force-resisting system.		

TABLE 9.2.2.3.2
Vertical Structural Irregularities

Irregularity Type and Description	Reference Section	Seismic Performance Category Application
1. Stiffness Irregularity: Soft Story A soft story is one in which the lateral stiffness is less than 70 percent of that in the story above or less than 80 percent of the average stiffness of the three stories above.	9.2.2.4.3	D and E
2. Weight (Mass) Irregularity Mass irregularity shall be considered to exist where the effective mass of any story is more than 150% of the effective mass of an adjacent story. A roof that is lighter than the floor below need not be considered.	9.2.2.4.3	D and E
3. Vertical Geometric Irregularity Vertical geometric irregularity shall be considered to exist where the horizontal dimension of the lateral force-resisting system in any story is more than 130% of that in an adjacent story.	9.2.2.4.3	D and E
4. In-Plane Discontinuity in Vertical Lateral Force-Resisting Elements An in-plane offset of the lateral force-resisting elements greater than the length of those elements. *	9.2.2.5.4.2	D and E
5. Discontinuity in Lateral Strength: Weak Story A weak story is one in which the story lateral strength is less than 80% of that in the story above. The story strength is the total strength of all seismic-resisting elements sharing the story shear for the direction under consideration.	9.2.2.5.2.4 9.2.2.5.4.2	B,C,D, and E

2. Irregularities Types 1 and 2 of Table 9.2.2.3.2 are not required to be considered for one- and two-story buildings.

9.2.2.4 Analysis Procedures. A structural analysis shall be made for all buildings in accordance with the requirements of this section. This section prescribes the minimum analysis procedure to be followed. However, use of an alternate generally accepted procedure, including the use of an approved site-specific spectrum, is permitted for any building if approved by the *authority having jurisdiction.* The limitations on the base shear stated in Section 9.2.4 apply to *any* such analysis.

9.2.2.4.1 Seismic Performance Category A. Regular or irregular buildings assigned to Category A are not required to be analyzed for seismic forces for the building as a whole. The provisions of Section 9.2.2.5.1apply.

9.2.2.4.2 Seismic Performance Categories B and C. The analysis procedures in Section 9.2.3 shall be used for regular or irregular buildings assigned to Category B or C or a more rigorous analysis shall be made.

9.2.2.4.3 Seismic Performance Categories D and E. The analysis procedures identified in Table 9.2.2.4.3 shall be used for buildings assigned to Categories D and E or a more rigorous analysis shall be made.

9.2.2.5 Design, Detailing Requirements, and Structural Component Load Effects. The design and detailing of the components of the seismic force-resisting system shall comply with the requirements of this section. Foundation design shall conform to the applicable requirements of Section 9.4. The materials and the systems composed of those materials shall conform to the requirements and limitations of Sections 9.5–9.9 for the applicable category.

9.2.2.5.1 Seismic Performance Category A. The design and detailing of buildings assigned to Category A shall comply with the requirements of this section.

9.2.2.5.1.1 *Load Path* Connections. All parts of the building between separation joints shall be interconnected *to form a continuous path to the seismic force-resisting system,* and the connections shall be capable of transmitting the seismic force (F_p) induced by the parts being connected. Any smaller portion of the building shall be tied to the remainder of the building with elements having a design strength capable of transmitting a seismic force of 1/3 of the seismic coefficient C_a, times the weight of the smaller portion or 5% of the portion's weight, whichever is greater. *For a building that is exempt from a full seismic analysis by Section 9.2.2.4.1, the main wind force-resisting system shall be deemed to be the seismic force-resisting system.*

A positive connection for resisting a horizontal force acting parallel to the member shall be provided for each beam, girder, or truss to its support. The connection shall have a minimum strength of 5% of the dead plus live load reaction. *One means to provide the strength is to use connecting elements such as slabs.*

TABLE 9.2.2.4.3
Analysis Procedures for Seismic Performance Categories D and E

	Building Description	Reference and Procedures
1	Buildings designated as regular up to 240 ft *(75 m)*	Section 9.2.3
2	Buildings that have only vertical structural irregularities of Type 1, 2, or 3 in Table 9.2.2.3.2 and have a height exceeding five stories or 65 ft (20 m) and all buildings exceeding 240 ft *(75 m)* in height	Section 9.2.4
3	All other buildings designated as having plan or vertical structural irregularities	Section 9.2.3 *plus the effect of the irregularity on* the dynamic response shall be analyzed.
4	Buildings in *Category III or IV per Table 1-1* in areas with A_a greater than 0.40 within 10 km of faults having the capability of generating magnitude 7 or greater earthquakes	A site-specific response spectra shall be used, but the design base shear shall not be less than that determined from Section 9.2.3.2
5	Buildings in areas with A_v of 0.2 and greater with a period of 0.7 sec or greater located on Soil Profile Type E sites.	A site-specific response spectra shall be used but the design base shear shall not be less than that determined from Section 9.2.3.2; also, the modal seismic design coefficient, C_{sm}, shall not be limited per Section 9.2.4.5

9.2.2.5.1.2 Anchorage of Concrete or Masonry Walls. Concrete and masonry walls shall be anchored to the roof and all floors that provide lateral support for the wall. The anchorage shall provide a direct connection between the walls and the roof or floor construction. The connections shall be capable of resisting the greater of a seismic lateral force (F_p) induced by the wall or 1,000 times the seismic coefficient C_a, pounds per lineal foot of wall (14,600 times C_a N/m). Walls shall be designed to resist bending between anchors where the anchor spacing exceeds 4 ft (1.2 m).

9.2.2.5.1.3 Anchorage of Nonstructural Systems. When required by Section 9.3, all portions or components of the building shall be anchored for the seismic force (F_p) prescribed therein.

9.2.2.5.2 Seismic Performance Category B. Buildings assigned to Category B shall conform to the requirements of Section 9.2.2.5.1 for Category A and the requirements of this section.

9.2.2.5.2.1 Component Load Effects. *Seismic load effects on components shall be determined from the load analysis as required by Section 9.2.2.4, by other portions of Section 9.2.2.5.2, and by Section 9.2.2.6. The second-order effects shall be included where applicable. Where these seismic load effects exceed the minimum load path connection forces given in Section 9.2.2.5.1, they shall govern. Components shall satisfy the load combinations in Section 2.*

9.2.2.5.2.2 Openings. Where openings occur in shear walls, diaphragms, or other plate-type elements, reinforcement at the edges of the openings shall be designed to transfer the stresses into the structure. The edge reinforcement shall extend into the body of the wall or diaphragm a distance sufficient to develop the force in the reinforcement.

9.2.2.5.2.3 *Direction of Seismic Load.* *The direction of application of seismic forces used in design shall be that which will produce the most critical load effect in each component. This requirement will be deemed satisfied if the design seismic forces are applied separately and independently in each of two orthogonal directions.*

9.2.2.5.2.4 Discontinuities in Vertical System. Buildings with a discontinuity in lateral capacity, vertical irregularity Type 5 as defined in Table 9.2.2.3.2, shall not be over two stories or 30 ft (9 m) in height where the "weak" story has a calculated strength of less than 65 percent of the story above.

Exception: The limit does not apply where the "weak" story is capable of resisting a total seismic force equal to 75 percent of the deflection amplification factor (C_d) times the design force prescribed in Section 9.2.3.

9.2.2.5.2.5 Nonredundant Systems. The design of a building shall consider the potentially adverse effect that the failure of a single member, connection, or component of the seismic force-resisting system would have on the stability of the building. *See Section 1.3.*

9.2.2.5.2.6 Collector Elements. Collector elements shall be provided that are capable of transferring the seismic forces originating in other portions of the building to the element providing the resistance to those forces.

9.2.2.5.2.7 Diaphragms. The deflection in the plane of the diaphragm, as determined by engineering analysis, shall not exceed the permissible deflection of the attached elements. Permissible deflection shall be that deflection which will permit the attached element to maintain its structural integrity under the individual loading and continue to support the prescribed loads.

Floor and roof diaphragms shall be designed to resist the following seismic forces: A minimum force equal to 50% of seismic coefficient C_a, times the weight of the diaphragm and other elements of the building attached thereto plus the portion of the seismic shear force at that level (V_x) required to be transferred to the components of the vertical seismic force-resisting system because of offsets or changes in stiffness of the vertical components above and below the diaphragm.

Diaphragms shall provide for both the shear and bending stresses resulting from these forces. Diaphragms shall have ties or struts to distribute the wall anchorage forces into the diaphragm. Diaphragm connections shall be positive connections, mechanical, or welded.

9.2.2.5.2.8 Bearing Walls. Exterior and interior bearing walls and their anchorage shall be designed for a force normal to the surface equal to seismic coefficient C_a, times the weight of wall (W_c), with a minimum force of 10% of the weight of the wall. Interconnection of wall elements and connections to supporting framing systems shall have sufficient ductility, rotational capacity, or sufficient strength to resist shrinkage, thermal changes, and differential foundation settlement when combined with seismic forces. *The connections shall also satisfy Section 9.2.2.5.1.2.*

9.2.2.5.2.9 Inverted Pendulum-Type Structures. Supporting columns or piers of inverted pendulum-type structures shall be designed for the bending moment calculated at the base determined using the procedures given in Section 9.2.3 and varying uniformly to a moment at the top equal to one-half the calculated bending moment at the base.

9.2.2.5.3 Seismic Performance Category C. Buildings assigned to Category C shall conform to the requirements of Section 9.2.2.5.2 for Category B and to the requirements of this section.

9.2.2.5.3.1 *Direction of Seismic Load.* For Buildings that have plan structural irregularity Type 5 in Table 9.2.2.3.1 *the critical direction requirement of Section 9.2.2.5.2.3 may be deemed to be satisfied* if components and their foundations *are* designed for the following orthogonal combination of prescribed loads: 100% of the forces for one direction plus 30% of the forces for the perpendicular direction. The combination requiring the maximum component strength shall be used.

9.2.2.5.4 Seismic Performance Categories D and E. Buildings assigned to Category D or E shall conform to the requirements of Section 9.2.2.5.3 for Category C and to the requirements of this section.

9.2.2.5.4.1 *Direction of Seismic Load.* *The independent orthogonal procedure given in Section 9.2.2.5.2.3 will not be satisfactory for the critical direction requirement for any building. The orthogonal combination procedure in Section 9.2.2.5.3.1 will be deemed satisfactory for any building.*

9.2.2.5.4.2 Plan or Vertical Irregularities. When the ratio of the strength provided in any story to the strength required is less than two-thirds of that ratio for the story immediately above, *the potentially adverse effect shall be analyzed and the strengths shall be adjusted to compensate for this effect.*

For buildings having a plan structural irregularity of Type 1, 2, 3, or 4 in Table 9.2.2.3.1 or a vertical structural irregularity of Type 4 in Table 9.2.2.3.2, the design forces determined from Section 9.2.3.2 shall be increased 25% for connections of diaphragms to vertical elements and to collectors and for connections of collectors to the vertical elements.

9.2.2.5.4.3 Vertical Seismic Forces. The vertical component of earthquake ground motion shall be considered in the design of horizontal cantilever and horizontal prestressed components. The load combinations used in evaluating such components shall include E as defined in Eq. (9.2.2.6-4) in Section 9.2.2.6. Horizontal cantilever structural components shall be designed for a minimum net upward force of 0.2 times the dead load in addition to the applicable load combinations of Section 9.2.2.6

9.2.2.6 Combination of Load Effects. The effects on the building and its components due to seismic forces shall be combined with gravity loads in accordance with the combination of load effects given in Section 2. For use with those combinations, the earthquake-induced force effect *shall include vertical and horizontal effects as given by Eq. (9.2.2.6-1) or, as applicable, Eqs. (9.2.2.6-2), (9.2.2.6-3), or (9.2.2.6-4). The term 0.5C_aD need not be included* where C_a is equal to or less than 0.05 in Eqs. (9.2.2.6-1), (9.2.2.6-2), (9.2.2.6-3) and (9.2.2.6-4).

For Eq. (5) in Section 2.3.2 or Eq. (4) in Section 2.4.1:

$$E = \pm 1.0\, Q_E + 0.5\, C_aD \qquad (9.2.2.6\text{-}1)$$

For Eq. (6) in Section 2.3.2 or Eq. (3) in 2.4.1:

$$E = \pm 1.0\, Q_E - 0.5\, C_aD \qquad (9.2.2.6\text{-}2)$$

where

$E =$ the effect of horizontal and vertical earthquake-induced forces;

$C_a =$ the seismic coefficient based upon the Soil Profile Type and the value of A_a as determined from Table 9.1.4.2.4.A;

$D =$ the effect of dead load, D; and

$Q_E =$ the effect of horizontal seismic (earthquake-induced) forces.

For columns supporting discontinuous lateral-force-resisting elements, the axial *compression* in the columns shall be computed using the following load *in Eq. (5) in Section 2.3.2 or Eq. (4) in Section 2.4.1:*

$$E = \left(\frac{2R}{5}\right)Q_E + 0.5 C_aD \qquad (9.2.2.6\text{-}3)$$

The axial forces in such columns need not exceed the capacity of other elements of the structure to transfer such loads to the column.

For brittle materials, systems and connections the following load also shall be used *in Eq. (6) in Section 2.3.2 or Eq. (3) in Section 2.4.1:*

$$E = \left(\frac{2R}{5}\right)Q_E - 0.5 C_aD \qquad (9.2.2.6\text{-}4)$$

The factor $(2R/5)$ shall be greater than or equal to 1.0.

9.2.2.7 Deflection and Drift Limits. The design story drift (Δ) as determined in Section 9.2.3.7 or 9.2.4.6, shall not exceed the allowable story drift (Δ_a) as obtained from Table 9.2.2.7 for any story. For structures with significant torsional deflections, the maximum drift shall include torsional effects. All portions of the building shall be designed and constructed to act as an integral unit in resisting seismic forces unless separated structurally by a distance sufficient to avoid damaging contact under total deflection (δ_x) as determined in Section 9.2.3.7.1

9.2.3 Equivalent Lateral Force Procedure

9.2.3.1 General. Section 9.2.3. provides required minimum standards for the equivalent lateral force procedure of seismic analysis of buildings. For purposes of analysis, the building is considered to be fixed at the base. See Section 9.2.2.4 for limitations on the use of this procedure.

9.2.3.2 Seismic Base Shear. The seismic base shear (V) in a given direction shall be determined in accordance with the following equation:

$$V = C_sW \qquad (9.2.3.2\text{-}1)$$

where

$C_s =$ the seismic response coefficient determined in accordance with Section 9.2.3.2.1; and

$W =$ the total dead load and applicable portions of other loads listed:

TABLE 9.2.2.7
Allowable Story Drift, $\Delta_a{}^a$

Building *	Category from Table 1-1		
	I & II	III	IV
Buildings, other than masonry shear wall or masonry wall frame buildings, four stories or less with interior walls, partitions, ceilings and exterior wall systems that have been designed to accommodate the story drifts.	$0.025\, h_{sx}{}^b$	$0.020\, h_{sx}$	$0.015\, h_{sx}$
All other buildings	$0.020\, h_{sx}$	$0.015\, h_{sx}$	$0.010\, h_{sx}$

$^a h_{sx}$ is the story height below Level x.

^{b}there shall be no drift limit for single-story buildings with interior walls, partitions, ceilings, and exterior wall systems that have been designed to accomodate the story drifts. The building separation requirement of Section 9.2.2.7 is not waived.

1. In areas used for storage, a minimum of 25% of the floor live load shall be applicable. *The 50-psf floor live load for passenger cars in parking garages need not be considered.*
2. Where an allowance for partition load is included in the floor load design, the actual partition weight or a minimum weight of 10 psf of floor area, whichever is greater, shall be applicable.
3. Total operating weight of permanent equipment and the effective contents of vessels.

Where the flat roof snow load (see Section 7.3) exceeds 30 psf, the design snow load shall be included in W. Where siting and load duration conditions warrant and the authority having jurisdiction approves, the amount of the snow load included in W may be reduced to no less than 20% of the design snow load.

9.2.3.2.1 Calculation of Seismic Response Coefficient. When the fundamental period of the building is computed, the seismic design coefficient (C_s) shall be determined in accordance with the following equation:

$$C_s = \frac{1.2C_v}{RT^{2/3}} \qquad (9.2.3.2.1\text{-}1)$$

where

C_v = the seismic coefficient based upon the Soil Profile Type and the value of A_v as determined from Section 9.1.4.2.3 or Table 9.1.4.2.4B;

R = the response modification factor in Table 9.2.2.2; and

T = the fundamental period of the building determined in Section 9.2.3.3.

A soil-structure interaction reduction *is permitted when determined using* Section 9.2.5 or other generally accepted procedures approved by the authority having jurisdiction are followed.

Alternatively, the seismic response coefficient, (C_s), need not be greater than the following equation:

$$C_s = \frac{2.5C_a}{R} \qquad (9.2.3.2\text{-}2)$$

where:

R = the response modification factor in Table 9.2.2.2

C_a = the seismic coefficient based upon the Soil Profile Type and the value of A_a as determined from Section 9.1.4.2.3 or Table 9.1.4.2.4A.

9.2.3.3 Period Determination. The fundamental period of the building (T) in the direction under consideration shall be established using the structural properties and deformational characteristics of the resisting elements in a properly substantiated analysis. The fundamental period (T) shall not exceed the product of the coefficient for upper limit on calculated period (C_u) from Table 9.2.3.3 and the approximate fundamental period (T_a) determined from Eq. (9.2.3.3-1).

$$T_a = C_T h_n^{3/4} \qquad (9.2.3.3.1\text{-}1)$$

where

C_T = 0.035 for buildings in which the lateral force-resisting system consists of moment resisting frames of steel providing 100% of the required lateral force resistance and such frames are not enclosed or adjoined by more rigid components tending to prevent the frames from deflecting when subjected to seismic forces (metric coefficient is 0.085);

C_T = 0.030 for buildings in which the lateral force-resisting system consists of moment resisting frames of reinforced concrete providing 100% of the required lateral force resistance and such frames are not enclosed or adjoined by more rigid components tending to prevent the frames from deflecting when subjected to seismic forces (metric coefficient is 0.073);

C_T = 0.030 for buildings in which the lateral force-resisting system consists of steel eccentrically braced frames acting along or with moment

TABLE 9.2.3.3
Coefficient for Upper Limit on Calculated Period

Seismic Coefficient (C_v)	Coefficient C_u
≥ 0.4	1.2
0.3	1.3
0.2	1.4
0.15	1.5
0.1	1.7
0.05	1.7

resisting frames (metric coefficient is 0.073);

$C_T = 0.020$ for all other buildings (metric coefficient is 0.049); and

$h_n = $ the height in feet (meters) above the base to the highest level of the building.

Alternately, it shall be permitted to determine the approximate fundamental period (T_a), in seconds, from the following equation for buildings not exceeding 12 stories in height in which the lateral force-resisting system consists entirely of concrete or steel moment resisting frames and the story height is at least 10 ft (3 m):

$$T_a = 0.1 N \qquad (9.2.3.3.1\text{-}2)$$

where N = number of stories.

9.2.3.4 Vertical Distribution of Seismic Forces.
The lateral seismic force (F_x) (kip or kN) induced at any level shall be determined from the following equations:

$$F_x = C_{vx}V \qquad (9.2.3.4\text{-}1)$$

and

$$C_{vx} = \frac{w_x h_x^k}{\displaystyle\sum_{i=1}^{n} w_i h_i^k} \qquad (9.2.3.4\text{-}2)$$

where

$C_{vx} = $ vertical distribution factor;

$V = $ total design lateral force or shear at the base of the building,(kip or kN);

w_i and $w_x = $ the portion of the total gravity load of the building (W) located or assigned to Level i or x;

h_i and $h_x = $ the height (feet or m) from the base to Level i or x; and

$k = $ an exponent related to the building period as follows: For buildings having a period of 0.5 sec or less, $k = 1$. For buildings having a period of 2.5 sec or more, $k = 2$. For buildings having a period between 0.5 and 2.5 sec, k shall be 2 or shall be determined by linear interpolation between 1 and 2.

9.2.3.5 Horizontal Shear Distribution and Torsion.
The seismic design story shear in any story (V_x) (kip or kN) shall be determined from the following equation:

$$V_x = \sum_{i=x}^{n} F_i \qquad (9.2.3.5)$$

where $F_i = $ the portion of the seismic base shear (V)(kip or kN) induced at Level i.

9.2.3.5.1 *Direct Shear.*
The seismic design story shear (V_x) (kip or kN) shall be distributed to the various vertical elements of the seismic force-resisting system in the story under consideration based on the relative lateral stiffness of the vertical resisting elements and the diaphragm.

9.2.3.5.2 Torsion.
The design shall include the torsional moment (M_t) (kip or kN) resulting from the location of the building masses plus the accidental torsional moments (M_{ta}) (kip or kN) caused by assumed displacement of the mass each way from its actual location by a distance equal to 5% of the dimension of the building perpendicular to the direction of the applied forces.

Buildings of Seismic Performance Categories C, D, and E, where Type 1 torsional irregularity exists as defined in Table 9.2.2.3.1 shall have the effects accounted for by increasing the accidental torsion at each level by a torsional amplification factor (A_x) determined from the following equation:

$$A_x = \left(\frac{\delta_{max}}{1.2\,\delta_{avg}} \right)^2 \qquad (9.2.3.5.1)$$

where

$\delta_{max} = $ the maximum displacement at Level x (in. or mm); and

$\delta_{avg} = $ the average of the displacements at the extreme points of the structure at Level x (in. or mm).

The torsional amplification factor (A_x) is not required to exceed 3.0. The more severe loading for each element shall be considered for design.

9.2.3.6 Overturning.
The building shall be designed to resist overturning effects caused by the seismic forces determined in Section 9.2.3.4. At any story, the increment of overturning moment in the story under consideration shall be distributed to the various vertical force-resisting elements in the same proportion as the distribution of the horizontal shears to those elements.

The overturning moments at Level x (M_x) (kip·ft or kN·m) shall be determined from the following equation:

$$M_x = \tau \sum_{i=x}^{n} F_i(h_i - h_x) \qquad (9.2.3.6)$$

where

$F_i =$ the portion of the seismic base shear (V) induced at Level i;

h_i and $h_x =$ the height (in feet or m) from the base to Level i or x;

$\tau =$ the overturning moment reduction factor, determined as follows:

for the top 10 stories, $\tau = 1.0$
for the 20th story from the top and below, $\tau = 0.8$
for stories between the 20th and 10th stories below the top, a value between 1.0 and 0.8 determined by a straight line interpolation.

The foundations of buildings, except inverted pendulum-type structures, shall be designed for the foundation overturning design moment (M_f) (kip·ft or kN·m) at the foundation-soil interface determined using the equation for the overturning moment at Level x (M_x) (kip·ft or kN·m) above with an overturning moment reduction factor (τ) of 0.75 for all building heights.

9.2.3.7 Drift Determination and P-Delta Effects. Story drifts and, where required, member forces and moments due to P-delta effects shall be determined in accordance with this section.

9.2.3.7.1 Story Drift Determination. The design story drift (Δ) shall be computed as the difference of the deflections at the top and bottom of the story under consideration. The deflections of Level x at the center of the mass (δ_x) (in. or mm) shall be determined in accordance with following equation:

$$\delta_x = C_d \delta_{xe} \qquad (9.2.3.7.1)$$

where:

$C_d =$ the deflection amplification factor in Table 9.2.2.2; and

$\delta_{xe} =$ the deflections determined by an elastic analysis.

The elastic analysis of the seismic force-resisting system shall be made using the prescribed seismic design forces of Section 9.2.3.4.

For determining compliance with the story drift limitation of Section 9.2.2.7, the deflections of Level x at the center of mass (δ_x) (in. or mm) shall be calculated as required in this section. For the purposes of this drift analysis only, the upper-bound limitation on the fundamental period specified in Section 9.2.3.3 *does not apply for computing* forces and displacements.

Where applicable, the design story drift (Δ) (in. or mm) shall be increased by the incremental factor relating to the P-delta effects as determined in Section 9.2.3.7.2.

9.2.3.7.2 P-Delta Effects. P-delta effects on story shears and moments, the resulting member forces and moments, and the story drifts induced by these effects are not required to be considered when the stability coefficient (θ) as determined by the following equation is equal to or less than 0.10:

$$\theta = \frac{P_x \Delta}{V_x h_{sx} C_d} \qquad (9.2.3.7.2\text{-}1)$$

where

$P_x =$ the total vertical design load at and above Level x (kip or kN); when computing P_x, no individual load factor need exceed 1.0;

$\Delta =$ the design story drift occurring simultaneously with V_x (in. or mm);

$V_x =$ the seismic shear force acting between Levels x and $x - 1$ (kip or kN);

$h_{sx} =$ the story height below Level x (in. or mm); and

$C_d =$ the deflection amplification factor in Table 9.2.2.2.

The stability coefficient (θ) shall not exceed θ_{max} determined as follows:

$$\theta_{max} = \frac{0.5}{\beta C_d} \leq 0.25 \qquad (9.2.3.7.2\text{-}2)$$

where β is the ratio of shear demand to shear capacity for the story between Level x and $x - 1$. This ratio may be conservatively taken as 1.0.

When the stability coefficient (θ) is greater than 0.10 but less than or equal to θ_{max}, the incremental factor related to P-delta effects (a_d) shall be determined by rational analysis. To obtain the story drift for including the P-delta effect, the design story drift determined in Section 9.2.3.7.1 shall be multiplied by $1.0/(1 - \theta)$.

When θ is greater than θ_{max}, the structure is potentially unstable and shall be redesigned.

When the P-delta effect is included in an automated analysis, Eq. (9.2.3.7.2-2) must still be satisfied, however, the value of θ computed from Eq. (9.2.3.7.2-1) using the results of the P-delta analysis may be divided by (1 + θ) before checking Eq. (9.2.3.7.2-2).

9.2.4 Modal Analysis Procedure

9.2.4.1 General. Section 9.2.4 provides required standards for the modal analysis procedure of seismic analysis of buildings. See Section 9.2.2.4 for requirements for use of this procedure. The symbols used in this method of analysis have the same meaning as those for similar terms used in Section 9.2.3, with the subscript m denoting quantities in the mth mode.

9.2.4.2 Modeling. The building shall be modeled as a system of masses lumped at the floor levels with each mass having one degree of freedom—that of lateral displacement in the direction under consideration.

9.2.4.3 Modes. The analysis shall include, for each of two mutually perpendicular axes, at least the lowest three modes of vibration or all modes of vibration with periods greater than 0.4 sec. The number of modes shall equal the number of stories for buildings less than three stories in height.

9.2.4.4 Periods. The required periods and mode shapes of the building in the direction under consideration shall be calculated by established methods of structural analysis for the fixed base condition using the masses and elastic stiffness of the seismic force-resisting system.

9.2.4.5 Modal Base Shear. The portion of the base shear contributed by the mth mode (V_m) shall be determined from the following equations:

$$V_m = C_{sm}W_m \qquad (9.2.4.5-1)$$

$$W_m = \frac{\left(\sum_{i=1}^{n} w_i \phi_{i\mu}\right)^2}{\sum_{i=1}^{n} w_i \phi_{i\mu}^2} \qquad (9.2.4.5-2)$$

where

C_{sm} = the modal seismic design coefficient determined herein;
W_m = the effective modal gravity load;
w_i = the portion of the total gravity load of the building at Level i; and
ϕ_{im} = the displacement amplitude at the ith level of the building when vibrating in its mth mode.

The modal seismic design coefficient (C_{sm}) shall be determined in accordance with the following equation:

$$C_{sm} = \frac{1.2C_v}{RT_m^{2/3}} \qquad (9.2.4.5-3)$$

where

C_v = The seismic coefficient based upon the Soil Profile Type and the value A_v as determined from Section 9.1.4.2.3 or Table 9.1.4.2.4B.
R = the response modification factor determined from Table 9.2.2.2 and
T_m = the modal period of vibration (in seconds) of the mth mode of the building.

The modal seismic design coefficient, C_{sm}, is not required to exceed Eq. (9.2.3.5-3a)

$$C_{sm} = \frac{2.5C_a}{R} \qquad (9.2.4.5-3a)$$

where

C_a = The seismic coefficient based upon the Soil Profile Type and the value of A_a as determined from Section 9.1.4.2.3 or Table 9.1.4.2.4A.

Exceptions:

1. The limiting value of Eq. (9.2.4.5-3a) is not applicable to Seismic Performance Category D and E buildings with a period of 0.7 sec or greater located on Soil Profile Type E or F *soils.*

2. For buildings on sites with Soil Profile Type D, E, or F, the modal seismic design coefficient, C_{sm}, for modes other than the fundamental mode, that have periods less than 0.3 sec the minimum C_{sm} shall be determined by the following equation:

$$C_{sm} = \frac{C_a}{R}(1.0 + 5.0T_m) \qquad (9.2.4.5-4)$$

3. For buildings where any modal period of vibration (T_m) exceeds 4.0 sec, the modal seismic design coefficient (C_{sm}) for that mode shall be determined by the following equation:

$$C_{sm} = \frac{3C_v}{RT_m^{4/3}} \qquad (9.2.4.5-5)$$

The reduction due to soil-structure interaction as determined in Section 9.2.5.3 *is permitted* to be used.

9.2.4.6 Modal Forces, Deflections, and Drifts. The modal force (F_{xm}) at each level shall be determined by the following equations:

$$F_{xm} = C_{vxm}V_m \qquad (9.2.4.6\text{-}1)$$

and

$$C_{vxm} = \frac{w_x\phi_{x\mu}}{\sum\limits_{i=1}^{n} w_i\phi_{im}} \qquad (9.2.4.6\text{-}2)$$

where

$C_{vsxm} =$ the vertical distribution factor in the mth mode;

$V_m =$ the total design lateral force or shear at the base in the mth mode;

w_i and $w_x =$ the portion of the total gravity load of the building (W) located or assigned to Level i or x;

$\phi_{xm} =$ the displacement amplitude at the xth level of the building when vibrating in its mth mode; and

$\phi_{im} =$ the displacement amplitude at the ith level of the building when vibrating in its mth mode.

The modal deflection at each level (δ_{xm}) shall be determined by the following equations:

$$\delta_{xm} = C_d\delta_{xem} \qquad (9.2.4.6\text{-}3)$$

and

$$\delta_{xem} = \left(\frac{g}{4\pi^2}\right)\left(\frac{T_m^2 F_{xm}}{w_x}\right) \qquad (9.2.4.6\text{-}4)$$

where

$C_d =$ the deflection amplification factor determined from Table 9.2.2.2;

$\delta_{xem} =$ the deflection of Level x in the mth mode at the center of the mass at Level x determined by an elastic analysis;

$g =$ the acceleration due to gravity (feet per second squared);

$T_m =$ the modal period of vibration, in seconds, of the mth mode of the building;

$F_{xm} =$ the portion of the seismic base shear in the mth mode, induced at Level x; and

$w_x =$ the portion of the total gravity load of the building (W) located or assigned to Level x.

The modal drift in a story (Δ_m) shall be computed as the difference of the deflections (δ_{xm}) at the top and bottom of the story under consideration.

9.2.4.7 Modal Story Shears and Moments. The story shears, story overturning moments, and the shear forces and overturning moments in walls and braced frames at each level due to the seismic forces determined from the appropriate equation in Section 9.2.4.6 shall be computed for each mode by linear static methods.

9.2.4.8 Design Values. The design value for the modal base shear (V_t), each of the story shear, moment and drift quantities, and the deflection at each level shall be determined by combining their modal values as obtained from Sections 9.2.4.6 and 9.2.4.7. The combination shall be carried out by taking the square root of the sum of the squares of each of the modal values or by the complete quadratic combination (CQC) method.

The base shear (V) using the equivalent lateral force procedure in Section 9.2.3 shall be calculated using a fundamental period of the building (T), in seconds, of 1.2 times the coefficient for upper limit on the calculated period (C_a) times the approximate fundamental period of the building (T_a). Where the design value for the modal base shear (V_t) is less than the calculated base shear (V) using the equivalent lateral force procedure, the design story shears, moments, drifts, and floor deflections shall be multiplied by the following modification factor:

$$\frac{V}{V_t} \qquad (9.2.4.8)$$

where

$V =$ the equivalent lateral force procedure base shear, calculated in accordance with this section and Section 9.2.3; and

$V_t =$ the modal base shear, calculated in accordance with this section.

The modal base shear (V_t) is not required to exceed the base shear from the equivalent lateral force procedure in Section 9.2.3.

Exception: For buildings in areas with an effective peak velocity related (A_v) value of 0.2 and greater with a period of 0.7 sec or greater located on Soil Profile Type E or F sites, the design base shear shall not be less than that determined using the equivalent lateral force procedure in Section 9.2.3 (see Section 9.2.2.4.3).

9.2.4.9 Horizontal Shear Distribution. The distribution of horizontal shear shall be in accordance with the requirements of Section 9.2.3.5.

9.2.4.10 Foundation Overturning. The foundation overturning moment at the foundation-soil interface is not prohibited from being reduced by 10%.

9.2.4.11 *P*-Delta Effects. The *P*-delta effects shall be determined in accordance with Section 9.2.3.7.2. The story drifts and story shears shall be determined in accordance with Section 9.2.3.7.1.

9.2.5 Soil Structure Interaction

9.2.5.1 General: *If the option to incorporate the effects of soil-structure interaction is exercised, the requirements of this section shall be used* in the determination of the design earthquake forces and the corresponding displacements of the building. *

The provisions for use with the equivalent lateral force procedure are given in Section 9.2.5.2. and those for use with the modal analysis procedure are given in Section 9.2.5.3.

9.2.5.2. Equivalent Lateral Force Procedure: The following requirements are supplementary to those presented in Sec 9.2.3.

9.2.5.2.1. Base Shear: To account for the effects of soil-structure interaction, the base shear (V) determined from Eq. (9.2.3.2-1) shall be reduced to:

$$\tilde{V} = V - \Delta V \qquad (9.2.5.2.1\text{-}1)$$

The reduction (ΔV) shall be computed as follows *and shall not exceed 0.3V:*

$$\Delta V = \left[C_s - \tilde{C}_s \left(\frac{0.05}{\tilde{\beta}} \right)^{0.4} \right] \overline{W} \quad \leq 0.3\,V \qquad (9.2.5.2.1\text{-}2)$$

where:

C_s = the seismic design coefficient computed from Eq. (9.2.3.2.1-1) using the fundamental natural period of the fixed base structure (T or T_a) as specified in Section 9.2.3.3;

$\tilde{C}_s$ = the value of C_s computed from Eq. (9.2.3.2.1-1) using the fundamental natural period of the flexibly

supported structure (T) defined in Section 9.2.5.2.1.1;

$\tilde{\beta}$ = The fraction of critical damping for the structure-foundation system determined in Section 9.2.5.2.1.2; and

$\overline{W}$ = the effective gravity load of the building, which shall be taken as $0.7W$, except that for buildings where the gravity load is concentrated at a single level, it shall be taken equal to W.

9.2.5.2.1.1 Effective Building Period: The effective period ($\tilde{T}$) shall be determined as follows:

$$\tilde{T} = T \sqrt{1 + \frac{\overline{k}}{K_y} \left(1 + \frac{K_y \overline{h}^2}{k_\theta} \right)} \qquad (9.2.5.2.1.1\text{-}1)$$

where:

T = the fundamental period of the building as determined in Section 4.2.2;

$\overline{k}$ = the stiffness of the building when fixed at the base, defined by the following:

$$\overline{k} = 4\pi^2 \left(\frac{\overline{W}}{gT^2} \right) \qquad (9.2.5.2.1.1\text{-}2)$$

$\overline{h}$ = the effective height of the building which shall be taken as 0.7 times the total height (h_n) except that for buildings where the gravity load is effectively concentrated at a single level, it shall be taken as the height to that level;

K_y = the lateral stiffness of the foundation defined as the static horizontal force at the level of the foundation necessary to produce a unit deflection at that level, the force and the deflection being measured in the direction in which the structure is analyzed;

K_θ = the rocking stiffness of the foundation defined as the static moment necessary to produce a unit average rotation of the foundation, the moment and rotation being measured in the direction in which the structure is analyzed; and

g = the acceleration of gravity.

The foundation stiffnesses (K_y and K_θ) shall be computed by established principles of foundation mechanics using soil properties that are compatible with the soil strain levels associated with the de-

TABLE 9.2.5.2.1.1
Values of G/G_o and v_s/v_{so}

| | Ground Acceleration Coefficient, (A_v) | | | |
	≤ 0.10	≤ 0.15	≤ 0.20	≥ 0.30
Value of G/G_o	0.81	0.64	0.49	0.42
Value of v_s/v_{so}	0.90	0.80	0.70	0.65

sign earthquake motion. The average shear modulus (G) for the soils beneath the foundation at large strain levels and the associated shear wave velocity (v_s) needed in these computations shall be determined from Table 9.2.5.2.1.1. where:

v_{so} = the average shear wave velocity for the soils beneath the foundation at small strain levels (10^{-3}% or less);

G_o = $\gamma v_{so}^2/g$ = the average shear modulus for the soils beneath the foundation at small strain levels; and

γ = the average unit weight of the soils.

Alternatively, for buildings supported on mat foundations that rest at or near the ground surface or are embedded in such a way that the side wall contact with the soil are not considered to remain effective during the design ground motion, the effective period of the building shall be determined as follows:

$$\tilde{T} = T\sqrt{1 + \frac{25\alpha r_a \overline{h}}{v_s^2 T^2}\left(1 + \frac{1.12 r_a \overline{h}^2}{r_m^3}\right)} \quad (9.2.5.2.1.1\text{-}3)$$

where:

α = the relative weight density of the structure and the soil defined by:

$$\alpha = \frac{\overline{W}}{\gamma A_o \overline{h}} \quad (9.2.5.2.1.1\text{-}4)$$

r_a and r_m = characteristic foundation lengths defined by:

$$r_a = \sqrt{\frac{A_o}{\pi}} \quad (9.2.5.2.1.1\text{-}5)$$

and

$$r_m = \sqrt[4]{\frac{4I_o}{\pi}} \quad (9.2.5.2.1.1\text{-}6)$$

where

A_o = the area of the load-carrying foundation; and

I_o = the static moment of inertia of the load-carrying foundation about a horizontal centroidal axis normal to the direction in which the structure is analyzed.

9.2.5.2.1.2 Effective Damping: The effective damping factor for the structure-foundation system $(\tilde{\beta})$ shall be computed as follows:

$$\tilde{\beta} = \beta_o + \frac{0.05}{(\tilde{T}/T)^3} \quad (9.2.5.2.1.2\text{-}1)$$

where:

β_o = the foundation damping factor as specified in Fig. 9.2.5.2.1.2.

The values of β_o corresponding to $A_v = 0.15$ in Fig. 9.2.5.2.1.2 shall be determined by averaging the results obtained from the solid lines and the dashed lines.

The quantity r in Fig. 9.2.5.2.1.2 is a characteristic foundation length that shall be determined as follows:

$$\text{For } \overline{h}/L_o \leq 0.5 \quad r = r_a = \sqrt{\frac{A_o}{\pi}} \quad (9.2.5.2.1.2\text{-}2)$$

$$\text{For } \overline{h}/L_o \geq 1 \quad r = r_m = \sqrt[4]{\frac{4I_o}{\pi}} \quad (9.2.5.2.1.2\text{-}3)$$

where:

L_o = the overall length of the side of the foundation in the direction being analyzed;

A_o = the area of the load-carrying foundation; and

I_o = the static moment of inertia of the load-carrying foundation about a horizontal centroidal axis normal to the direction in which the structure is analyzed.

For intermediate values of $\overline{h}/L_o$, the value of r shall be determined by linear interpolation.

Exception: For buildings supported on point bearing piles and in all other cases where the foundation soil consists of a soft stratum of reasonably uniform properties underlain by a much stiffer, rock-like deposit with an abrupt increase in stiffness, the factor β_o in Eq. (9.2.5.2.1.2-1) shall be replaced by:

$$\beta'_o = \left(\frac{4D_s}{v_s\tilde{T}}\right)^2 \beta_o \qquad (9.2.5.2.1.2-4)$$

if $4D_s/v_s\tilde{T} < 1$, where D_s is the total depth of the stratum.

The value of $\tilde{\beta}$ computed from Eq. (9.2.5.2.1.2-1), both with or without the adjustment represented by Eq. (9.2.5.2.1.2-4), shall in no case be taken as less than $\tilde{\beta} = 0.05$.

9.2.5.2.2 Vertical Distribution of Seismic Forces: The distribution over the height of the building of the reduced total seismic force ($\tilde{v}$) shall be considered to be the same as for the building without interaction.

9.2.5.2.3 Other Effects: The modified story shears, overturning moments, and torsional effects about a vertical axis shall be determined as for structures without interaction using the reduced lateral forces.

The modified deflections ($\tilde{\delta}_x$) shall be determined as follows:

$$\tilde{\delta}_x = \frac{\tilde{V}}{V}\left[\frac{M_o h_x}{K_\theta} + \delta_x\right] \qquad (9.2.5.2.3-1)$$

where:

M_o = the overturning moment at the base determined in accordance with Section 9.2.3.6 using the unmodified seismic forces and not including the reduction permitted in the design of the foundation;

h_x = the height above the base to the level under consideration; and

δ_x = the deflections of the fixed base structure as determined in Section 9.2.3.7.1 using the unmodified seismic forces.

The modified story drifts and P-delta effects shall be evaluated in accordance with the provisions of Section 9.2.3.7 using the modified story shears and deflections determined in this section.

9.2.5.3. Modal Analysis Procedure: The following provisions are supplementary to those presented in Section 9.2.4.

9.2.5.3.1. Modal Base Shears: To account for the effects of soil-structure interaction,

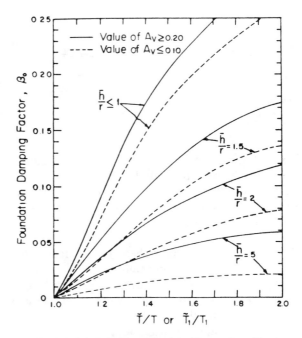

FIG. 9.2.5.2.1.2. Foundation Damping Factor

the base shear corresponding to the fundamental mode of vibration (V_1) *shall* be reduced to:

$$\tilde{V}_1 = V_1 - \Delta V_1 \qquad (9.2.5.3.1-1)$$

The reduction (ΔV_1) shall be computed in accordance with Eq. (9.2.5.2.1-2) with $\overline{W}$ taken as equal to the gravity load $\overline{W}_1$ defined by Eq. (9.2.4.5-2), C_s computed from Eq. (9.2.4.5-3) using the fundamental period of the fixed base building (T_1), and $\tilde{C}_s$ computed from Eq. (9.2.4.5-3) using the fundamental period of the elastically supported building ($\tilde{T}_1$).

The period $\tilde{T}_1$ shall be determined from Eq. (9.2.5.2.1.1-1), or from Eq. (9.2.5.2.1.1-3) when applicable, taking $T = \tilde{T}_1$, evaluating $\bar{k}$ from Eq. (9.2.5.2.1.1-2) with $\overline{W} = \overline{W}_1$, and computing $\bar{h}$ as follows:

$$\bar{h} = \frac{\displaystyle\sum_{i=1}^{n} w_i\phi_{i1}h_j}{\displaystyle\sum_{i=1}^{n} w_i\phi_{i1}} \qquad (9.2.5.3.1-2)$$

The aforementioned designated values of $\overline{W}$, $\bar{h}$, T, and $\tilde{T}$ also shall be used to evaluate the factor α from Eq. (9.2.5.2.1.1-4) and factor β_o from Fig. 9.2.5.2.1.2. No reduction shall be made in the shear components contributed by the higher modes of vibration. The reduced base shear ($\tilde{V}_I$) shall in no case be taken less than $0.7V_I$.

9.2.5.3.2. Other Modal Effects: The modified modal seismic forces, story shears, and overturning moments shall be determined as for buildings without interaction using the modified base shear ($\tilde{V}_I$) instead of V_I. The modified modal deflections ($\tilde{\delta}_{xm}$) shall be determined as follows:

$$\tilde{\delta}_{xI} = \frac{\tilde{V}_1}{V_1}\left[\frac{M_{01}h_x}{K_\theta} + \delta_{x1}\right] \qquad (9.2.5.3.2\text{-}1)$$

and

$$\tilde{\delta}_{xm} = \delta_{xm} \qquad \text{for m} = 2,3,\ldots \qquad (9.2.5.3.2\text{-}2)$$

where:

$M_{o1} =$ the overturning base moment for the fundamental mode of the fixed-base building, as determined in Section 9.2.4.7. using the unmodified modal base shear V_1; and

$\delta_{xm} =$ the modal deflections at Level x of the fixed-base building as determined in Section 9.2.4.6. using the unmodified modal shears, V_m.

The modified modal drift in a story ($\tilde{\Delta}_m$) shall be computed as the difference of the deflections ($\tilde{\delta}_{xm}$) at the top and bottom of the story under consideration.

9.2.5.3.3. Design Values: The design values of the modified shears, moments, deflections, and story drifts shall be determined as for structures without interaction by taking the square root of the sum of the squares of the respective modal contributions. In the design of the foundation, *it shall be permitted* to reduce the overturning moment at the foundation-soil interface determined in this manner by 10% as for structures without interaction.

The effects of torsion about a vertical axis shall be evaluated in accordance with the provisions of Section 9.2.3.5. and the *P*-delta effects shall be evaluated in accordance with the provisions of Section 9.2.3.7.2., using the story shears and drifts determined in Section 9.2.5.3.2.

9.2.6 Provisions for Seismically Isolated Structures

9.2.6.1 General: Every seismically isolated structure and every portion thereof shall be designed and constructed in accordance with the requirements of this section and the applicable requirements of Section 9.1.

The lateral-force-resisting system and the isolation system shall be designed to resist the deformations and stresses produced by the effects of seismic ground motions as provided in this section.

9.2.6.2 Criteria Selection

9.2.6.2.1 Basis for Design: The procedures and limitations for the design of seismically isolated buildings shall be determined considering zoning, site characteristics, vertical acceleration, cracked section properties of concrete and masonry members, category per Table 1-1, configuration, structural system, and height in accordance with Section 9.2.2 except as noted below.

9.2.6.2.2 Stability of the Isolation System: The stability of the vertical load-carrying elements of the isolation system shall be verified by analysis and test, as required, for lateral seismic displacement equal to the total maximum displacement.

9.2.6.2.3 *Structural Category:* All portions of the building, including the structure above the isolation system, shall be assigned a *category per Table 1-1.*

9.2.6.2.4 Configuration Requirements: Each building shall be designated as being regular or irregular on the basis of the structural configuration above the isolation system.

9.2.6.2.5 Selection of Lateral Response Procedure

9.2.6.2.5.1 General: Seismically isolated buildings *except those defined in Section 9.2.6.2.5.2* shall be designed using the dynamic lateral response procedure of Section 9.2.6.4.

9.2.6.2.5.2 Equivalent-Lateral-Force Procedure: Seismically isolated buildings *meeting the following requirements* shall be designed using either the equivalent-lateral-response procedure of Section 9.2.6.3 or the *dynamic lateral response procedure of Section 9.2.6.4:*

1. The building is located at least 15 km from all active faults;
2. The building is located on a Soil Profile Type A, B, C, or D site;
3. The structure above the isolation interface is less than or equal to four stories or 65 ft (19.8 m) in height;
4. The isolated period of the building, T_I, is less than or equal to 3.0 sec;
5. The isolated period of the building, T_I, is greater than three times the elastic, fixed-base period of the building above the isola-

tion system as determined by Eqs. (9.2.3.3.1-1) or (9.2.3.3.1-2);

6. The structure above the isolation system is of regular configuration; and

7. The isolation system meets all of the following criteria:

 a. The effective stiffness of the isolation system at the design displacement is greater than one third of the effective stiffness at 20% of the design displacement;

 b. The isolation system is capable of producing a restoring force as specified in Section 9.2.6.6.2.4;

 c. The isolation system has force-deflection properties that are independent of the rate of loading;

 d. The isolation system has force-deflection properties that are independent of vertical load and bilateral load; and

 e. The isolation system does not limit maximum capable earthquake displacement to less than M_M times the total design displacement.

9.2.6.2.5.3 Dynamic Analysis: * The dynamic lateral response procedure of Section 9.2.6.4 shall be used as specified below.

9.2.6.2.5.3.1 Response-spectrum analysis: Response-spectrum analysis shall not be used for design of a seismically isolated building unless:

1. The building is located on a Soil Profile Type A, B, C, D, or E site; and

2. The isolation system meets the criteria of Item 7 of Section 9.2.6.2.5.2.

9.2.6.2.5.3.2 Time-history analysis: Time-history analysis *shall be permitted* for design of any seismically isolated building and shall be used for design of all seismically isolated buildings not meeting the criteria of Section 9.2.6.2.5.3.1.

9.2.6.2.5.3.3 Site-specific design spectra: Site-specific ground-motion spectra of the design earthquake and the maximum capable earthquake developed in accordance with Section 9.2.6.4.4.1 shall be used for design and analysis of all seismically isolated buildings if any one of the following conditions apply:

1. The building is located on a Soil Profile Type E or F site; or

2. The building is located within 15 km of an active fault; or

3. The isolated period of the building, T_I, is greater than 3.0 sec.

9.2.6.3 Equivalent-Lateral Force Procedure

9.2.6.3.1 General: Except as provided in Section 9.2.6.4, every seismically isolated building or portion thereof shall be designed and constructed to resist minimum earthquake displacements and forces as specified by this section and the applicable requirements of Section 9.2.3.

9.2.6.3.2 Deformation Characteristics of the Isolation System: Minimum lateral earthquake design displacements and forces on seismically isolated buildings shall be based on the deformation characteristics of the isolation system.

The deformation characteristics of the isolation system shall explicitly include the effects of the wind-restraint system if such a system is used to meet the design requirements of this document.

The deformation characteristics of the isolation system shall be based on properly substantiated tests performed in accordance with Section 9.2.6.9.

9.2.6.3.3 Minimum Lateral Displacements

9.2.6.3.3.1 Design Displacement: The isolation system shall be designed and constructed to withstand minimum lateral earthquake displacements that act in the direction of each of the main horizontal axes of the building in accordance with the following:

$$D = \frac{gA_vF_vN_sT_I}{4\pi^2B_I} \qquad (9.2.6.3.3.1)$$

where

g = acceleration of gravity. The units of the acceleration of gravity, g, are in./sec^2 (mm/sec^2) if the units of the design displacement, D, are inches (mm);

A_v = the seismic coefficient representing the effective peak velocity-related acceleration as determined in Section 9.1.4.1

F_v = the soil coefficient as determined from Table 9.1.4.2.3B; for calculation of *D substitute the value of A_vN_s for A_v in Table 9.1.4.2.3B.*

N_s = numerical coefficient related to both the proximity of the building to an active fault and fault magnitude as set forth in Table 9.2.6.3.3.1A.

T_I = period of seismically isolated build-

78

TABLE 9.2.6.3.3.1A
Near-Field Site Response Coefficient, N_s

Closest Distance, d_F, to Active Fault	Maximum Capable Earthquake Magnitude, M_{MCE}, of Active Fault[a,b]		
	$M_{MCE} \geq 8.0$	$M_{MCE} = 7.0$	$M_{MCE} \leq 6.0$
$d_F \geq 15$ km (9 mi)	1.0	1.0	1.0
$d_F = 10$ km (6 mi)	1.2	1.0	1.0
$d_F \leq 5$ km (3 mi)	1.5	1.3	1.1

[a]Location and maximum capable earthquake magnitude, M_{MCE}, of active faults shall be established from properly substantiated geotechnical data (e.g., most recent mapping of active faults by the U.S. Geological Survey).

[b] The near-field site response coefficient shall be based on linear interpolation of values of the closest distance, d_F, and maximum capable earthquake magnitude, M_{MCE}, other than those given.

ing, in seconds (sec), in the direction under consideration, as prescribed by Eq. (9.2.6.3.3.2).

B_I = numerical coefficient related to the effective damping of the isolation system as set forth in Table 9.2.6.5.3.3.1B.

9.2.6.3.3.2 Isolated-Building Period:
The isolated-building period, T_I, shall be determined using the deformational characteristics of the isolation system in accordance with the following equation:

$$T_I = 2\pi \sqrt{\frac{W}{k_{min}g}} \qquad (9.2.6.3.3.2)$$

where

W = total seismic dead load weight of the building above the isolation interface;
k_{min} = minimum effective stiffness of the

isolation system at the design displacement in the horizontal direction under consideration; and
g = acceleration due to gravity.

9.2.6.3.3.3 Total Design Displacement: The total design displacement, D_T, of elements of the isolation system shall include additional displacement due to actual and accidental torsion calculated considering the spatial distribution of the lateral stiffness of the isolation system and the most disadvantageous location of mass eccentricity.

The total design displacement, D_T, of elements of an isolation system with uniform spatial distribution of lateral stiffness shall not be taken as less than that prescribed by the following equation:

$$D_T = D\left(1 + y_p \frac{12e_p}{b_p^2 + d_p^2}\right) \qquad (9.2.6.3.3.3)$$

Exception: Where the isolation system is shown by calculation to be configured to resist torsion accordingly, D_T shall be at least 1.1 times D.

where

D = design displacement, in inches (mm), at the center of rigidity of the isolation system in the direction under consideration as prescribed by Eq. (9.2.6.3.3.1);
y_p = the distance, in feet (mm), between the center of rigidity of the isolation system rigidity and the element of interest measured perpendicular to the direction of seismic loading under consideration;

TABLE 9.2.6.3.3.1B
Damping Coefficient, B_I

Effective Damping, β_I (Percentage of Critical)[a,b]	B_I Factor
≤2%	0.8
5%	1.0
10%	1.2
20%	1.5
30%	1.7
40%	1.9
≥50%	2.0

[A]The damping coefficient shall be based on the effective damping of the isolation system determined in accordance with the requirements of Section 9.2.6.9.5.2.

[B]The damping coefficient shall be based on linear interpolation for effective damping values other than those given.

e_p = the actual eccentricity, in feet (mm), measured in plan between the center of mass of the structure above the isolation interface and the center of rigidity of the isolation system, plus accidental eccentricity, in feet (mm), taken as 5 percent of the maximum building dimension perpendicular to the direction of force under consideration;

b_p = the shortest plan dimension of the structure, in feet (mm), measured perpendicular to d_p; and

d_p = the longest plan dimension of the structure, in feet (mm).

9.2.6.3.3.4 Total Maximum Displacement:

The total maximum displacement, D_{TM}, required for verification of isolation system stability in the most critical direction of horizontal response shall be calculated in accordance with the following:

$$D_{TM} = M_M D_{TC} \qquad (9.2.6.3.3.4)$$
*

where

M_M = numerical coefficient related to maximum capable earthquake response as set forth in Table 9.2.6.3.3.4;

TABLE 9.2.6.3.3.4
Maximum Capable Earthquake Displacement Coefficient, M_M

Peak Velocity-Related Acceleration, A_v	Effective Response Region[a,b]	
	Constant Acceleration	Constant Velocity
0.40	1.2	1.25
0.30	1.33	1.5
0.20	1.5	1.75
0.15	1.67	2.0
0.10	2.0	2.5
0.05	2.5	3.0

[a]Except for construction of design spectra, as required in Section 9.2.6.4.4.1, the value of M_M shall be that specified for constant velocity.

[b]For construction of design spectra, as required in Section 9.2.6.4.4.1, the value of M_M specified for constant acceleration shall apply to all periods from 0 seconds to the transition period (i.e., 0.4 sec for Soil Profile Types A and B; 0.6 sec for Soil Profile Types C and D; and 0.9 sec for Soil Profile Type E), and the value of M_M specified for constant velocity shall apply to all periods greater than the transition period. The product $M_M A_v N$ in the constant velocity region need not exceed the product $M_M A_v N$ at the transition period.

D_{TC} = the total design displacement for the maximum capable earthquake in inches (mm) including both translational displacement at the center of rigidity, D_c, and the component of torsional displacement in the direction under consideration *as specified in Section 9.2.6.3.3.3 but instead substituting D_c for D; and*

D_c = the design displacement, in inches (mm), at the center of rigidity of the isolation systems in the direction under consideration as prescribed by Eq. (9.2.6.3.3.1) *except the equation is multiplied by M_M and F_v is determined from Table 9.1.4.2.3.B by substituting $M_M A_v$ for A_v.*

9.2.6.3.4 Minimum Lateral Forces
9.2.6.3.4.1 Isolation System and Structural Elements at or below Isolation System:

The isolation system, the foundation, and all structural elements below the isolation system shall be designed and constructed to withstand a minimum lateral seismic force, V_b, using all of the appropriate provisions for a nonisolated building where:

$$V_b = k_{max} D \qquad (9.2.6.3.4.1)$$

where

V_b = the minimum lateral seismic design force or shear on elements of the isolation system or elements below the isolation system as prescribed by Eq. (9.2.6.3.4.1);

k_{max} = maximum effective stiffness of the isolation system at the design displacement in the horizontal direction under consideration; and

D = design displacement, in inches (mm), at the center of rigidity of the isolation system in the direction under consideration as prescribed by Eq. (9.2.6.3.3.1).

9.2.6.3.4.2 Structural Elements above Isolation System:

The structure above the isolation system shall be designed and constructed to withstand a minimum shear force, V_s, using all of the appropriate provisions for a nonisolated building where:

$$V_s = \frac{k_{max} D}{R_I} \qquad (9.2.6.3.4.2)$$

where

k_{max} = maximum effective stiffness of the isolation system at the design displacement in the horizontal direction under consideration.

D = design displacement, in inches (mm), at the center of rigidity of the isolation system in the direction under consideration as prescribed by Eq. (9.2.6.3.3.1).

R_I = numerical coefficient related to the type of lateral-force-resisting system above the isolation system.

The R_I factor shall be based on the type of lateral-force-resisting system used for the structure above the isolation system and shall be 3/8 of the R value given in Table 9.2.2.2 with an upper bound value not to exceed 2.0 and a lower bound value not to be less than 1.0.

9.2.6.3.4.3 Limits on V_s: The value of V_s shall not be taken as less than the following:

1. The lateral seismic force required by Section 2.2 for a fixed-base building of the same weight, W, and a period equal to the isolated period, T_I;
2. The base shear corresponding to the factored design wind load; and
3. The product of 1.5 times the lateral seismic force required to fully activate the isolation system (e.g., 1.5 times the yield level of a softening system, the ultimate capacity of a sacrificial wind-restraint system, or the static friction level of a sliding system).

9.2.6.3.5 Vertical Distribution of Force. The total force shall be distributed over the height of the structure above the isolation interface in accordance with the following equation:

$$F_x = \frac{V_s w_x h_x}{\sum\limits_{i=1}^{n} w_i h_i} \qquad (9.2.6.3.5)$$

where

V_s = total lateral seismic design force or shear on elements above the isolation system as prescribed by Eq. (9.2.6.3.4.2);

W_x = portion of W that is located at or assigned to Level $i, n,$ or x, respectively;

h_x = height above the base Level $i, n,$ or x, respectively;

w_i = portion of W that is located at or assigned to Level $i, n,$ or x, respectively; and

h_i = height above the base Level $i, n,$ or x, respectively.

At each level designated as x, the force, F_x, shall be applied over the area of the building in accordance with the mass distribution at the level. Stresses in each structural element shall be calculated as the effect of force, F_x, applied at the appropriate levels above the base.

9.2.6.3.6 Drift Limits: The maximum interstory drift of the structure above the isolation system shall not exceed $0.010h_{sx}$. The drift shall be calculated by Eq. (9.2.3.7.1) with the C_d factor of the isolated structure equal to the R_I factor defined in Section 9.2.7.3.4.2.

9.2.6.4 Dynamic Lateral Response Procedure

9.2.6.4.1 General: As required by Section 9.2.6.2, every seismically isolated building or portion thereof shall be designed and constructed to resist earthquake displacements and forces as specified in this section and the applicable requirements of Section 9.2.4.

9.2.6.4.2 Isolation System and Structural Elements below the Isolation System: The total design displacement of the isolation system shall not be taken as less than 90% of D_T as specified by Section 9.2.6.3.3.3.

The total maximum displacement of the isolation system shall not be taken as less than 80% of D_{TM} as prescribed by Eq. (9.2.6.3.3.4).

The design lateral shear force on the isolation system and structural elements below the isolation system shall not be taken as less than 90% of V_b as prescribed by Eq. (9.2.6.3.4.1).

The limits of the first and third paragraphs of Section 9.2.6.4.2 shall be evaluated using values of D_T and D_{TM} determined in accordance with Section 9.2.6.3.3 except that D' *shall not* be used in lieu of D *unless* D' is prescribed by the equation:

$$D' = \frac{D}{\sqrt{1 + (T/T_I)^2}} \qquad (9.2.6.4.2)$$

where

D = design displacement, in inches (mm), at the center of rigidity of the isolation system in the direction under

81

consideration as prescribed by Eq. (9.2.6.3.3.1).

$T =$ elastic, fixed-base period of the structure above the isolation system as determined by Section 9.2.3.2.2.

$T_I =$ period of seismically isolated building, in seconds (sec), in the direction under consideration as prescribed by Eq. (9.2.6.3.3.2).

9.2.6.4.3 Structural Elements above Isolation System: The design lateral shear force on the structure above the isolation system, if regular in configuration, shall not be taken as less than 80% of $k_{max}D/R_I$ or less than the limits specified by Section 9.2.6.3.4.3.

Exception: The design lateral shear force on the structure above the isolation system, if regular in configuration, *shall not* be less than 60% of $k_{max}D/R_I$, *when* time-history analysis is used for design of the structure.

The design lateral shear force on the structure above the isolation system, if irregular in configuration, shall not be taken as less than $k_{max}D/R_I$ or less than the limits specified by Section 9.2.6.3.4.3.

Exception: The design lateral shear force on the structure above the isolation system, if irregular in configuration, *shall not* be less than 80% of $k_{max}D/R_I$, *when* time-history analysis is used for design of the structure.

9.2.6.4.4 Ground Motion

9.2.6.4.4.1 Design Spectra: Properly substantiated site-specific spectra are required for design of all buildings with an isolated period, T_I, greater than 3.0 sec or located on a Soil Profile Type E or F site or located within 15 km of an active fault. Buildings that do not require site-specific spectra and for which site-specific spectra have not been calculated shall be designed using spectra developed using the procedure presented in Table 9.2.6.4.4.1.

A design spectrum shall be constructed for the design earthquake. This design spectrum shall not be taken as less than the response spectrum developed using Table 9.2.6.4.4.1 for the appropriate Soil Profile Type.

Exception: If a site-specific spectrum is calculated for the design earthquake, the design spectrum *shall not* be less than 80% of the response spectrum developed using Table 9.2.6.4.4.1 for the appropriate Soil Profile Type.

A design spectrum shall be constructed for the maximum capable earthquake. This design spectrum shall not be taken as less than the spectrum developed using Table 9.2.6.4.4.1 for the appropriate Soil Profile Type. This design spectrum shall be used to determine the total maximum displacement and overturning forces for design and testing of the isolation system.

Exception: If a site-specific spectrum is calculated for the maximum capable earthquake, the design spectrum *shall not* be less than 80% of the response spectrum developed using Table 9.2.6.4.4.1 for the appropriate Soil Profile Type.

9.2.6.4.4.2 Time Histories: Pairs of horizontal ground-motion time-history components shall be selected from not less than three recorded

TABLE 9.2.6.4.4.1
Construction of Response Spectra (Free Field, Elastic, Smoothed, 5% Damping)

Step 1 Select A_a and A_v from Maps 3 and 4.

Step 2 Select the appropriate Soil Profile Type from Section 1.4.2.

Step 3 Determine the corresponding values of the soil coefficients F_a and F_v and F_a' and F_v' from Tables 9.1.4.2.3a and 9.1.4.2.3b. The values of F_a and F_v shall be determined using a value of $A_v = A_v N_s$ and $A_a = A_a N_s$ for the design spectra. The values of F_a' and F_v' shall be determined using a value of $A_a = M_M A_a N_s$ and $A_v = M_M A_v N_s$ for the maximum capable response spectra.

Step 4 Compute the (short period) constant spectral acceleration portion of the response as follows:

$$\text{design spectra } S_A = 2.5 F_a A_a N_s \qquad\qquad (9.2.6.4.4.1.\text{-}1)$$

$$\text{maximum capable spectra } S_A = 2.5 M_M F'_a A_a N_s \qquad\qquad (9.2.6.4.4.1\text{-}2)$$

Step 5 Compute the (longer period) constant velocity portion of the spectrum (S_A decreases as $1/T$ where $T =$ period) as follows:

$$\text{design spectra } S_A = S_A = F_v A_v N_s\left(\frac{1}{T}\right) \qquad\qquad (9.2.6.4.4.1\text{-}3)$$

$$\text{maximum design spectra } S_A = M_M F'_v A_v N_s\left(\frac{1}{T}\right) \qquad\qquad (9.2.6.4.4.1\text{-}4)$$

Step 6 At each period (T), the elastic response spectrum is the lesser of the two values from Eq. (9.2.6.4.4.1-1) and (9.2.6.4.4.1-2) so that Eq. (9.2.6.4.4.1-1) defines S_A in the low-period range and Eq. (9.2.6.4.4.1-2) defines S_A in the higher period range. The period at which the transition from Eq. (9.2.6.4.4.1-1) to Eq. (9.2.6.4.4.1-2) occurs varies as a function of: (a) the Soil Profile Type; (b) A_a; and (c) A_v.

events. For each pair of horizontal ground-motion components, the square root sum of the squares (SRSS) of the 5% damped spectrum of the scaled, horizontal components shall be constructed. The motions shall be scaled such that the average value of the SRSS spectra does not fall below 1.3 times the 5% damped spectrum of the design earthquake (or maximum capable earthquake) by more than 10 percent in the period range of T_I, as determined by Eq. (9.2.6.3.3.2), for periods from T_I minus 1.0 sec to T_I plus 1.0 sec.

The duration of the time histories shall be consistent with the magnitude and source characteristics of the design earthquake (or maximum capable earthquake).

Time histories developed for sites within 15 km of a major active fault shall incorporate near-fault phenomena.

9.2.6.4.5 Mathematical Model

9.2.6.4.5.1 General: The mathematical models of the isolated building including the isolation system, the lateral-force-resisting system, and other structural elements shall conform to Section 9.2.4.2 and to the requirements of Sections 9.2.6.4.5.2 and 9.2.6.4.5.3, herein.

9.2.6.4.5.2 Isolation System: The isolation system shall be modeled using deformational characteristics developed and verified by test in accordance with the requirements of Section 9.2.6.3.2. The isolation system shall be modeled with sufficient detail to:

1. Account for the spatial distribution of isolator units;
2. Calculate translation, in both horizontal directions, and torsion of the building above the isolation interface considering the most disadvantageous location of mass eccentricity;
3. Assess overturning/uplift forces on individual isolator units; and
4. Account for the effects of vertical load, bilateral load, and/or the rate of loading if the force deflection properties of the isolation system are dependent on one or more of these attributes.

9.2.6.4.5.3 Isolated Building

9.2.6.4.5.3.1 Displacement: The maximum displacement of each floor and the total design displacement and total maximum displacement across the isolation system shall be calculated using a model of the isolated building that in-

corporates the force-deflection characteristics of nonlinear elements of the isolation system and the lateral-force-resisting system.

Isolation systems with nonlinear elements include, but are not limited to, systems that do not meet the criteria of Item 7 of Section 9.2.6.2.5.2.

Lateral-force-resisting systems with nonlinear elements include, but are not limited to, irregular structural systems designed for a lateral force less than $k_{max}D/R_I$ and regular structural systems designed for a lateral force less than 80% of $k_{max}D/R_I$.

9.2.6.4.5.3.2 Forces and displacements in key elements: Design forces and displacements in key elements of the lateral force-resisting system shall not be calculated using a linear elastic model of the isolated structure unless:

1. Pseudo-elastic properties assumed for nonlinear isolation-system components are based on the maximum effective stiffness of the isolation system and
2. All key elements of the lateral-force-resisting system are linear.

9.2.6.4.6 Description of Analysis Procedures

9.2.6.4.6.1 General: Response-spectrum and time-history analyses shall be performed in accordance with Section 9.2.4 and the requirements of this section.

9.2.6.4.6.2 Input Earthquake: The design earthquake shall be used to calculate the total design displacement of the isolation system and the lateral forces and displacements of the isolated structure. The maximum capable earthquake shall be used to calculate the total maximum displacement of the isolation system.

9.2.6.4.6.3 Response-Spectrum Analysis. Response-spectrum analysis shall be performed using a damping value equal to the effective damping of the isolation system or 30% of critical, whichever is less.

Response-spectrum analysis used to determine the total design displacement and the total maximum displacement shall include simultaneous excitation of the model by 100% of the most critical direction of ground motion and 30% of the ground motion on the orthogonal axis. The maximum displacement of the isolation system shall be calculated as the vectorial sum of the two orthogonal displacements.

The design shear at any story shall not be less than the story shear obtained using Eq. (9.2.6.3.5) and a value of V_s taken as that equal to the base shear obtained from the response-spectrum analysis in the direction of interest.

9.2.6.4.6.4 Time-History Analysis: Time-history analysis shall be performed with at least three appropriate pairs of horizontal time-history components as defined in Section 9.2.6.4.4.2.

Each pair of time histories shall be applied simultaneously to the model considering the most disadvantageous location of mass eccentricity. The maximum displacement of the isolation system shall be calculated from the vectorial sum of the two orthogonal components at each time step.

The parameter of interest shall be calculated for each time-history analysis. If three time-history analyses are performed, the maximum response of the parameter of interest shall be used for design. If seven or more time-history analyses are performed, the average value of the response parameter of interest shall be used for design.

9.2.6.4.7 Design Lateral Force

9.2.6.4.7.1 Isolation System and Structural Elements at or below Isolation System: The isolation system, foundation, and all structural elements below the isolation system shall be designed using all of the appropriate provisions for a nonisolated building and the forces obtained from the dynamic analysis without reduction.

9.2.6.4.7.2 Structural Elements above Isolation System: Structural elements above the isolation system shall be designed using the appropriate provisions for a nonisolated building and the forces obtained from the dynamic analysis reduced by a factor of R_I. The R_I factor shall be based on the type of lateral-force-resisting system used for the structure above the isolation system.

9.2.6.4.7.3 Scaling of Results: When the factored lateral shear force on structural elements, determined using either response spectrum or time-history analysis, is less than the minimum level prescribed by Section 9.2.6.4.2 and 9.2.6.4.3, all response parameters, including member forces and moments, shall be adjusted upward proportionally.

9.2.6.4.7.4 Drift Limits: Maximum interstory drift corresponding to the design lateral force including displacement due to vertical deformation of the isolation system shall not exceed the following limits:

1. The maximum interstory drift of the structure above the isolation system calculated by response spectrum analysis shall not exceed $0.015h_{sx}$; and
2. The maximum interstory drift of the structure above the isolation system calculated by

time-history analysis considering the force-deflection characteristics of nonlinear elements of the lateral force-resisting system shall not exceed $0.020h_{sx}$.

Drift shall be calculated using Eq. (9.2.3.7.1) with the C_d factor of the isolated structure equal to the R_I factor defined in Section 9.2.6.3.4.2.

The secondary effects of the maximum capable earthquake lateral displacement Δ of the structure above the isolation system combined with gravity forces shall be investigated if the interstory drift ratio exceeds $0.010/R_I$.

9.2.6.5 Lateral Load on Elements of Buildings and Nonstructural Components Supported by Buildings

9.2.6.5.1 General: Parts or portions of an isolated building, permanent nonstructural components and the attachments to them, and the attachments for permanent equipment supported by a building shall be designed to resist seismic forces and displacements as prescribed by this section and the applicable requirements of Section 9.3.

9.2.6.5.2 Forces and Displacements:

9.2.6.5.2.1 Components at or above Isolation Interface: Elements of seismically isolated buildings and nonstructural components, or portions thereof, that are at or above the isolation interface shall be designed to resist a total lateral seismic force equal to the maximum dynamic response of the element or component under consideration.

Exception: Elements of seismically isolated buildings and nonstructural components or portions * designed to resist total lateral seismic force as prescribed by Eq. (9.2.2.6-1) or (9.2.2.6-2) as appropriate.

9.2.6.5.2.2 Components Crossing Isolation Interface: Elements of seismically isolated buildings and nonstructural components, or portions thereof, that cross the isolation interface shall be designed to withstand the total maximum displacement.

9.2.6.5.2.3 Components below Isolation Interface: Elements of seismically isolated buildings and nonstructural components, or portions thereof, that are below the isolation interface shall be designed and constructed in accordance with the requirements of Section 9.2.2.

9.2.6.6 Detailed System Requirements

9.2.6.6.1 General: The isolation system and the structural system shall comply with the material requirements of Sections 9.5–9.9. In addition, the isolation system shall comply with the detailed system requirements of this section and the structural system shall comply with the detailed system requirements of this section and the applicable portions of Section 9.2.2.

9.2.6.6.2 Isolation System

9.2.6.6.2.1 Environmental Conditions: In addition to the requirements for vertical and lateral loads induced by wind and earthquake, the isolation system shall be designed with consideration given to for other environmental conditions including aging effects, creep, fatigue, operating temperature, and exposure to moisture or damaging substances.

9.2.6.6.2.2 Wind Forces: Isolated buildings shall resist design wind loads at all levels above the isolation interface. At the isolation interface, a wind restraint system shall be provided to limit lateral displacement in the isolation system to a value equal to that required between floors of the structure above the isolation interface.

9.2.6.6.2.3 Fire Resistance: Fire resistance for the isolation system shall meet that required for the building columns, walls, or other structural elements.

9.2.6.6.2.4 Lateral-Restoring Force: The isolation system shall be configured to produce a restoring force such that the lateral force at the total design displacement is at least $0.025W$ greater than the lateral force at 50% of the total design displacement.

Exception: The isolation system need not be configured to produce a restoring force, as required above, provided the isolation system is capable of remaining stable under full vertical load and accommodating a total maximum displacement equal to the greater of either 3.0 times the total design displacement or $36M_MC_aN_s$ in. (or $915M_MC_aN_s$ mm).

9.2.6.6.2.5 Displacement Restraint: The isolation system shall not be configured to include a displacement restraint that limits lateral displacement due to the maximum capable earthquake to less than M_M times the total design displacement unless the seismically isolated building is designed in accordance with the following criteria when more stringent than the requirements of Section 9.2.6.2:

1. Maximum capable earthquake response is calculated in accordance with the dynamic analysis requirements of Section 9.2.6.4 explicitly considering the nonlinear characteristics of the isolation system and the structure above the isolation system;

2. The ultimate capacity of the isolation system and structural elements below the isolation system shall exceed the strength and displacement demands of the maximum capable earthquake;

3. The structure above the isolation system is checked for stability and ductility demand of the maximum capable earthquake; and

4. The displacement restraint does not become effective at a displacement less than 0.75 times the total design displacement unless it is demonstrated by analysis that earlier engagement does not result in unsatisfactory performance.

9.2.6.6.2.6 Vertical-Load Stability: Each element of the isolation system shall be designed to be stable under the full-design-vertical load at a horizontal displacement equal to the total maximum displacement. Full-design-vertical load shall be computed using maximum and minimum vertical loads based on the combination of factored gravity and seismic loads as specified in Section 9.2.2.6. The seismic load E is given by Eq. (9.2.2.6-1) and (9.2.2.6-2) where C_a in these equations is replaced by $M_MN_sC_a$. The vertical force due to horizontal earthquake load, Q_E, shall be based on peak response due to the maximum capable earthquake.

9.2.6.6.2.7 Overturning: The factor of safety against global structural overturning at the isolation interface shall not be less than 1.0 for required load combinations. All gravity and seismic loading conditions shall be investigated. Seismic forces for overturning calculations shall be based on the maximum capable earthquake and W shall be used for the vertical restoring force.

Local uplift of individual elements is permitted provided the resulting deflections do not cause overstress or instability of the isolator units or other building elements.

9.2.6.6.2.8 Inspection and Replacement: Access for inspection and replacement of all components of the isolation system shall be provided.

9.2.6.6.2.9 Quality Control: A quality control testing program for isolator units shall be established by the engineer responsible for the structural design.

9.2.6.6.3 Structural System

9.2.6.6.3.1 Horizontal Distribution of Force: A horizontal diaphragm or other structural elements shall provide continuity above the isolation interface and shall have adequate strength and ductility to transmit forces (due to nonuniform ground motion) from one part of the building to another.

9.2.6.6.3.2 Building Separations: Minimum separations between the isolated building and surrounding retaining walls or other fixed obstructions shall not be less than the total maximum displacement.

9.2.6.6.3.3 Nonbuilding Structures: These shall be designed and constructed in accordance with the requirements of Section 9.2.7 using design displacements and forces calculated in accordance with Section 9.2.6.3 or 9.2.6.4.

9.2.6.7 Foundations: Foundations shall be designed and constructed in accordance with the requirements of Section 4 using design forces calculated in accordance with Section 9.2.6.3 or 9.2.6.4, as appropriate.

9.2.6.8 Design and Construction Review

9.2.6.8.1 General: A design review of the isolation system and related test programs shall be performed by an independent engineering team including persons licensed in the appropriate disciplines and experienced in seismic analysis methods and the theory and application of seismic isolation.

9.2.6.8.2 Isolation System: Isolation system design review shall include, but not be limited to, the following:

1. Review of site-specific seismic criteria including the development of site-specific spectra and ground motion time histories and all other design criteria developed specifically for the project;
2. Review of the preliminary design including the determination of the total design displacement of the isolation system design displacement and the lateral force design level;
3. Overview and observation of prototype testing (Section 9.2.6.9);
4. Review of the final design of the entire structural system and all supporting analyses; and
5. Review of the isolation system quality control testing program (Section 9.2.6.6.2.9).

9.2.6.9 Required Tests of the Isolation System

9.2.6.9.1 General: The deformation characteristics and damping values of the isolation system used in the design and analysis of seismically isolated buildings shall be based on tests of a selected sample of the components prior to construction as described in this section.

The isolation system components to be tested shall include the wind-restraint system if such a system is used in the design.

The tests specified in this section are for establishing and validating the design properties of the isolation system and shall not be considered as satisfying the manufacturing quality control tests of Section 9.2.6.6.2.9.

9.2.6.9.2 Prototype Tests

9.2.6.9.2.1 General: Prototype tests shall be performed separately on two full-size specimens of each predominant type and size of isolator unit of the isolation system. The test specimens shall include the wind restraint system as well as individual isolator units if such systems are used in the design. Specimens tested shall not be used for construction.

9.2.6.9.2.2 Record: For each cycle of tests, the force-deflection and hysteretic behavior of the test specimen shall be recorded.

9.2.6.9.2.3 Sequence and Cycles: The following sequence of tests shall be performed for the prescribed number of cycles at a vertical load equal to the average $Q_D + 0.5Q_L$ on all isolator units of a common type and size:

1. Twenty fully reversed cycles of loading at a lateral force corresponding to the wind design force;
2. Three fully reversed cycles of loading at each of the following increments of the total design displacement—0.25, 0.50, 0.75, and 1.0;
3. Three fully reversed cycles of loading at the total maximum displacement; and
4. $15F_v/B_I$, but not less than 10, fully reversed cycles of loading at 1.0 times the total design displacement.

If an isolator unit is also a vertical-load-carrying element, then Item 2 of the sequence of cyclic tests specified previously shall be performed for two additional vertical load cases. The first is given by the combination of the average dead load plus half the live load plus the earthquake load from Eq. (9.2.2.6-1). The second is given by the average dead load minus the earthquake load from Eq. (9.2.2.6-2). In Eqs. (9.2.2.6-1) and (9.2.2.6-2) where C_a is replaced by C_aN_s and where the vertical force due to horizontal earthquake load, Q_E, shall be based on peak response due to the design earthquake. In these tests, the combined vertical load shall be taken as the typical or average downward force on all isolator units of a common type and size.

9.2.6.9.2.4 Units Dependent on Loading Rates: If the force-deflection properties of the isolator units are dependent on the rate of loading, each set of tests specified in Section 9.2.6.9.2.3 shall be performed at a frequency, f, in the range of 0.1–1.0 times the inverse of the effective period, T_s. The frequency, f, shall be the minimum frequency of testing at which the effective stiffness and the effective damping at the design displacement are at least 85% of the corresponding values when the isolator unit is tested at a frequency equal to the inverse of period T_s.

If reduced-scale prototype specimens are used to quantify rate-dependent properties of isolators, the reduced-scale prototype specimens shall be of the same type and material and be manufactured with the same processes and quality as full-scale prototypes and shall be tested at a frequency that represents full-scale prototype loading rates.

The force-deflection properties of an isolator unit shall be considered to be dependent on the rate of loading if there is greater than a plus or minus 15% difference in the effective stiffness and the effective damping at the design displacement when tested at a frequency equal to the inverse of the effective period of the isolated building and when tested at any frequency in the range of 0.1–2.0 times the inverse of the effective period of the isolated building.

9.2.6.9.2.5 Units Dependent on Bilateral Load: If the force-deflection properties of the isolator units are dependent on bilateral load, the tests specified in Sections 9.2.6.9.2.3 and 9.2.6.9.2.4 shall be augmented to include bilateral load at the following increments of the total design displacement: 0.25 and 1.0, 0.50 and 1.0, 0.75 and 1.0, and 1.0 and 1.0.

If reduced-scale prototype specimens are used to quantify bilateral-load-dependent properties, the reduced scale specimens shall be of the same type and material and manufactured with the same processes and quality as full-scale prototypes.

The force-deflection properties of an isolator unit shall be considered to be dependent on bilateral load if the bilateral and unilateral force-deflection properties have greater than a 15% difference in effective stiffness at the design displacement.

9.2.6.9.2.6 Downward-Vertical Load: Isolator units that carry vertical load shall be statically tested for maximum and minimum downward vertical load at the total maximum displacement. In these tests, maximum and minimum vertical load on any one isolator unit of a common type and size shall be based on the combination of factored gravity and seismic loads as specified in Section 9.2.2.6. The seismic load E is given by Eq. (9.2.2.6-1) and Eq.

(9.2.2.6-2), where C_a in these equations is replaced by $M_M N_s C_a$ and the vertical force due to horizontal earthquake load, Q_E, is based on the peak response of the maximum capable earthquake.

9.2.6.9.2.7 Sacrificial-Wind-Restraint Systems: If a sacrificial-wind-restraint system is to be utilized, the ultimate capacity shall be established by test.

9.2.6.9.2.8 Testing Similar Units: The prototype tests are not required if an isolator unit is of similar size and of the same type and material as a prototype isolator unit that has been previously tested using the specified sequence of tests.

9.2.6.9.3 Determination of Force-Deflection Characteristics: The force-deflection characteristics of the isolation system shall be based on the cyclic load test results for each fully reversed cycle of loading.

The effective stiffness of an isolator unit shall be calculated for each cycle of loading as follows:

$$k_{\text{eff}} = \frac{F_I^+ - F_I^-}{\Delta_I^+ - \Delta_I^-} \qquad (9.2.6.9.3)$$

where F_I^+ and F_I^- are the maximum positive and maximum negative forces, respectively; and Δ_I^+ and Δ_I^- are the maximum positive and maximum negative test displacements, respectively.

If the minimum effective stiffness is to be determined, $F^+{}_{min}$ and $F^-{}_{min}$ shall be used in the equation.

If the maximum effective stiffness is to be determined, $F^+{}_{max}$ and $F^-{}_{max}$ shall be used in the equation.

9.2.6.9.4 System Adequacy: The performance of the test specimens shall be assessed as adequate if the following conditions are satisfied:

1. For each increment of test displacement specified in Item 2 of Section 9.2.6.9.2.3 and for each vertical load case specified in Section 9.2.6.9.2.3:
   there is no greater than a 15% difference between the effective stiffness at each of the three cycles of test and the average value of effective stiffness for each test specimen;

2. For each increment of test displacement specified in Item 2 of Section 9.2.6.9.2.3 and for each vertical load case specified in Section 9.2.6.9.2.3;
   there is no greater than a 15% difference in the average value of effective stiffness of the two test specimens of a common type and

size of the isolator unit over the required three cycles of test;

3. For each specimen there is no greater than a plus or minus 20% change in the initial effective stiffness of each test specimen over the $15F\sqrt{B_I}$, but not less than 10, cycles of test specified in Item 3 of Section 9.2.6.9.2.3;

4. For each specimen there is no greater than a 20% decrease in the initial effective damping over for the $15F\sqrt{B_I}$, but not less than 10, cycles of test specified in Section 9.2.6.9.2.3; and

5. All specimens of vertical-load-carrying elements of the isolation system remain stable up to the total maximum displacement for static load as prescribed in Section 9.2.6.9.2.6 and shall have a positive incremental force-carrying capacity.

9.2.6.9.5 Design Properties of the Isolation System

9.2.6.9.5.1 Effective Stiffness: The minimum and maximum effective stiffness of the isolation system shall be determined as follows:

1. The value of k_{min} shall be based on the minimum effective stiffness of individual isolator units as established by the cyclic tests of Item 2 of Section 9.2.6.9.2.3 at a displacement amplitude equal to the design displacement;

2. The value of k_{max} shall be based on the maximum effective stiffness of individual isolator units as established by the cyclic tests of Item 2 of Section 9.2.6.9.2.3 at a displacement amplitude equal to the design displacement; and

3. For isolator units that are found by the tests of Section 9.2.6.9.2.3, 9.2.6.9.2.4, or 9.2.6.9.2.5 to have force-deflection characteristics that vary with vertical load, rate of loading or bilateral load, respectively, the value of k_{max} shall be increased and the value of k_{min} shall be decreased, as necessary, to bound the effects of measured variation in effective stiffness.

9.2.6.9.5.2 Effective Damping: The effective damping, β_I, of the isolation system shall be calculated as follows:

$$\beta_I = \frac{total\ area}{2\pi k_{max} D^2} \qquad (9.2.6.9.5)$$

where the total area shall be taken as the sum of the areas of the hysteresis loops of all isolator units and the hysteresis loop area of each isolator unit shall be taken as the minimum area of the three hysteresis loops established by the cyclic tests of Item 2 of Section 9.2.6.9.2.3 at a displacement amplitude equal to the design displacement and

k_{max} = maximum effective stiffness of the isolation system at the design displacement in the horizontal direction under consideration.

D = design displacement, in inches (mm), at the center of rigidity of the isolation system in the direction under consideration as prescribed by Eq. (9.2.6.3.3.1).

9.2.7. Nonbuilding Structures
9.2.7.1 General
9.2.7.1.1: Nonbuilding structures include all self-supporting structures, other than buildings, *vehicular* bridges, dams, and *other structures excluded in Section 9.1.2* that are supported by the earth, that carry gravity loads, and that are required to resist the effects of earthquake. Nonbuilding structures shall be designed to resist the minimum lateral forces specified in this section. Design shall conform to the applicable provisions of other sections as modified by this section.

9.2.7.1.2: The design of nonbuilding structures shall provide sufficient strength and ductility, consistent with the requirements specified herein for buildings, to resist the effects of seismic ground motions as represented by these design forces:

a. Applicable strength and other design criteria shall be obtained from other portions of Section 9 or its referenced codes and standards.

b. When applicable strength and other design criteria are not contained in or referenced by Section 9, such criteria shall be obtained from approved national standards. Where approved national standards define acceptance criteria in terms of allowable stresses as opposed to strength, the design seismic forces shall be obtained from this Section and *used directly with allowable stresses specified in the national standards*. Detailing shall be in accordance with the approved national standards.

9.2.7.1.3: The weight W for nonbuilding structures shall include all dead load as defined for buildings in Section 9.2.3.2. For purposes of calculating design seismic forces in nonbuilding structures, W also shall include all normal operating contents for items such as tanks, vessels, bins, and piping.

9.2.7.1.4: The fundamental period of the nonbuilding structure shall be determined by rational methods as prescribed in Section 9.2.3.3.

9.2.7.1.5: The drift limitations of Section 9.2.2.7 need not apply to nonbuilding structures. Drift limitations shall be established for structural and nonstructural elements whose failure would cause life-safety hazards. *P*-delta effects shall be considered for structures whose drifts exceed one-half the values in Section 9.2.2.7.

9.2.7.1.6: For nonbuilding structures supporting flexible nonstructural elements whose combined gravity weight exceeds 25% of the structure at sites where the seismic coefficient C_a is greater than or equal to 0.20, the interaction effect between the structure and the supported element shall be *analyzed*.

9.2.7.2: The lateral force procedure for nonbuilding structures with structural systems similar to buildings (those with structural systems listed in Table 9.2.2.2) shall be selected in accordance with the force and detailing requirements of Section 9.2.2.1.

Exception: Intermediate moment frames of reinforced concrete shall be permitted at sites where the seismic coefficient C_a is greater than or equal to 0.20 if:

1. The nonbuilding structure is less than 50 ft (15.2 m) in height; and
2. $R = 3.0$ is used for design.

9.2.7.2.1: If hazardous contents are supported, increase the seismic base shear (V) by 50%.

9.2.7.3: Nonbuilding structures that have a fundamental period, T, less than 0.06 sec, including their anchorages, shall be designed for the lateral force obtained from the following:

$$V = 0.60\, C_a W \qquad (9.2.7.3)$$

where:

V = seismic design force applied to a nonbuilding structure;
C_a = the seismic coefficient based upon the Soil Profile Type and the Value of A_a as determined from Section 9.1.4.2.3, or Table 9.1.4.2.4a; and

W = nonbuilding structure operating weight.

The force shall be distributed with height in accordance with Section 9.2.3.4.

9.2.7.4: Flat-bottom tanks or other tanks with supported bottoms, founded at or below grade, shall be designed to resist seismic forces calculated using the procedures in Section 9.3.3.9.2.

9.2.7.5: Nonbuilding structures that are not covered by Sections 9.2.7.2–9.2.7.4 shall be designed to resist minimum seismic lateral forces not less than those determined in accordance with the requirements of Section 9.2.3.2 with the following additions and exceptions:

1. The factor R shall be as given in Table 9.2.7.5. The ratio of $1.2\, C_v/RT^{2/3}$ used in design shall not be less than $0.50\, C_a$.
2. The vertical distribution of the lateral seismic forces in nonbuilding structures covered by this section may be determined:
   a. Using the requirements of Section 9.2.3.4; or
   b. Using the procedures of Section 9.2.4.

Irregular structures at sites where the seismic coefficient C_a is greater than or equal to 0.20 and that cannot be modeled as a single mass shall use the procedures of Section 9.2.4.

3. Where an approved national standard provides a basis for the earthquake resistant design of a particular type of nonbuilding structure covered by Section 9.2.7, such a standard *shall not* be used *unless* the following limitations are met:
   a. The seismic ground acceleration, and the seismic coefficient, shall be in conformance with the requirements of Sections 9.1.4.1, 9.1.4.2, and *9.1.4.4*, respectively; and
   b. The values for total lateral force and total base overturning moment used in design shall not be less than 80% of the value that is obtained using this standard.

9.3 Architectural, Mechanical, and Electrical Components and Systems

9.3.1 General. Section 9.3 establishes minimum design criteria for architectural, mechanical, electrical, and nonstructural systems, components, and elements permanently attached to buildings, including supporting structures and attachments (hereinafter

TABLE 9.2.7.5
R Factors for Nonbuilding Structures

Nonbuilding Structure Type	R
Vessels (including tanks and pressurized spheres) on braced or unbraced legs	
Hazardous contents	1.5
All others	2
Cast-in-place concrete silos and chimneys having walls continuous to the foundation	3.5
All other distributed mass cantilever structures not covered above including stacks, chimneys, silos, and skirt-supported	
Vertical vessels	
Hazardous contents	2
All other	3
Trussed towers (freestanding or guyed), guyed stacks, and chimneys	3
Inverted pendulum type structures	2
Cooling towers	3.5
Bins and hoppers on braced or unbraced legs	3
Signs and billboards	3.5
Amusement structures and monuments	2
All other self-supporting structures not covered above	3

referred to as "components"). The design criteria establish minimum equivalent static force levels and relative displacement demands for the design of components and their attachments to the structure, recognizing ground motion and structural amplification, component toughness and weight, and performance expectations. Categories for buildings are defined in *Table 1-1*. For the purposes of this section, components shall be considered to have the same Category as that of the building that they occupy or to which they are attached unless otherwise noted.

In addition, all components are assigned a component importance factor (I_p) in this chapter. The default value for I_p is 1.00 for typical components in normal service. Higher values for I_p are assigned for components that contain hazardous substances, must have a higher level of assurance of function, or otherwise require additional attention because of their life-safety characteristics. Component importance factors are prescribed in Section 9.3.1.5.

All architectural, mechanical, electrical, and other nonstructural components in buildings shall be designed and constructed to resist the equivilant static forces and displacements determined in accordance with this Section. The design and evaluation of support structures and architectural components and equipment shall consider their flexibility as well as their strength.

Exceptions:

1. All components in Seismic Performance Category A.
2. Architectural components in Seismic Performance Category B *provided that* the importance factor (I_p) is equal to 1.0.

3. Mechanical and electrical components and systems in buildings assigned to Seismic Performance Categories B and C *provided that* the importance factor (I_p) is equal to 1.0.
4. Mechanical and electrical components in all Seismic Performance Categories that are mounted at 4 ft (1.2 m) or less above a floor level and weigh 400 lb (180 Kg) or less, *provided that* the importance factor (I_p) is equal to 1.0.
5. *Breakaway walls referred to in Section 5.3.2.2, however Section 9.2.2.2.4.2 shall be satisfied.*

The interrelationship of components and their effect on each other shall be considered so that the failure of an architectural, mechanical, or electrical component shall not cause the failure of a nearby critical architectural, mechanical, or electrical component that is essential to remain in place. *

9.3.1.1 References and Standards: The following references and standards are to be considered part of these provisions to the extent referred to in this chapter:

[9.3-1] API STD 650, Welded Steel Tanks For Oil Storage, American Petroleum Institute (API), 1993.

[9.3-2] ASME A17.1, Safety Code For Elevators and Escalators, American Society of Mechanical Engineers (ASME), 1993.

[9.3-3] ASME B31, Code For Pressure Piping, American Society of Mechanical Engineers (ASME), 1993.

[9.3-4] Boiler And Pressure Vessel Code, American Society of Mechanical Engineers (ASME), 1993.

[9.3-5] ASTM C635, Standard Specification For The Manufacture, Performance, and Testing of Metal Suspension Systems For Acoustical Tile And Lay-in Panel Ceilings, American Society For Testing and Materials (ASTM), 1991.

[9.3-6] ASTM C636, Standard Practice For Installation Of Metal Ceiling Suspension Systems For Acoustical Tile And Lay-in Panels, American Society For Testing And Materials (ASTM), 1992.

[9.3-7] D100, Welded Steel Tanks For Water Storage, American Water Works Association (AWWA), 1984.

*

[9.3-11] SP-58, Pipe Hangers and Supports—Materials, Design, and Manufacture, Manufacturers Standardization Society of the Valve and Fitting Industry (MSS), 1988.

[9.3-12] NFPA-13, Standard for the Installation of Sprinkler Systems, National Fire Protection Association (NFPA), 1991.

*

[9.3-13] Specification for the Design, Testing, and Utilization of Industrial Steel Storage Racks, Rack Manufacturers Institute (RMI), 1990.

9.3.1.2 Component Force Transfer. Components shall be attached such that the component forces are transferred to the structure of the building. Component seismic attachments shall be bolted, welded, adhered or otherwise positively fastened without consideration of frictional resistance produced by the effects of gravity.

The design documents shall include sufficient information relating to the attachments to verify compliance with the requirements of Section 9.3.

9.3.1.3 Seismic Forces: Seismic forces (F_p) shall be determined in accordance with Eq. (3.1.3-1):

$$F_p = 4.0\ C_a I_p W_p \qquad (9.3.1.3\text{-}1)$$

Alternatively, F_p may be computed in accordance with Eq. 3.1.3-2 through Eq. 3.1.3-5:

$$F_p = \frac{a_p A_p I_p W_p}{R_p} \qquad (9.3.1.3\text{-}2)$$

$$A_p = C_a + (A_r - C_a)\left(\frac{x}{h}\right) \qquad (9.3.1.3\text{-}3)$$

$$A_r = 2.0 A_s \le 4.0 C_a \qquad (9.3.1.3\text{-}4)$$

$$F_p(\text{min}) = 0.5 C_a I_p W_p \qquad (9.3.1.3\text{-}5)$$

where

F_p = Seismic design force centered at the component's center of gravity and distributed relative to component's mass distribution;

a_p = Component amplification factor that varies from 1.00 to 2.50 (select appropriate value from Table 9.3.2.2 or Table 9.3.3.2);

A_p = Component acceleration coefficient (expressed as a percentage of gravity) at point of attachment to structure;

I_p = Component importance factor that varies from 1.00 to 1.50 (see Section 9.3.1.5);

W_p = Component operating weight;

R_p = Component response modification factor that varies from 1.50 to 6.00 (select appropriate value from Table 9.3.2.2 or Table 9.3.3.2);

C_a = Seismic coefficient as determined in Section 9.1.4.2.3. or Table 9.1.4.2.4A;

A_r = Component acceleration coefficient (expressed as a percentage of gravity) at structure roof level;

x = Elevation in structure of center of gravity of component relative to grade elevation;

h = Average roof elevation of structure relative to grade elevation;

A_s = Structure response acceleration coefficient (expressed as a percentage of gravity):

$$A_s = \frac{1.2 C_v}{T^{2/3}} \le 2.5 C_a$$

Note that A_s shall be calculated for each principle horizontal direction of the structure. The largest value for A_s shall be utilized in determining A_r;

C_v = Seismic coefficient as determined in Section 9.1.4.2.3 or Table 9.1.4.2.4B; and

T = Effective fundamental period of the structure as determined in Sections 9.2.3.3 and 9.2.4.4.

The force (F_p) shall be applied independently vertically, longitudinally, and laterally in combination with other normal loads associated with the component.

When positive and negative wind loads exceed F_p for nonbearing exterior wall, these wind loads shall govern the design. Similarly when the building code horizontal loads exceed F_p for interior partitions, these building code loads shall govern the design.

9.3.1.4 Seismic Relative Displacements:

Seismic relative displacements (D_p) shall be determined in accordance with the following equations:

For two connection points on the same building or structural system, use the smaller of:

$$D_p = \delta_{xA} - \delta_{yA} \qquad (9.3.1.4\text{-}1)$$

or

$$D_p = (X - Y)\frac{\Delta_{aA}}{h_{sx}} \qquad (9.3.1.4\text{-}2)$$

For two connection points on separate buildings or structural systems, use the smaller of:

$$D_p = |\delta_{xA}| + |\delta_{yB}| \qquad (9.3.1.4\text{-}3)$$

or

$$D_p = \frac{X\Delta_{aA}}{h_{sx}} + \frac{Y\Delta_{aB}}{h_{sx}} \qquad (9.3.1.4\text{-}4)$$

where

D_p = Relative seismic displacement that the component must be designed to accommodate;

δ_{xA} = Deflection at building level x of Building A, determined by analysis as defined in Section 9.2.3.7.1;

δ_{yA} = Deflection at building level y of Building A, determined by analysis as defined in Section 9.2.3.7.1;

δ_{xB} = Deflection at building level x of Building B, determined by analysis as defined in Section 9.2.3.7.1;

δ_{yB} = Deflection at building level y of Building B, determined by analysis as defined in Section 9.2.3.7.1;

X = Height of upper support attachment at level x as measured from grade;

Y = Height of lower support attachment at level y as measured from grade;

Δ_{aA} = Allowable story drift for Building A as defined in Table 9.2.2.7;

Δ_{aB} = Allowable story drift for Building B as defined in Table 9.2.2.7; and

h_{sx} = Story height used in the definition of the allowable drift Δ_a in Table 9.2.2.7. Note that Δ_a/h_{sx} = the drift index.

The effects of seismic relative displacements shall be considered in combination with displacements caused by other loads as appropriate.

9.3.1.5 Component Importance Factor:

The component importance factor (I_p) shall be selected as follows:

$I_p = 1.5$ Life-safety component required to function after an earthquake (e.g., fire protection sprinkler system).

$I_p = 1.5$ Component contains material that would be significantly hazardous if released.

$I_p = 1.5$ Component poses a significant life—safety hazard if separated from primary structure (e.g., parapets, exterior wall panels).

$I_p = 1.5$ Component can block a means of egress or exitway if damaged (e.g., exit stairs).

$I_p = 1.0$ All other components.

9.3.2 Architectural Component Design

9.3.2.1 General: Architectural systems, components, or elements (hereinafter referred to as "components") listed in Table 9.3.2.2 and their attachments shall meet the requirements of Sections 9.3.2.2–9.3.2.9.

9.3.2.2 Architectural Component Forces and Displacements: Architectural components shall meet the force requirements of Section 9.3.1.3 and Table 9.3.2.2.

Components supported by chains or otherwise "hung" from above are not required to meet the seismic force requirements of this section provided that they cannot significantly damage any other component when subject to seismic motion and they have ductile or articulating connections to the structure at the point of attachment.

9.3.2.3 Architectural Component Deformation. Architectural components that could pose a life-safety hazard shall be designed for the seismic relative displacement requirements of Section 9.3.1.4. Architectural components shall be designed for vertical deflection due to joint rotation of cantilever structural members.

9.3.2.4 Exterior Wall Panel Connections. Exterior nonbearing wall panels that are attached to or enclose the structure shall be designed to meet the force and displacement provisions of Section 9.3.1.3 and 9.3.1.4. Connections to resist the seismic forces shall accomodate displacements of the structure and wall panel from other forces and effects. Such elements shall be supported by means of structural connections or by mechanical connections and fasteners. The support system shall be designed in accordance with the following:

TABLE 9.3.2.2
Architectural Component Coefficients

Architectural Component or Element	$a_p{}^a$	$R_p{}^b$
Interior Nonbearing Walls and Partitions		
Stair and elevator enclosures	1	3.0
Other vertical enclosures	1	3.0
Area separation walls or fire walls	1	3.0
Plain (unreinforced) masonry walls	1	1.5
All other walls and partitions	1	3.0
Cantilever Elements		
Parapets	2.5	1.5
Chimneys	2.5	1.5
Stacks	2.5	3.0
Exterior Nonbearing Walls	1^d	3.0
Exterior Wall Panels		
Panel	1	3.0
Connecting members and fasteners	1^d	3.0
Veneer		
Ductile materials and attachments	1	4.0
Nonductile materials and attachments	1	1.5
Penthouses	2.5	4.0
Ceilings		
All	1	1.5
Racks and Cabinets		
Storage racks more than 8 ft (2.4 m) in height	2.5	4.0^c
Storage racks detailed in accordance with the provisions of Section 5	2.5	6.0^c
Storage cabinets and laboratory equipment	1	3.0
Access Floors		
Special access floors (designed in accordance with Section 9.3.2.7.2)	2.5	6.0
All other	2.5	3.0
Appendages and Ornamentations	1	3.0
Other Rigid Components		
Ductile materials and attachments	1	4.0
Nonductile materials and attachments	1	1.5
Other Flexible Components		
Ductile materials and attachments	2.5	4.0
Nonductile materials and attachments	2.5	1.5

Notes

^{a}A lower value for a_p shall not be used unless justified by detailed dynamic analysis. The value for a_p shall not be less than 1.00. The value of a_p = 1 is for equipment generally regarded rigid and rigidly attached. The value of a_p = 2.5 is for equipment generally regarded as flexible or flexibly attached. See Section 9.1.7 for definitions of rigid and flexible.

^bR_p = 1.5 for anchorage design when component anchorage is provided by expansion anchor bolts, shallow chemical anchors, or shallow (non-ductile) cast-in-place anchors or when the component is constructed of nonductile materials. R_p = 0.75 for powder-actuated fasteners (shot pins). Shallow anchors are those with an embedment length-to-bolt diameter ratio of less than 8.

^{c}Storage racks over 8 ft in height shall be designed in accordance with the provisions of Section 9.3.2.9.1.

^{d}Where flexible diaphragms provide lateral support for walls and partitions, the value of a_p shall be increased to 2.0 for the center one-half of the span.

a. Connections and panel joints shall allow for the story drift caused by relative seismic displacements (D_p) determined in Section 9.3.1.4.

b. Connections to permit movement in the plane of the panel for story drift shall be sliding connections using slotted or oversize holes, connections that permit movement by bending of steel, or other connections that provide equivalent sliding or ductile capacity.

c. The connecting member itself shall have sufficient ductility and rotation capacity to preclude fracture of the concrete or brittle failures at or near welds.

*

9.3.2.5 Out-of-Plane Bending. Transverse or out-of-plane bending or deformation of a component or system that is subjected to forces as determined in Section 9.3.2.2 shall not exceed the deflection capability of the component or system.

9.3.2.6 Suspended Ceilings. Suspended ceilings shall meet the requirements of Sections 9.3.2.6.1, 9.3.2.6.2, and 9.3.2.6.7. *In addition*, suspended ceilings shall meet the requirements of

93

either Section 9.3.2.6.3, 9.3.2.6.4, 9.3.2.6.5, or 9.3.2.6.6.

9.3.2.6.1 Seismic Forces: Unless exempted by Section 9.3.2.6.4.2 or compliance with Section 9.3.2.6.5 is demonstrated, suspended ceilings shall be designed to meet the force provisions of Section 9.3.1.3 and the additional provisions of the following sections.

The weight of the ceiling, W_p, shall include the ceiling grid and panels; light fixtures if attached to, clipped to, or laterally supported by the ceiling grid; and other components which are laterally supported by the ceiling.

The seismic force, F_p, shall be transmitted through the ceiling attachments to the building structural elements or the ceiling-structure boundary.

Design of anchorage and connections shall be in accordance with these provisions.

For ceiling areas exceeding 2,500 sq ft (232 m²), analyses shall be performed to determine if seismic separation joints in the ceiling system are required.

9.3.2.6.2 Installation: The manufacture and installation of suspended ceilings shall meet the requirements of ASTM C635 and ASTM C636. Conduit, piping, ducts, and cabling shall be supported independently of the suspended ceiling system, including vertical supports and bracing elements. Flexible connections shall be used for all ductwork interfaces with the ceiling grid. Diagonal bracing of mechanical or electrical components attached to the ceiling system *shall not be used unless* the diagonal bracing is incorporated into the design of the lateral force resisting system for the ceiling system.

9.3.2.6.3 Industry Standard Construction: Suspended ceilings shall be designed and constructed in accordance with Section 9.3.2.6.3 or one of Sections 9.3.2.6.4, 9.3.2.6.5, or 9.3.2.6.6.

9.3.2.6.3.1: Suspended ceilings shall be designed and installed in accordance with *a method approved by the authority having jurisdiction,* except that seismic forces shall be determined in accordance with Sections 9.3.1.3 and 9.3.2.6.1.

9.3.2.6.3.2: Suspended ceilings in Seismic Performance Categories D and E shall be designed and installed *as for Categories B and C.* In addition, if lateral bracing wires are provided, compression struts between the runners and the supporting structure shall be provided at the points of wire attachment to the runners.

9.3.2.6.3.3 Sprinkler heads and other penetrations in Seismic Performance Categories B and C shall have a minimum of 1/4 in. (6 mm)

clearance on all sides. Sprinkler heads and other penetrations in Seismic Performance Categories D and E shall have a minimum of 1/2 in. (12 mm) clearance on all sides.

Smaller gaps around penetrations are permitted if it is demonstrated that the penetration stem has adequate flexibility to accommodate 1/2 in. (12 mm) of displacement without exceeding allowable stresses.

9.3.2.6.4 Unbraced Construction: *Suspended ceilings shall be designed and constructed in accordance with Section 9.3.2.6.4 or one of Sections 9.3.2.6.3, 9.3.2.6.5, or 9.3.2.6.6.* Ceiling panels shall be designed such that the edges of the panels are positioned on the closure angle such that they have a maximum wall clearance of 0.25 w all around and an object clearance, c, around all ceiling penetrations where w and c are as defined in the following paragraphs.

9.3.2.6.4.1: *The following terms are defined:*

$w =$ perimeter width in length units, the width of the supporting closure angle at the perimeter of the ceiling system, usually at a wall surface, building column, or seismic separation joints;

$c =$ object clearance in length units, the clear dimension between the ceiling panels and stiff penetrating objects such as sprinkler heads or HVAC grills;

$h =$ plenum height in length units, the length of the supporting member from the bottom of the ceiling system to the supporting structure attachment point;

$\Delta =$ calculated suspended ceiling lateral deflection, in length units, with respect to the supporting structure when the seismic forces of Section 9.3.2.6.1 are applied at the suspended ceiling elevation; and

$g =$ acceleration of gravity in length units per second per second.

9.3.2.6.4.2: Ceiling systems which meet both of the following requirements need not be designed for seismic forces or displacements:

$$w \geq \frac{C_v\sqrt{gh}}{10}$$

$$c \geq \frac{C_v\sqrt{gh}}{40}$$

9.3.2.6.4.3: Ceiling systems which do not meet both of the requirements of Section 9.3.2.6.4.2 shall be designed such that both of the following requirements are met:

$$w \geq 2\Delta$$

$$c \geq 0.5\Delta$$

9.3.2.6.5 Braced Construction: *Suspended ceilings shall be designed and constructed in accordance with Section 9.3.2.6.5 or one of Sections 9.3.2.6.3, 9.3.2.6.4, or 9.3.2.6.6.*

9.3.2.6.5.1: Where substantiating seismic force calculations are not provided, horizontal restraints shall be effected by four 0.1196 in. (2.7 mm) wires secured to the main runner within 2 in. (51 mm) of the cross-runner intersection and splayed 90° from each other at an angle not exceeding 45° from the plane of the ceiling. These horizontal restraint points shall be placed approximately 12 ft (3.66 m) on center in both directions with the first placement no more than 6 ft (1.83 m) from each wall. These horizontal restraint points shall be in a nonsymmetrical pattern to minimize diaphragm loads.

The perimeter width (*w*) of the supporting closure angle shall be a minimum of 2 in. (51 mm) in Seismic Performance Categories D and E and a minimum of 1 in. (25 mm) in Seismic Performance Categories B and C. In Seismic Performance Categories D and E, compression struts shall be located at each horizontal restraint point.

Sprinkler heads and other penetrations in Seismic Performance Categories B and C shall have a minimum of 1/2-in. (12-mm) clearance on all sides. Sprinkler heads and other penetrations in Seismic Performance Categories D and E shall have a minimum of 1-in. (25-mm) clearance on all sides.

The minimum clearance around penetrations is not required if it is demonstrated that the penetration stem has adequate flexibility to accommodate 1/2 in. (12 mm) of displacement without exceeding allowable stresses.

9.3.2.6.5.2: If rigid braces are used instead of the described wires described in Section 9.3.2.6.5.1, attachment of the bracing elements to the structure above shall be adequate to limit lateral deflections to less than 1/4 in. (6 mm) for the loads prescribed in Section 9.3.1.3. Sprinkler heads and other penetrations shall have a minimum of 1/4-in. (6-mm) clearance on all sides.

9.3.2.6.5.3: Lateral force bracing members shall be spaced a minimum of 6 in. (152 mm) from all piping or duct work that is not provided with its own bracing restraints for horizontal forces. Bracing members shall be attached to the grid and to the supporting structure in such a manner that they provide support for the horizontal seismic design force or 200 lb (890 N), whichever is greater. Lateral force bracing for ceilings with plenum depths exceeding 8 ft (2.44 m), measured from the supporting structure to the grid surface, shall be designed and detailed to meet the force and displacement requirements of Section 9.3.1.3 and 9.3.1.4.

9.3.2.6.6 Integral Ceiling/Sprinkler Construction: *Suspended ceilings shall be designed and constructed in accordance with Section 9.3.2.6.6 or one of Sections 9.3.2.6.3, 9.3.2.6.4, or 9.3.2.6.5.* As an alternate to providing large clearances around sprinkler system penetrations through ceiling systems, the sprinkler system and ceiling grid may be designed and tied together as an integral unit. Such a design shall consider the mass and flexibility of all elements involved, including: ceiling system, sprinkler system, light fixtures, and mechanical (HVAC) appurtenances. The design shall be performed by a registered engineer.

9.3.2.6.7 Partitions: In Seismic Performance Categories D and E, ceiling bracing members shall not be used to brace ceiling-high partitions and partitions penetrating the ceiling.

9.3.2.7 Access Floors

9.3.2.7.1 General: Access floors shall be designed to meet the force provisions of Section 9.3.1.3 and the additional provisions of this section. The weight of the access floor, W_p, shall include the weight of the floor system, 100% of the weight of all equipment fastened to the floor, and 25% of the weight of all equipment supported by, but not fastened to the floor. The seismic force, F_p, shall be transmitted from the top surface of the access floor to the supporting structure.

Overturning effects of equipment fastened to the access floor panels also shall be considered. The ability of "slip on" heads for pedestals shall be evaluated for suitability to transfer overturning effects of equipment.

When checking individual pedestals for overturning effects, the maximum concurrent axial load shall not exceed the portion of W_p assigned to the pedestal under consideration.

9.3.2.7.2 Special Access Floors: Access floors shall be considered to be "special access floors" if they are designed to comply with the following considerations:

1. Connections transmitting seismic loads consist of mechanical fasteners, concrete anchors, welding, or bearing. Design load capacities comply with recognized design codes and/or certified test results.
2. Seismic loads are not transmitted by friction, produced solely by the effects of gravity, powder-actuated fasteners (shot pins), or adhesives.
3. The bracing system shall be designed considering the destabilizing effects of individual members buckling in compression.
4. Bracing and pedestals are of structural or mechanical shape produced to ASTM specifications that specify minimum mechanical properties. Electrical tubing shall not be used.
5. Floor stringers that are designed to carry axial seismic loads and that are mechanically fastened to the supporting pedestals are used.

9.3.2.8 Partitions: Partitions that are tied to the ceiling and all partitions greater than 6 ft (1.8 m) in height shall be laterally braced to the building structure. Such bracing shall be independent of any ceiling splay bracing. Bracing shall be spaced to limit horizontal deflection at the partition head to be compatible with ceiling deflection requirements as determined in Section 9.3.2.6 for suspended ceilings and Section 9.3.2.2 for other systems.

9.3.2.9 Steel Storage Racks

9.3.2.9.1 At Grade Elevation: Storage racks installed at grade elevation shall be designed, fabricated, and installed in accordance with the *Specification for the Design, Testing, and Utilization of Industrial Steel Storage Racks* [9.3-13] and the following requirements:

a. If designed as a building structure, requirements of Section 9.2 shall be met. *R* shall be taken as 4, unless higher values are supported by test results or a higher value of *R* is used and the full detailing requirements of Sections 9.2, 9.5, and A.9.5 are met.
b. If designed as an architectural component or system, seismic design forces shall not be less than that required by Section 9.3.1.3.
c. Dead load weight (*W*) in seismic force calculations shall not be less than the weight of the storage rack plus 67% of the rated load of the rack placed on all levels.

9.3.2.9.2 Above-Grade Elevations: Storage racks installed at elevations above-grade shall be designed, fabricated, and installed in accordance with the *Specification for the Design, Testing, and Utilization of Industrial Steel Storage Racks* [9.3-13] and the following requirements:

a. Storage racks shall meet the force and displacement requirements of Sections 9.3.1.3 and 9.3.1.4.
b. Dead Load weight (*W*) in seismic force calculations shall not be less than the weight of the storage rack plus 67% of the rated load of the rack placed on all levels.

9.3.3 Mechanical and Electrical Component Design

9.3.3.1 General: Attachments and equipment supports for the mechanical and electrical systems, components, or elements (hereinafter referred to as "components") shall meet the requirements of Sections 9.3.3.2–9.3.3.16.

9.3.3.2 Mechanical and Electrical Component Forces and Displacements: Mechanical and electrical components shall meet the force and seismic relative displacement requirements of Sections 9.3.1.3 and 9.3.1.4, and Table 9.3.3.2.

When complex equipment such as valves and valve operators, turbines and generators, and pumps and motors *are* functionally connected by mechanical links not capable of transferring the seismic loads or accommodating seismic relative displacements, *the design shall protect such links by alternative methods.*

Components supported by chains or otherwise "hung" from above are not required to meet the seismic force requirements of this section provided that they cannot significantly damage any other component when subject to seismic motion **and** they have ductile connections to the building at the point of attachment.

9.3.3.3 Mechanical and Electrical Component Period. The fundamental period of the mechanical and electrical component (and its attachment to the building), T_p, shall be determined by the following equation provided that the component and attachment can be reasonably represented analytically by a simple spring and mass single-degree-of-freedom system:

$$T_p = 2\pi\sqrt{\frac{W_p}{K_p g}} \tag{9.3.3.3}$$

where

T_p = Component fundamental period;

96

TABLE 9.3.3.2
Mechanical and Electrical Components Seismic Coefficients

Mechanical and Electrical Component or Element	$a_p{}^a$	$R_p{}^b$
General Mechanical Equipment		
Boilers and furnaces	1.0	3.0
Pressure vessels on skirts and free-standing	2.5	3.0
Stacks	2.5	3.0
Cantilevered chimneys	2.5	1.5
Other	1.0	3.0
Manufacturing and Process Machinery		
General	1.0	3.0
Conveyors (nonpersonnel)	2.5	3.0
Piping Systems	2.5	4.0
Storage Tanks and Spheres		
Flat bottom (anchored)	2.5	4.0
Flat bottom (unanchored)	2.5	3.0
On braced or unbraced legs	2.5	2.0
HVAC Systems		
Ductwork	2.5	6.0
Equipment		
Vibration isolated	2.5	4.0
Nonvibration isolated	1.0	4.0
In-line equipment	1.0	3.0
Other	1.0	4.0
Elevator Components	1.0	3.0
Trussed Towers (free-standing of guyed)	2.5	3.0
General Electrical Equipment		
Communication	1.0	4.0
Bus ducts, conduit, cable tray	2.5	6.0
Panelboards, battery racks	2.5	3.0
Motor control centers, switchgear	2.5	3.0
Other	1.0	3.0
Lighting Fixtures	1.0	1.5

^{a}A lower value for a_p shall not be used unless justified by detailed dynamic analyses. The value for a_p shall not be less than 1.00. The value of $a_p = 1$ is for equipment generally regarded as rigid or rigidly attached. The value of $a_p = 2.5$ is for equipment generally regarded as flexible or flexibly attached. See Section 9.1.7 for definitions of rigid and flexible.

$^bR_p = 1.5$ for anchorage design when component anchorage is provided by expansion anchor bolts, shallow chemical anchors, or shallow nonductile cast-in-place anchors or when the component is constructed of nonductile materials. $R_p = 0.75$ for powder-actuated fasteners (shot pins). Shallow anchors are those with an embedment length-to-bolt diameter ratio of less than 8.

W_p = Component operating weight;

g = Gravitational acceleration; and

K_p = Stiffness of resilient support system of the component and attachment, determined in terms of load per unit deflection at the center of gravity of the component.

Note that consistent units must be used.

Otherwise, determine the fundamental period of the component in seconds (T_p) from experimental test data or by a properly substantiated analysis.

9.3.3.4 Mechanical and Electrical Component Attachments. The stiffness of mechanical and electrical component attachments shall be designed such that the load path for the component performs its intended function.

9.3.3.5 Component Supports: Mechanical and electrical component supports and the means by which they are attached to the component shall be designed for the forces determined in Section 9.3.1.3 and in conformance with Sections 9.5–9.9, as appropriate, for the materials comprising the means of attachment. Such supports include structural members, braces, frames, skirts, legs, saddles, pedestals, cables, guys, stays, snubbers, and tethers *as well as* elements forged or cast as a part of the mechanical or electrical component. If standard or proprietary supports are used, they shall be designed by either load rating (i.e., testing) or for the calculated seismic forces. In addition, the stiffness of the support, when appropriate, shall be designed such that the seismic load path for the component performs its intended function.

Component supports shall be designed to accommodate the seismic relative displacements between points of support determined in accordance with Section 9.3.1.4.

In addition, the means by which supports are attached to the component, except when integral (i.e., cast or forged), shall be designed to accommodate both the forces and displacements determined in accordance with Sections 9.3.1.3 and 9.3.1.4. If the value of $I_p = 1.5$ for the component, the local region of the support attachment point to the component shall be evaluated for the effect of the load transfer on the component wall.

9.3.3.6 Component Certification. The manufacturer's certificate of compliance with the force requirements of the Section shall be submitted to the regulatory agency when required by the contract documents or when required by the regulatory agency.

9.3.3.7 Utility and Service Lines at Buildings Interfaces. At the interface of adjacent structures or portions of the same building that are capable of moving independently, utility lines shall be provided with adequate flexibility to accommodate the differential movement.

9.3.3.8 Site-Specific Considerations. The possible interruption of utility service shall be investigated in relation to designated seismic systems in Category IV per Table 1-1. Specific attention shall be given to the vulnerability of underground utilities and utility interfaces between the structure and the ground where Soil Profile Type E or F is present, and where the seismic coefficient C_v at the underground utility or at the base of the structure is equal to or greater than 0.15.

9.3.3.9 Storage Tanks

9.3.3.9.1 Above-Grade Storage Tanks: Attachments and supports for storage tanks mounted above grade in buildings or structures shall be designed to meet the force provisions of Section 9.3.1.3. The weight of the storage tank (W_p) shall include the weight of the tank structure and appurtenances and the operating weight of the contents at maximum rated capacity.

9.3.3.9.2 At-Grade Storage Tanks: Flat bottom storage tanks mounted at grade shall be designed to meet the force provisions of either [9.3-1], [9.3-7], or Section 9.3.1.3.

In addition, tanks designated with an I_p of 1.5 or tanks greater than 20 ft (6.2 m) in diameter or tanks that have a height-to-diameter ratio greater than 1.0 shall also be designed to meet the following addition requirements:

1. Sloshing effects shall be considered.
2. Piping connections to steel storage tanks shall consider the potential uplift of the tank

wall during earthquakes. Unless otherwise calculated, the following displacements shall be assumed for all side-wall connections and bottom penetrations:
   a. Vertical displacement of 2 in. (51 mm) for anchored tanks;
   b. Vertical displacement of 12 in. (305 mm) for unanchored tanks; and
   c. Horizontal displacement of 8 in. (203 mm) for unanchored tanks with a diameter of 40 ft (12.2 m) or less.

9.3.3.10 HVAC Ductwork: Attachments and supports for HVAC ductwork systems shall be designed to meet the force and displacement provisions of Sections 9.3.1.3 and 9.3.1.4 and the additional provisions of this section. In addition to their attachments and supports, ductwork systems designated as having an $I_p = 1.5$ themselves shall be designed to meet the force and displacement provisions of Sections 9.3.1.3 and 9.3.1.4 and the additional provisions of this section.

Seismic restraints are not required for HVAC ducts with $I_p = 1.0$ if either of the following conditions are met:

a. HVAC ducts are suspended from hangers 12 in. (305 mm) or less in length from the top of the duct to the supporting structure. The hangers shall be detailed to avoid significant bending of the hangers; or
b. HVAC ducts have a cross-sectional area of less than 6 sq ft (0.557 m²).

HVAC duct systems fabricated and installed in accordance with standards *approved by the authority having jursidiction* shall be deemed to meet the lateral bracing requirements of this section.

Equipment items installed in-line with the duct system (e.g., fans, heat exchangers, and humidifiers) weighing more than 75 lb (344 N) shall be supported and laterally braced independent of the duct system and shall meet the force requirements of Section 9.3.1.3.

9.3.3.11 Piping Systems: Attachments and supports for piping systems shall be designed to meet the force and displacement provisions of Sections 9.3.1.3 and 9.3.1.4 and the additional provisions of this section. In addition to their attachments and supports, piping systems designated as having $I_p = 1.5$ themselves shall be designed to meet the force and displacement provisions of Sections 9.3.1.3 and 9.3.1.4 and the additional provisions of this section.

Seismic effects that shall be analyzed in the design of a piping system include the dynamic effects of the piping system, its contents, and, when appropriate, its supports. The interaction between the piping system and the supporting structures, including other mechanical and electrical equipment shall also be analyzed.

9.3.3.11.1 Pressure Piping Systems: Pressure piping systems designed and constructed in accordance with ASME B31, *Code for Pressure Piping* [9.3-3] shall be deemed to meet the force, displacement, and other provisions of this section. In lieu of specific force and displacement provisions provided in the ASME B31, the force and displacement provisions of Sections 9.3.1.3 and 9.3.1.4 shall be used.

9.3.3.11.2 Fire Protection Sprinkler Systems: Fire protection sprinkler systems designed and constructed in accordance with NFPA 13, *Standard for the Installation of Sprinkler Systems* [9.3-12] shall be deemed to meet the other requirements of this section., except the force and displacement requirements of Sections 9.3.1.3 and 9.3.1.4 shall be satisfied.

9.3.3.11.3 Other Piping Systems: Piping designated as having an $I_p = 1.5$ but not designed and constructed in accordance with ASME B31 [9.3-3] or NFPA 13 [9.3-12] shall meet the following:

a. The design strength for seismic loads in combination with other service loads and appropriate environmental effects shall not exceed the following:
  1. For piping systems constructed with ductile materials (e.g., steel, aluminum or copper), 90% of the piping material yield strength.
  2. For threaded connections with ductile materials, 70% of the piping material yield strength.
  3. For piping constructed with nonductile materials (e.g., plastic, cast iron, or ceramics), 25% of the piping material minimum specified tensile strength.
  4. For threaded connections in piping constructed with nonductile materials, 20% of the piping material minimum specified tensile strength.
b. Provisions shall be made to mitigate seismic impact for piping components constructed of nonductile materials or in cases where material ductility is reduced (e.g., low-temperature applications).
c. Piping shall be investigated to ensure that the piping has adequate flexibility between support attachment points to the structure, ground, other mechanical and electrical equipment, or other piping.
d. Piping shall be investigated to ensure that the interaction effects between it and other piping or constructions are acceptable.

9.3.3.11.4 Supports and Attachments for Other Piping: Attachments and supports for piping not designed and constructed in accordance with ASME B31 [9.3-3] or NFPA 13 [9.3-12] shall meet the following provisions:

a. Attachments and supports transferring seismic loads shall be constructed of materials suitable for the application and designed and constructed in accordance with a nationally recognized structural code such as, when constructed of steel, the AISC *Manual of Steel Construction* [9.5-1], [9.5-2] or MSS SP-58, *Pipe Hangers and Supports—Materials, Design, and Manufacture* [9.3-11].
b. Attachments embedded in concrete shall be suitable for cyclic loads.
c. Rod hangers may be considered seismic supports if the length of the hanger from the supporting structure is 12 in. (305 mm) or less. Rod hangers shall not be constructed in a manner that would subject the rod to bending moments.
d. Seismic supports are not required for:
  1. Ductile piping in Seismic Performance Category D or E designated as having an $I_p = 1.5$ and a nominal pipe size of 1 in. (25 mm) or less when provisions are made to protect the piping from impact or to avoid the impact of larger piping or other mechanical equipment.
  2. Ductile piping in Seismic Performance Category A, B, or C designated as having an $I_p = 1.5$ and a nominal pipe size of 2 in. (50 mm) or less when provisions are made to protect the piping from impact or to avoid the impact of larger piping or other mechanical equipment.
  3. Ductile piping in Seismic Performance Category D or E designated as having an $I_p = 1.0$ and a nominal pipe size of 3 in. (75 mm) or less.

---

4. Ductile piping in Seismic Performance Category A, B, or C designated as having an $I_p = 1.0$ and a nominal pipe size of 6 in. (150 mm) or less.

e. Seismic supports shall be constructed so that support engagement is maintained.

9.3.3.12 Boilers and Pressure Vessels: Attachments and supports for boilers and pressure vessels shall be designed to meet the force and displacement provisions of Sections 9.3.1.3 and 9.3.1.4 and the additional provisions of this section. In addition to their attachments and supports, boilers and pressure vessels designated as having an $I_p = 1.5$ themselves shall be designed to meet the force and displacement provisions of Sections 9.3.1.3 and 9.3.1.4.

The seismic *design* of a boiler or pressure vessel shall include *analysis* of the following: the dynamic effects of the boiler or pressure vessel, its contents, and its supports; sloshing of liquid contents; loads from attached components such as piping; and the interaction between the boiler or pressure vessel and its support.

9.3.3.12.1 ASME Boilers and Pressure Vessels: Boilers or pressure vessels designed in accordance with the ASME *Boiler and Pressure Vessel Code* [9.3-4] shall be deemed to meet the force, displacement, and other requirements of this section. In lieu of the specific force and displacement provisions provided in the ASME code, the force and displacement provisions of Sections 9.3.1.3 and 9.3.1.4 shall be used.

9.3.3.12.2 Other Boilers and Pressure Vessels: Boilers and pressure vessels designated as having an $I_p = 1.5$ but not constructed in accordance with the provisions of the ASME code [9.3-4] shall meet the following provisions:

a. The design strength for seismic loads in combination with other service loads and appropriate environmental effects shall not exceed the following:
1. For boilers and pressure vessels constructed with ductile materials (e.g., steel, aluminum or copper), 90% of the material minimum specified yield strength.
2. For threaded connections in boilers or pressure vessels or their supports constructed with ductile materials, 70% of the material minimum specified yield strength.
3. For boilers and pressure vessels constructed with nonductile materials (e.g.,

plastic, cast iron, or ceramics), 25% of the material minimum specified tensile strength.
4. For threaded connections in boilers or pressure vessels or their supports constructed with nonductile materials, 20% of the material minimum specified tensile strength.

b. Provisions shall be made to mitigate seismic impact for boiler and pressure vessel components constructed of nonductile materials or in cases where material ductility is reduced (e.g., low-temperature applications).

c. Boilers and pressure vessels shall be investigated to ensure that the interaction effects between them and other constructions are acceptable.

9.3.3.12.3 Supports and Attachments for Other Boilers and Pressure Vessels: Attachments and supports for boilers and pressure vessels shall meet the following provisions:

a. Attachments and supports transferring seismic loads shall be constructed of materials suitable for the application and designed and constructed in accordance with nationally recognized structural code such as, when constructed of steel, the AISC *Manual of Steel Construction* [9.5-1], [9.5-2].

b. Attachments embedded in concrete shall be suitable for cyclic loads.

c. Seismic supports shall be constructed so that support engagement is maintained.

9.3.3.13 Mechanical Equipment, Attachments and Supports: Attachments and supports for mechanical equipment not covered in Sections 9.3.3.8–9.3.3.12 or 9.3.3.16 shall be designed to meet the force and displacement provisions of Sections 9.3.1.3 and 9.3.1.4 and the additional provisions of this section. In addition to their attachments and supports, such mechanical equipment designated as having an $I_p = 1.5$, itself, shall be designated to meet the force and displacement provisions of Sections 9.3.1.3 and 9.3.1.4 and the additional provisions of this section.

The seismic *design* of mechanical equipment, attachments and their supports shall include *analysis* of the following: the dynamic effects of the equipment, its contents, and when appropriate its supports. The interaction between the equipment and the supporting structures, including other mechanical and electrical equipment, shall also be considered.

9.3.3.13.1 Mechanical Equipment: Mechanical equipment designated as having an $I_p = 1.5$ shall meet the following provisions.

a. The design strength for seismic loads in combination with other service loads and appropriate environmental effects shall not exceed the following:
  1. For mechanical equipment constructed with ductile materials (e.g., steel, aluminum, or copper), 90% of the equipment material minimum specified yield strength.
  2. For threaded connections in equipment constructed with ductile materials, 70% of the material minimum specified yield strength.
  3. For mechanical equipment constructed with nonductile materials (e.g., plastic, cast iron, or ceramics), 25% of the equipment material minimum tensile strength.
  4. For threaded connections in equipment constructed with nonductile materials, 20% of the material minimum specified yield strength.
b. Provisions shall be made to mitigate seismic impact for equipment components constructed of nonductile materials or in cases where material ductility is reduced (e.g., low-temperature applications).
c. The possibility for loadings imposed on the equipment by attached utility or service lines due to differential motions of points of support from separate structures shall be evaluated.

9.3.3.13.2 Attachments and Supports for Mechanical Equipment: Attachments and supports for mechanical equipment shall meet the following provisions:

a. Attachments and supports transferring seismic loads shall be constructed of materials suitable for the application and designed and constructed in accordance with a nationally recognized structural code such as, when constructed of steel, AISC, *Manual of Steel Construction* [9.5-1], [9.5-2].
b. Friction clips shall not be used for anchorage attachment.
c. Expansion anchors shall not be used for me-

chanical equipment rated over 10 hp (7.45 kW).
  Exception:
  Undercut expansion anchors.
d. Drilled and grouted-in-place anchors for tensile load applications shall use either expansive cement or expansive epoxy grout.
e. Supports shall be specifically evaluated if weak-axis bending of light-gage support steel is relied on for the seismic load path.
f. Components mounted on vibration isolation systems shall have a bumper restraint or snubber in each horizontal direction. The design force shall be taken as $2F_p$. *The intent is to prevent excessive movement and to avoid fracture of support springs and any nonductile components of the isolators.*
g. Seismic supports shall be constructed so that support engagement is maintained.

9.3.3.14 Electrical Equipment, Attachments, and Supports: Attachments and supports for electrical equipment shall be designed to meet the force and displacement provisions of Sections 9.3.1.3 and 9.3.1.4 and the additional provisions of this section. In addition to their attachments and supports, electrical equipment designated as having $I_p = 1.5$, itself, shall be designed to meet the force and displacement provisions of Sections 9.3.1.3 and 9.3.1.4 and the additional provisions of this section.

The seismic design of other electrical equipment shall include analysis of the following: the dynamic effects of the equipment, its contents, and when appropriate its supports. The interaction between the equipment and the supporting structures, including other mechanical and electrical equipment, shall also be considered.

9.3.3.14.1 Electrical Equipment: Electrical equipment designated as having an $I_p = 1.5$ shall meet the following provisions:

a. The design strength for seismic loads in combination with other service loads and appropriate environmental effects shall not exceed the following:
  1. For electrical equipment constructed with ductile material (e.g., steel, aluminum, or copper), 90% of the equipment material minimum specified yield strength.
  2. For threaded connections in equipment constructed with ductile materials, 70% of the material minimum specified yield strength.

3. For electrical equipment constructed with nonductile materials (e.g., plastic, cast iron, or ceramics), 25% of the equipment material minimum tensile strength.

4. For threaded connections in equipment constructed with nonductile materials, 20% of the material minimum specified yield strength.

b. Provisions shall be made to mitigate seismic impact for equipment components constructed of nonductile materials or in cases where material ductility is reduced (e.g., low temperature applications).

c. The possibility for loadings imposed on the equipment by attached utility or service lines due to differential motion of points of support from separate structures shall be evaluated.

d. Batteries on racks shall have wrap-around restraints to ensure that the batteries will not fall off the rack. Racks shall be evaluated for sufficient lateral and longitudinal load capacity.

e. Internal coils of dry type transformers shall be positively attached to their supporting substructure within the transformer enclosure.

f. Slide out components in electrical control panels shall have a latching mechanism to hold contents in place.

g. Structural design of electrical cabinets shall be in conformance with standards of the industry that are accpetable to the authority having jurisdiction. Large cutouts in the lower shear panel shall be specifically evaluated if an evaluation is not provided by the manufacturer.

h. The attachment of additional items weighing more than 100 lb (440 N) shall be specifically evaluated if not provided by the manufacturer.

9.3.3.14.2 Attachments and Supports for Electrical Equipment: Attachments and supports for electrical equipment shall meet the following provisions:

a. Attachments and supports transferring seismic loads shall be constructed of materials suitable for the application and designed and constructed in accordance with a nationally recognized structural code such as, when constructed of steel, AISC, *Manual of Steel Construction* [9.5-1], [9.5-2].

b. Friction clips shall not be used for anchorage attachment.

c. Oversized washers shall be used at bolted connections through the base sheet metal if the base is not reinforced with stiffeners.

d. Supports shall be specifically evaluated if weak-axis bending of light gage support steel is relied on for the seismic load path.

e. The supports for linear electrical equipment such as cable trays, conduit, and bus ducts shall be designed to meet the force and displacement provisions of Sections 9.3.1.3 and 9.3.1.4 only if any of the following situations apply:
Supports are cantilevered up from the floor;
Supports include bracing to limit deflection;
Supports are constructed as rigid welded frames;
Attachments into concrete utilize nonexpanding insets, shot pins, or cast iron embedments; or
Attachments utilize spot welds, plug welds, or minimum size welds as defined by AISC [9.5-1], [9.5-2].

9.3.3.15 Alternate Seismic Qualification Methods: As an alternative to the analysis methods implicit in the design methodology described above, equipment testing is an acceptable method to determine seismic capacity. Thus, adaptation of a nationally recognized standard for qualification by testing that is acceptable to the authority having jursidicion is an acceptable alternate, so long as the equipment seismic capacity equals or exceeds the demand expressed in Sections 9.3.1.3 and 9.3.1.4.

9.3.3.16 Elevator Design Requirements. Elevators shall meet the force and displacement provisions of Section 9.3.3.2 unless exempted by either Section 9.1.3.4 or 9.3.1 Elevators designed in accordance with the seismic provisions of the *ASME Safety Code for Elevators and Escalators* [9.3-2] shall be deemed to meet the seismic force requirements of this section, except as modified herein.

9.3.3.16.1 Elevators and Hoistway Structural System. Elevators and hoistway structural systems shall be designed to meet the force and displacement provisions of Sections 9.3.1.3 and 9.3.1.4.

9.3.3.16.2 Elevator Machinery and Controller Supports and Attachments. Elevator machinery and controller supports and attachments shall be designed to with meet the force and displacement provisions of Sections 9.3.1.3 and 9.3.1.4.

9.3.3.16.3 Seismic Controls. Seismic switches shall be provided for all elevators addressed by Section 9.3.3.16. including those meeting therequirements of the ASME reference, provided they operate with a speed of 150 ft/min (46 m/m) or greater.

Seismic switches shall provide an electrical signal indicating that structural motions are of such a magnitude that the operation of elevators may be impaired. Upon activation of the seismic switch, elevator operations shall conform to provisions in the *ASME Safety Code for Elevators and Escalators* [9.3-2] except as noted herein. The seismic switch shall be located at or above the highest floor serviced by the elevators. The seismic switch shall have two horizontal perpendicular axes of sensitivity. Its trigger level shall be set to 30% of the acceleration of gravity.

In facilities where the loss of the use of an elevator is a life-safety issue, the elevator *shall only* be used after the seismic switch has triggered provided that:

1. The elevator shall operate no faster than the service speed,
2. Before the elevator is occupied, it is operated from top to bottom and back to top to verify that it is operable, and
3. The individual putting the elevator back in service should ride the elevator from top to bottom and back to top to verify acceptable performance.

9.3.3.16.4 Retainer Plates. Retainer plates are required at the top and bottom of the car and counterweight.

9.4 Foundation Design Requirements

9.4.1 General. Section 9.4 *sets requirements for loads that foundations must resist and for investigations to establish critical geotechnical* parameters.*

9.4.2 Seismic Performance Category A. *There are no special requirements for the foundations of buildings assigned to Category* A.

9.4.3 Seismic Performance Category B. *The determination of the site coefficient (Section 9.1.4.2) shall be documented* and the resisting capacities of the foundations, subjected to the prescribed seismic forces of Sections 9.1 through 9.6, shall meet the following requirements:

9.4.3.1 Structural *Components*. The *design* strength of foundation components subjected to seismic forces alone or in combination with other prescribed loads and their detailing requirements shall conform to the requirements of Sections 9.5–9.9.*

9.4.3.2 Soil Capacities.* For the load combination including earthquake as specified in Section 9.2.2.6 the capacity of the foundation soil in bearing or the capacity of the soil interface between pile, pier, or caisson and the soil must be sufficient to resist loads at acceptable strains considering both the short duration of loading and the dynamic properties of the soil.

9.4.4 Seismic Performance Category C. Foundations for buildings assigned to Category C shall conform to all of the requirements for Categories A and B and to the additional requirements of this section.

9.4.4.1 Investigation. *When required by* the authority having jurisdiction, a written report shall be *submitted.* The report shall include, in addition to the evaluations required in Section 9.4.3, the results of an investigation to determine the potential hazards due to slope instability, liquefaction, and surface rupture due to faulting or lateral spreading, all as a result of earthquake motions.

9.4.4.2 Pole-Type Structures. Construction employing posts or poles as columns embedded in earth or embedded in concrete footings in the earth may be used to resist both axial and lateral loads. The depth of embedment required for posts or poles to resist seismic forces shall be determined by means of the design criteria established in the foundation investigation report.

9.4.4.3 Foundation Ties. Individual pile caps, drilled piers, or caissons shall be interconnected by ties. All ties shall have a design strength in tension or compression, greater than a force equal to 25% of the effective peak velocity-related acceleration (A_v) times the larger pile cap or column factored dead plus factored live load unless it can be demonstrated that equivalent restraint can be provided by reinforced concrete beams within slabs on grade or reinforced concrete slabs on grade or confinement by competent rock, hard cohesive soils, very dense granular soils, or other approved means.

9.4.4.4 Special Pile Requirements. Concrete piles, concrete filled steel pipe piles, drilled piers, or caissons *require minimum bending, shear, tension, and elastic strain capacities. Refer to Section A.9.7.4.4 for supplementary provisions.*

9.4.5 Foundation Requirements for Seismic Performance Categories D and E. Foundations for buildings assigned to Categories D and E shall conform to all of the requirements for Category C construction and to the additional requirements of this section.

9.4.5.1 Investigation. The owner shall submit to the authority having jurisdiction a written report that includes an evaluation *of the items in Section 9.4.4.1* and the determination of lateral pressures on basement and retaining walls due to earthquake motions.

9.4.5.2 Foundation Ties. Individual spread footings founded on soil defined in Section 9.1.4.2 as Soil Profile Type E or F shall be interconnected by ties. Ties shall conform to Section 9.4.4.3.

9.4.5.3 Special Pile Requirements. Piling shall be designed to withstand maximum imposed curvatures resulting from seismic forces for free-standing piles, in loose granular soils and in Soil Profile Types E or F. Piles subject to such deformation shall be designed and detailed in accordance with provisions for special moment frames (Sec. 9.5.10 or 9.6.3.3) for a length equal to 120% of the flexural length (point of fixity to pile cap). *Refer to Section A.9.4.5.3 for supplementary provisions in addition to those given in Section A.9.4.4.4.*

9.5 Steel

9.5.1 Reference Documents. The design, construction and quality of steel components that resist seismic forces shall conform to the requirements of the references listed in this section except that modifications are necessary to make the references compatible with the provisions of this document. *Appendix A.9.5 provides supplementary provisions for this compatibility.*

[9.5-1] Load and Resistance Factor Design Specification for Structural Steel Buildings (LRFD). American Institute of Steel Construction (AISC), 1993.

[9.5-2] Allowable Stress Design and Plastic Design Specification for Structural Steel Buildings (ASD). American Institute of Steel Construction, June 1, 1989.

[9.5-3] Seismic Provisions for Structural Steel Buildings. American Institute of Steel Construction, 1992.

[9.5-4] Specification for the Design of Cold-formed Steel Structural Members. American Iron and Steel Institute (AISI), August 10 1986 (Dec. 11, 1989, Addendum).

[9.5-5] Load and Resistance Factor Design Specification for Cold-Formed Steel Structural Members. American Iron and Steel Institute, Mar. 1991.

[9.5-6] ASCE 8-90, Specification for the Design of Cold-formed Stainless Steel Structural Members. ASCE, 1990.

[9.5-7] Standard Specification, Load Tables and Weight Tables for Steel Joists and Joist Girders. Steel Joist Institute, 1992.

[9.5-8] The Criteria for Structural Applications for Steel Cables for Buildings. AISI, 1973.

9.6 Structural Concrete

9.6.1 Reference Documents. The quality and testing of materials and the design and construction of structural concrete components that resist seismic forces shall conform to the requirements of the references listed in this section except that modifications are necessary to make the reference compatible with the provisions of this document. *Appendix A.9.6 provides the supplementary provisions for this compatibility. The load combinations of Section 2.4.1 are not applicable for design of reinforced concrete to resist earthquake loads.*

[9.6-1] Building Code Requirements for Reinforced Concrete. American Concrete Institute, ACI 318-89, 1992.

[9.6-2] Building Code Requirements for Structural Plain Concrete. American Concrete Institute (ACI), 318.1-89 1992.

9.7 Reserved for Composite Structures*

9.8 Masonry

9.8.1 Reference Documents. *The design, construction, and quality assurance of masonry components that resist seismic forces shall conform to the requirements of the reference listed in this section.*

[9.8-1] Building Code Requirements for Masonry Structures, ACI 530-*95*/ASCE 5-*95*/TMS 402-*95*, and Specifications for Masonry Structures, ACI 530.1-*95*/ASCE 6-*95*/TMS 602-*95*.

9.9 Wood

9.9.1 Reference Documents. The quality, testing, design, and construction of members and their fastenings in wood systems that resist seismic forces shall conform to the requirements of the reference documents listed in this section except that modifications are necessary to make the references compatible with the provisions of this document. *Section A.9.9 provides the details of such modifications to the application of these references, for both conventional and engineered wood construction.*

[9.9-1] National Design Specification for Wood Construction including Design Values for Wood Construction (NDS Supplement). ANSI/NFoPA NDS-1991, 1991.

[9.9-2] American Softwood Lumber Standard, Voluntary Product Standard, 20–94, National Institute of Standards and Technology, 1986.

[9.9-3] Softwood Plywood—Construction and Industrial. PS 1-83, 1983.

[9.9-4] Wood Particle Board. ANSI A208.1, 1989.

[9.9-5] Wood Based Structural Use Panels. PS 2-92, 1992.

[9.9-6] American National Standard for Wood Products—Structural Glued Laminated Timber. ANSI/AIIC, A190.1, 1992.

[9.9-7] Wood Poles - Specifications and Dimensions. ANSI 05.1, 1992.

[9.9-8] One- and Two-Family Dwelling Code. Council of American Building Officials (CABO), 1989.

[9.9-9] Gypsum Wallboard. ASTM C36-84, 1984.

[9.9-10] Fiberboard Nail-Base Sheathing. ASTM D2277-87, 1987.

*

[9.9-12] Performance Policies and Standards for Structural Use Panels. APA PRP-108, 1988.

[9.9-13] Standard Specification for Establishing and Monitoring Structural Capacities of Prefabricated Wood I-Joists. ASTM D 5055, 1994.

[9.9.-14] National Design Standard for Metal Plate Connected Wood Truss Construction. ANSI/TPI 1-1995, 1995.

10. Ice Loads—Atmospheric Icing

*10.1 Definitions

Freezing rain or drizzle: rain or drizzle falling into a shallow layer of subfreezing air at the earth's surface. The water freezes on contact with the ground or a structure to form glaze ice.

Snow: considered to be an atmospheric ice accretion when it adheres to a structure by capillary forces, freezing and/or sintering. Roof snow loads are covered in Section 7.

In-cloud icing: occurs on structures in supercooled clouds and fogs. The droplets colliding with the structure freeze to form rime ice.

Hoarfrost: an accumulation of ice crystals formed by direct deposition of water vapor from the air onto a structure.

Ice-sensitive structures: open structures including, but not limited to, lattice structures, overhead lines, suspension and cable-stayed bridges, aerial cable systems (e.g., for skilifts and logging operations), amusement rides, open catwalks, ladders, railings, flagpoles and signs.

Components and appurtenances: elements attached to the structure that are not part of the main structural system and will be exposed to atmospheric icing. Examples are conductors, wires, cables, insulators, antennas, radar and handrails.

*10.2 General

Atmospheric ice loads due to ice accretions formed by freezing rain and drizzle, snow, in-cloud icing and hoarfrost shall be considered in the design of ice-sensitive structures throughout the United States.

*10.3 Design for Ice Loads

The radial thickness of an ice accretion is assumed to be uniform over the exposed surface of all structural members, components, and appurtenances. The application of a uniform equivalent radial ice thickness to a variety of cross-sectional shapes is shown in Fig. 10-1. When historical ice accretion thicknesses and associated densities are known for the region of interest, the design ice thickness and accretion density shall be determined from this data for the appropriate mean recurrence interval. When ice accretion data are not available the design values shall be estimated by the analysis of meteorological information for the appropriate mean recurrence interval. The quality of the measured or estimated ice load information and the length of the record must be taken into account in determining the design ice load. Alternatively, the local jurisdiction is not prohibited from establishing the design ice thickness and density. Mean recurrence intervals for each structure category in Table 1-1 are given in Table 10-1.

Dynamic loads such as galloping and aeolian vibration that are caused or enhanced by an ice accretion on a flexible structural member, component or appurtenance are not covered in this section.

**TABLE 10-1
Mean Recurrence Intervals for Structure Categories**

Structure Category	Mean Recurrence Interval (years)
I	25
II	50
III	50
IV	100

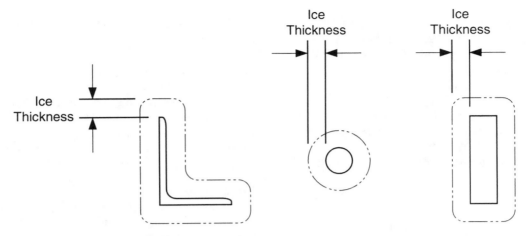

**FIG. 10-1 Application of Uniform Equivalent Radial Ice Thicknesses to a Variety of
Cross-Sectional Shapes**

*10.3.1 Weight of Ice

The weight of ice per linear foot is the product of the accretion density and the cross-sectional area of the accretion.

*10.3.2 Wind on Ice Covered Structures

Ice accreted on structural members, components and appurtenances increases the projected area of the structure exposed to wind. Wind loads on this increased projected area shall be used in the design of ice-sensitive structures.

*10.3.3 Partial Loading

The effects of a partial ice load shall be considered. Partial loading of ice-sensitive structures occurs, for example, when the exposure of the structure varies either vertically or horizontally or when accreted ice falls off only part of the structure.

APPENDIX A.9 SUPPLEMENTAL PROVISIONS

A.9.1 Purpose. *These provisions are not directly related to computation of earthquake loads, but they are deemed essential for satisfactory performance in an earthquake when designing with the loads determined from Section 9, due to the substantial cyclic inelastic strain capacity assumed to exist by the load procedures in Section 9. These supplemental provisions form an integral part of Section 9.*

A.9.1.6 Quality Assurance. This section provides minimum requirements for quality assurance for seismic force resisting and other designated seismic systems. These requirements supplement the testing and inspection requirements contained in the reference standards given in Sections 9.1–9.9. As a minimum, the quality-assurance provisions apply to the following:

1. The seismic force-resisting systems in buildings assigned to Seismic Performance Categories C, D, and E.
2. Other designated seismic systems in buildings assigned to Seismic Performance Categories C, D, and E *for which the component importance factor I_p is 1.5.*

The following standards are referenced in the provisions for inspection and testing:

[A.9.1.6-1] ANSI/AWS D1.1-94, Structural Welding Code

[A.9.1.6-2] ASTM A435-90, Specification for Straight Beam Ultrasound Examination of Steel Plates, 1990.

[A.9.1.6-3] ASTM A898-91, Specification for Straight Beam Ultrasound Examination for Rolled Steel Shapes, 1991.

A.9.1.6.1 Quality Assurance Plan. A quality assurance plan shall be submitted to the authority having jurisdiction.

A.9.1.6.1.1 Details of Quality Assurance Plan. The quality assurance plan shall specify the designated seismic systems or seismic force-resisting system in accordance with Section A.9.1.6 that are subject to quality assurance. The person responsible for the design of a designated seismic system shall be responsible for the portion of the quality assurance plan applicable to that system. The special inspections and special tests needed to establish that the construction is in conformance with these provisions shall be included in the portion of the quality assurance plan applicable to the designated seismic system.

A.9.1.6.1.2 Contractor Responsibility. Each contractor responsible for the construction of a designated seismic system or component listed in the quality assurance plan shall submit a written statement to the regulatory authority having jurisdiction prior to the commencement of work on the system or component. The statement shall contain the following:

1. Acknowledgment of awareness of the special requirements contained in the quality assurance plan.
2. Acknowledgment that control will be exercised to obtain conformance with the design documents approved by the authority having jurisdiction.
3. Procedures for exercising control within the contractor's organization, the method and frequency of reporting, and the distribution of the reports.
4. The person exercising such control and that person's position in the organization.

A.9.1.6.2 Special Inspection. The building owner shall employ special inspector(s) to observe the construction of all designated seismic systems in accordance with the quality assurance plan for the following construction work:

A.9.1.6.2.1 Foundations. Continuous special inspection is required during driving of piles, and placement of concrete in deep foundations. Periodic special inspection is required during construction of drilled piles and caisson work, the placement of concrete in shallow foundations, and the placement of reinforcing steel.

A.9.1.6.2.2 Reinforcing Steel

A.9.1.6.2.2.1. Periodic special inspection during and upon completion of the placement of reinforcing steel in intermediate and special moment frames of concrete and concrete shear walls.

A.9.1.6.2.2.2. Continuous special inspection during the welding of reinforcing steel resisting flexural and axial forces in intermediate and special moment frames of concrete, in boundary members of concrete shear walls, and welding of shear reinforcement.

A.9.1.6.2.3 Structural Concrete. Periodic special inspection during and on completion of the placement of concrete in intermediate and special moment frames, and in boundary members of concrete shear walls.

A.9.1.6.2.4 Prestressed Concrete. Periodic special inspection during the placement and after the completion of placement of prestressing steel and continuous special inspection is required during all stressing and grouting operations and during the placement of concrete.

A.9.1.6.2.5 Structural Masonry

A.9.1.6.2.5.1. Periodic special inspection during the preparation of mortar, the laying of masonry units, and placement of reinforcement; and prior to placement of grout;

A.9.1.6.2.5.2. Continuous special inspection during welding of reinforcement, grouting, consolidation, and reconsolidation.

A.9.1.6.2.6. Structural Steel

A.9.1.6.2.6.1. special inspection is required for all structural welding.

Exception: Periodic special inspection for single-pass fillet or resistance welds and welds loaded to less than 50% of their design strength shall be the minimum requirement, provided the qualifications of the welder and the welding electrodes are inspected at the beginning of the work and all welds are inspected for compliance with the approved construction documents at the completion of welding.

A.9.1.6.2.6.2. Periodic special inspection is required in accordance with [9.5-1] or [9.5-2] for installation and tightening of fully tensioned high-strength bolts in slip-critical connections and in connections subject to direct tension. Bolts in connections identified as not being slip-critical or subject to direct tension need not be inspected for bolt tension other than to ensure that the plies of the connected elements have been brought into snug contact.

A.9.1.6.2.7 Structural Wood

A.9.1.6.2.7.1. Continuous special inspection during all field gluing operations of elements of the seismic-force-resisting system.

A.9.1.6.2.7.2. Periodic special inspection is required for nailing, bolting, anchoring and other fastening of all seismic components including drag struts, braces, and hold downs.

A.9.1.6.2.8 Architectural Components. Special inspection for architectural components shall be as follows:

1. Periodic special inspection during the erection and fastening of exterior cladding, interior and exterior nonloadbearing walls, and veneer in Seismic Performance Categories D and E and

   Exceptions: (a) Buildings 30 ft (9.2 m) or less in height; and (b) Cladding and veneer weighing 5 lb/sq ft (25 kg/m²) or less.

2. Periodic special inspection during the anchorage of access floors and storage racks 8 ft (2.5 m) or greater in height in Seismic Performance Categories D and E.

A.9.1.6.2.9 Mechanical and Electrical Components. Special inspection for mechanical and electrical components shall be as follows:

1. Periodic special inspection during the anchorage of electrical equipment for emergency or standby power systems in Seismic Performance Categories C, D, and E;
2. Periodic special inspection during the installation of anchorage of all other electrical equipment in Seismic Performance Category E;
3. Periodic special inspection during the installation for flammable, combustible, or highly toxic piping systems and their associated mechanical units in Seismic Performance Categories C, D, and E; and
4. Periodic special inspection during the installation of HVAC ductwork that will contain hazardous materials in Seismic Performance Categories C, D and E.

A.9.1.6.3 Testing. The special inspector shall be responsible for verifying that the special test requirements are performed by an approved testing agency for the types of work in designated seismic systems listed below.

A.9.1.6.3.1 Reinforcing and Prestressing Steel. Special testing of reinforcing and prestressing steel shall be as follows:

A.9.1.6.3.1.1. Examine certified mill test reports for each shipment of reinforcing steel used to resist flexural and axial forces in reinforced concrete intermediate and special moment frames and boundary members of reinforced concrete or reinforced masonry shear walls and determine conformance with specification requirements.

A.9.1.6.3.1.2. Where ASTM A615 reinforcing steel is used to resist earthquake-induced flexural and axial forces in special moment frames and in wall boundary elements of shear walls in buildings of Seismic Performance Category D and E, verify that the requirements of Section 22.2.5.1 of [9.6-1] have been satisfied.

A.9.1.6.3.1.3. Where ASTM A615 reinforcing steel is to be welded, verify that chemical tests have been performed to determine weldability in accordance with Section 3.5.2 of [9.6-1].

A.9.1.6.3.2 Structural Concrete. Samples of structural concrete shall be obtained at the project site and tested in accordance with requirements of [9.6-1] (see Section 9.6.1).

A.9.1.6.3.3 Structural Masonry. Quality-assurance testing of structural masonry shall be in accordance with the requirements of [9.8-1].

A.9.1.6.3.4 Structural Steel. Special testing of structural steel shall be as follows:

A.9.1.6.3.4.1. Welded connections for moment frames and eccentrically-braced frames shall be tested by nondestructive methods conforming to [A.9.1.6-1], Section 9.5 and 9.6. All complete penetration groove welds contained in joints and splices shall be 100 % tested either by ultrasonic testing or by other approved methods.

Exception: The minimum nondestructive testing rate for an individual welder shall be reduced to 25% with the concurrence of the design professional(s) of record, provided that the reject rate is demonstrated to be 5 percent or less of the welds tested for the welder.

A.9.1.6.3.4.2. Partial penetration groove welds when used in column splices designed to resist tension resulting from the prescribed seismic design forces shall be tested by ultrasonic testing or other approved methods at a rate established by the design professional(s) of record.

A.9.1.6.3.4.3. Base metal thicker than 1.5 in. (38 mm) when subject to through-thickness weld shrinkage strains shall be ultrasonically tested for discontinuities behind and adjacent to such welds after joint completion. Any material discontinuities shall be accepted or rejected on the basis of [A.9.1.6-2] or [A.9.1.6-3], and criteria as established by the design professional(s) of record and the contract documents.

A.9.1.6.3.5 Mechanical and Electrical Equipment. As required to ensure compliance with the seismic design provisions herein, the facility designer shall clearly state the applicable requirements on contract documents. Each manufacturer of these designated components shall test or analyze the component and its mounting system or anchorage as required and shall submit a certificate of compliance for review and acceptance by the person responsible for the design of the designated seismic system and for approval by the authority having jurisdiction. The basis of certification shall be by actual test on a shaking table, by three-dimensional shock tests, by an analytical method using dynamic characteristics and forces, by the use of experience data (i.e., historical data demonstrating acceptable seismic performance), or by more rigorous analysis providing for equivalent safety. The special inspector shall examine the designated seismic system component and shall determine whether its anchorages and label conform with the certificate of compliance.

A.9.1.6.3.6 Seismic-Isolated Structures. For required system tests, see Section A.9.2.6.9.

A.9.1.6.4 Reporting and Compliance Procedures. Each special inspector shall furnish to the authority having jurisdiction, the owner, the persons preparing the quality assurance plan, and the contractor copies of regular weekly progress reports of his observations, noting therein any uncorrected deficiencies and corrections of previously reported deficiencies. All deficiencies shall be brought to the immediate attention of the contractor for correction. At completion of construction, each special inspector shall submit a final report to the authority having jurisdiction certifying that all inspected work was completed substantially in accordance with approved construction documents. Work not in compliance shall be described in the final report. At completion of construction, the building contractor shall submit a final report to the authority having jurisdiction certifying that all construction work incorporated into the designated seismic systems was constructed substantially in accordance with the construction documents and applicable workmanship requirements. Work not in compliance shall be described in the final report. The contractor shall correct all deficiencies as required.

A.9.4 Supplementary Foundation Requirements

A.9.4.4.4 Special Pile Requirements for Category C. All concrete piles and concrete filled pipe piles shall be connected to the pile cap by embedding the pile reinforcement in the pile cap for a distance equal to the development length as specified in [9.6-1] or by the use of field-placed dowels anchored in the concrete pile. For deformed bars, the development length is the full development length for compression without reduction in length for excess area.

Where special reinforcement at the top of the pile is required, alternative measures for laterally confining concrete and maintaining toughness and ductile-like behavior at the top of the pile *shall be allowed* provided due consideration is given to forcing the hinge to occur in the confined region. Where a minimum length for reinforcement or the extent of closely spaced confinement reinforcement is specified at the top of the pile, provisions shall be made so that those specified lengths or extents are maintained after pile cut-off.

A.9.4.4.4.1 Uncased Concrete Piles. A minimum reinforcement ratio of 0.0025 shall be provided for uncased cast-in-place concrete drilled piles, drilled piers, or caissons in the top one-third of the pile length or a minimum length of 10 ft below the ground. There shall be a minimum of four bars with closed ties (or equivalent spirals) of a minimum 1/4 in. diameter provided at 16-longitudinal-bar-diameter maximum spacing with a maximum spacing of 4 in. in the top 2 ft of the pile. Reinforcement detailing requirements shall be in conformance with Section A.9.6.6.2.

A.9.4.4.4.2 Metal-Cased Concrete Piles. Reinforcement requirements are the same as for uncased concrete piles.

Exception: Spiral welded metal-casing of a thickness not less than No. 14 gauge is considered as providing concrete confinement equivalent to the closed ties or equivalent spirals required in an uncased concrete pile, provided that the metal casing is adequately protected against possible deleterious action due to soil constituents, changing water levels, or other factors indicated by boring records of site conditions.

A.9.4.4.4.3 Concrete-Filled Pipe. Minimum reinforcement 0.01 times the cross-sectional area of the pile concrete shall be provided in the top of the pile with a length equal to two times the required cap embedment anchorage into the pile cap.

A.9.4.4.4.4 Precast Concrete Piles. Longitudinal reinforcement shall be provided for precast concrete piles with a minimum steel ratio of 0.01. Ties or equivalent spirals shall be provided at a maximum 16-bar-diameter spacing with a maximum spacing of 4 in. in the top 2 ft. Reinforcement shall be full length.

A.9.4.4.4.5 Precast-Prestressed Piles. The upper 2 ft of the pile shall have No. 3 ties minimum at not over 4-in. spacing or equivalent spirals. Where pile cap connection is made by means of developing pile reinforcing strand, a connection capable of dissipating energy shall be provided.

A.9.4.5.3 Special Pile Requirements for Category D

A.9.4.5.3.1 Uncased Concrete Piles. A minimum reinforcement ratio of 0.005 shall be provided for uncased cast-in-place concrete piles, drilled piers, or caissons in the top one-half of the pile length or a minimum length of 10 ft below ground. There shall be a minimum of four bars with closed ties or equivalent spirals provided at 8-longitudinal-bar-diameter maximum spacing with a maximum spacing of 3 in. in the top 4 ft of the pile. Ties shall be a minimum of No. 3 bars for up to 20-in. diameter piles and No. 4 bars for piles of larger diameter.

A.9.4.5.3.2 Metal-Cased Concrete Piles. Reinforcement requirements are the same as for uncased concrete piles.

Exception: Spiral welded metal-casing of a thickness not less than No. 14 gauge is considered as providing concrete confinement equivalent to the closed ties or equivalent spirals required in an uncased concrete pile, provided that the metal casing is adequately protected against deleterious action due to soil constituents, changing water levels, or other factors indicated by boring records of site conditions.

A.9.4.5.3.3 Precast Concrete Piles. Ties in precast concrete piles shall conform to the requirements of Section A.9.6 for at least the top half of the pile.

A.9.4.5.3.4 Precast-Prestressed Piles. For the body of fully embedded foundation piling subjected to vertical loads only, or where the design bending moment does not exceed 0.20 M_{nb} (where M_{nb} is the unfactored ultimate moment capacity at balanced strain conditions as defined in [9.6-1], spiral reinforcing shall be provided such that $\rho_s \geq 0.006$.

A.9.4.5.3.5 Steel Piles. The connection between the pile cap and steel piles or unfilled steel pipe piles shall be designed for a tensile force equal to 10% of the pile compression capacity.

A.9.5 Supplementary Provisions for Steel
A.9.5.1 General
A.9.5.1.1 Structural Steel by Strength Design. *If the allowable stress load combinations of*

Section 2.4.1 are used, Section A.9.5.1.2 shall be satisfied. Otherwise, the strength load combinations of Section 2.3.2 shall be used to design structural steel for the earthquake loads given Section 9.

A.9.5.1.2 Allowable Stress Design. When using the load combinations of Sec. 2.4.1, the allowable strength of members and connections shall be determined from allowable stress set forth in the following:

Structural Steel, [9.5-2]
Cold Formed Steel, [9.5-4]
Cold Formed Stainless Steel, [9.5-6, Appendix E]
Steel Joists and Joist Girders, [9.5-7]
Steel Cables, [9.5-8]

The one-third increase in allowable stress given in reference documents [9.5-2] and [9.5-6, Appendix E] or the 0.75 factor on loads given in reference [9.5-4] for use with seismic loads is permitted. The load combination adjustment factors of Section 2.4.3 shall not be used. The increase in allowable stress given in part 2 of [9.5-3] for structural steel or Section A.9.5.3 for cold formed steel to approximate strength shall not be used in conjunction with the load combination of Section 2.4.1.

For structural steel members designed using [9.5-2], Section A.9.5.2.1 and the provisions of [9.5-3] shall also be satisfied, including the detailed proportioning rules that are stated in terms of strength for Seismic Performance Categories C (as limited in section 2.2 of [9.5-3], D, and E.

For light framed walls, the provisions of Section A.9.5.7 shall also be satisfied, when required by Section A.9.5.6.3.

A.9.5.2 Structural Steel Seismic Requirements: The design of structural steel members and connections to resist seismic forces shall be in accordance with [9.5-1] or [9.5-2]. When using the provisions of [9.5-2] to compute the capacity of members to resist seismic forces, allowable stresses shall be converted into design strengths using the provisions of [9.5-3, part II, sections 3.2 and 3.3]. When required, structural steel members also shall be designed in accordance with [9.5-3] as modified by the requirements of this section, except that the definition of E shall be as defined in these provisions and that the term C_a shall be substituted for A_v throughout. Also, [9.5-3, Section 8.2c] shall be deleted and replaced with the following: 8.2c Connection Strength: Connection configurations utilizing welds or high strength bolts shall demonstrate, by approved cyclic testing results or calculations, the ability to sustain inelastic

rotation and to develop the strength criteria in Section 8.2a considering the expected value of yield strength and strain hardening.

*

A.9.5.2.1 Requirements for Special Concentrically Braced Frames (SCBF): Special CBFs shall be designed in accordance with the requirements of [9.5-3] for concentrically braced frames except as modified herein. The reference to section and paragraph numbers are those of [9.5-3]. The following modifications shall apply to special CBFs and shall not modify the requirements for ordinary CBFs in [9.5-3]:

1. Sec. 9.2.a—Shall not apply to SCBF.
2. Sec. 9.2.b—Revise as follows:
   "**9.2.b Compressive Design Strength:** The design strength of a bracing member in axial compression shall not exceed $\phi_c P_n$."
3. Sec. 9.2.d—Revise as follows:
   "**9.2.d Width-thickness Ratio:** Width-thickness ratios of stiffened and unstiffened compression elements of braces shall comply with Sec. B5 of [5-1]. Braces shall be compact (i.e., $\lambda < \lambda_p$). The width-thickness ratio of angle sections shall not exceed $52/\sqrt{F_y}$. Circular sections shall have an outside diameter to wall thickness ratio not exceeding $1,300/F_y$; rectangular tubes shall have outside wall width-thickness ratio not exceeding $110/\sqrt{F_y}$ unless the circular section or tube walls are stiffened."
4. Sec. 9.2.e—Revise as follows:
   "**9.2.e Built-up Member Stitches:** For all built-up braces, the spacing of stitches shall be uniform and not less than two stitches shall be used:
   "1. For a brace in which stitches can be subjected to postbuckling shear, the spacing of stitches shall be such that the slenderness ratio, L/r, of individual elements between the stitches does not exceed 0.4 times the governing slenderness ratio of the built-up member. The total shear strength of the stitches shall be at least equal to the tensile strength of each element.
   "2. For braces that can buckle without causing shear in the stitches, the spacing of the stitches shall be such that the slenderness ratio, L/r, of the individual elements between the stitches does not exceed 0.75 times the governing slenderness ratio of the built-up member."

111

5. Sec. 9.4.a—Revise as follows:

   "**9.4.a V and Inverted V Type Bracing:**
   V and inverted *V* braced frames shall comply with the following:

   "1. A beam intersected by braces shall be continuous between columns.

   "2. A beam intersected by braces shall be capable of supporting all tributary dead and live loads assuming the bracing is not present.

   "3. A beam intersected by braces shall be capable of resisting the combination of load effects by Eq. (3-5) and (3-6) of [9.5-3] except that the term Q_b shall be substituted for the term E where $Q_b =$ the maximum unbalanced load effect applied to the beam by the braces. This load effect shall be permitted to be calculated using a minimum of P_y for the brace in tension and a maximum of $0.3\phi_c P_n$ for the brace in compression.

   "4. The top and bottom flanges of the beam at the point of intersection of *V* braces shall be designed to support a lateral force equal to 1.5 percent of the nominal beam flange strength, $F_y b_f t_f$."

6. Sec. 9.4.b—Delete in its entirety without replacement.

7. Sec. 9.5—Delete in its entirety without replacement.

8. Add a new section as follows:

   "**9.5 Columns:**

   "**9.5.a Compactness:** Columns used in SCBFs shall be compact according to Section B5 of the *Specification*. The outside wall width-thickness ratio of rectangular tubes used for columns shall not exceed $110/\sqrt{F_y}$ unless otherwise stiffened.

   "**9.5.b Splices:** In addition to meeting the requirements of Section 6.2, column splices in SCBFs also shall be designed to develop the nominal shear strength and 50% of the nominal moment strength of the section."

A.9.5.3 Cold-Formed Steel Seismic Requirements. The design of cold-formed carbon or low-alloy steel to resist seismic loads shall be in accordance with the provisions of [9.5-4], [9.5-5], and [9.5-6] except as modified by this section. The reference to section and paragraph numbers are to those of the particular specification modified.

A.9.5.3.1. Reference [9.5-4]—The nominal strength of members and connections shall be as specified therein except that the nominal strength for shear and web crippling shall be determined by multiplying the allowable strength by 1.7. Design strengths shall be determined by multiplying the strengths by resistance factors as stated herein. The following resistance factors, ϕ, shall be used:

Shear strength with $h/t > \sqrt{(Ek_v/F_y)}$	$\phi = 0.9$
Shear strength with $h/t \leq \sqrt{(Ek_v/F_y)}$	$\phi = 1.0$
Web crippling of members with single unreinforced webs	$\phi = 0.75$
Web crippling of I sections	$\phi = 0.8$
All other cases	$\phi = 1.55/\Omega$

where

$h =$ height of shear element;

$t =$ thickness of shear element;

$E =$ modulus of elasticity, ksi;

$k_v =$ shear buckling coefficient;

$F_y =$ specified minimum yield stress of the type of steel being used, ksi; and

$\Omega =$ overall factor of safety.

A.9.5.3.2. Reference [9.5-4]—*Revise Section A4.4 by deleting the reference to earthquake loads, except when following the provision of Section A.9.5.1.2.*

A.9.5.3.3. Reference [9.5-5]—Modify Section A5.1.4 by substituting a load factor of 1.0 in place of 1.5 for nominal earthquake load.

A.9.5.3.4. Reference [9.5-6]—Modify Section 1.5.2 by substituting a load factor of 1.0 in place of 1.5 for nominal earthquake load.

A.9.5.4 Seismic Requirements for Steel Deck Diaphragms: Steel deck diaphragms shall be made from materials conforming to the requirements of Ref. 9.5-4, 9.5-4, or 9.5-6. Nominal strengths shall be determined in accordance with approved analytical procedures or with test procedures prepared by a licensed design professional experienced in testing of cold-formed steel assemblies and approved by the authority having jurisdiction. Design strengths shall be determined by multiplying the nominal strength by a resistance factor, ϕ, equal to 0.60 for mechanically connected diaphragms and equal to 0.50 for welded diaphragms. The steel deck installation for the building, including fasteners, shall comply with the test assembly arrangement. Quality standards established for the nominal strength test shall be the minimum standards required for the steel deck installation, including fasteners.

A.9.5.5 Steel Cables. The design strength of steel cables shall be determined by the provisions of [9.5-8] except as modified by this Section. Reference [9.5-8, section 5d] shall be modified by substituting $1.5(T_4)$ when T_4 is the net tension in cable due to dead load, prestress, live load, and seismic load. A load factor of 1.1 shall be applied to the prestress force to be added to the load combination of Section 3.1.2 of [9.5-8].

A.9.5.6 Seismic Provisions for Steel Structural Members: Steel structures and structural elements therein that resist seismic forces shall be designed in accordance with the applicable provisions of Sections A.9.5.2–A.9.5.5. In addition, steel structures also shall be designed in accordance with the requirements of Sections A.9.5.6.1, A.9.5.6.2, and A.9.5.6.3 for the appropriate Seismic Performance Category.

A.9.5.6.1 Seismic Performance Categories A and B. Buildings assigned to Seismic Performance Category A or B shall be of any construction permitted by the references in Section 9.5.1.

A.9.5.6.2 Seismic Performance Category C. Unless otherwise required by the provisions of this section, Seismic Performance Category C buildings shall be of any construction permitted by the references in Section 9.5.1.

A.9.5.6.3 Seismic Performance Categories D and E. Buildings assigned to Seismic Performance D or E shall be designed in accordance with the additional provisions of [9.5-3] for structural steel buildings and Section A.9.5.7 for light framed walls.

A.9.5.7 Light Framed Wall Requirements. Cold-formed steel stud wall systems designed in accordance with [9.5-4], [9.5-5], or [9.5-6] shall when required by the provisions of Section A.9.5.6.3 also comply with the requirements of this section.

A.9.5.7.1 Boundary Members. All boundary members, chords, and collectors shall be designed to transmit the axial force induced by the specified loads of Section 9.

A.9.5.7.2 Connections. Connections of diagonal bracing members, top chord splices, boundary members and collectors shall have a design strength equal to or greater than the nominal tensile strength of the members being connected or $(2R/5)$ times the design seismic forces. The term $2R/5$ shall not be taken less than unity. The pullout resistance of screws shall not be used to resist seismic forces.

A.9.5.7.3 Braced Bay Members. In systems where the lateral forces are resisted by braced frames, the vertical and diagonal members of braced bays shall be anchored such that the tracks are not required to resist tensile forces by bending of the track or track web. Both flanges of studs in a bracing bay shall be braced to prevent lateral torsional buckling.

A.9.5.7.4 Diagonal Braces. Provision shall be made for pretensioning or other methods of installation of tension-only bracing to prevent loose diagonals.

A.9.6 Supplementary Provisions for Structural Concrete

A.9.6.1 Modifications to Referenced Documents

A.9.6.1.1 Modifications to [9.6-1]

A.9.6.1.1.1 *The load combinations for earthquake load in [9.6-1] shall be replaced with the load combinations of Section 2.3.2 multiplied by a factor of 1.1, which accounts for an incompatibility between the ϕ factors of [9.6-1] and the load factors of this document.*

A.9.6.1.1.2 The application requirements of sections 21.2.1.3 and 21.2.1.4 of [9.6-1] shall be replaced with the provisions of Sections A.9.6.3 through A.9.6.7.
*

A.9.6.1.2 Modifications to [9.6-2] Amend Section 1.2.3 by deleting the words "earthquake or."

A.9.6.2. Bolts and Headed Stud Anchors in Concrete.* The design strength of bolts and headed stud anchors embedded in concrete shall be determined using Section A.9.6.2.

A.9.6.2.1 Load Factor Multipliers. The required design strength shall include a multiplier of 2 times the load combinations of Section 2.3.2 if special inspection *of the anchors* is not provided or of 1.3 if it is provided. When anchors are embedded in the tension zone of a member, the required design strength shall include a multiplier of 3 if special inspection is not provided or of 2 if it is provided.

A.9.6.2.2 Strength of Anchors.* The strength of headed bolts and headed studs solidly cast in concrete shall be taken as the *average* of 10 tests for each concrete strength and anchor size or calculated as the minimum of P_s or ϕP_c in tension and V_s or ϕV_c in shear when:

$$P_s = 0.9 A_b f_s'$$

and

$$\phi P_c = \phi \lambda \sqrt{f_c'}\,(2.8 A_s + 4 A_t)$$

where

A_b = Area (in square inches) of bolt or stud. Must be used with the corresponding steel properties to determine the weakest part of the assembly in tension. In shear, the insert leg need not be checked.

A_s = The sloping area (in square inches) of an assumed failure surface. The surface to be that of a cone or truncated pyramid radiating at a 45° slope from the bearing edge of the anchor or anchor group to the surface. For thin sections with anchor groups, the failure surface shall be assumed to follow the extension of this slope through to the far side rather than truncate as in A_t.

A_t = The area (in square inches) of the flat bottom of the truncated pyramid of an assumed concrete failure surface. When anchors in a group are closer together than twice their embedment length, the failure surface pyramid is assumed to truncate at the anchor bearing edge rather than form separate cones.

f'_c = Concrete strength, 6,000-psi limit for design.

f'_s = Ultimate tensile strength (in psi) of the bolt, stud, or insert leg wires not to be taken greater than 60,000 psi. For A307 bolts or A108 studs, f'_s shall be assumed to be 60,000.

λ = 1 for normal weight, 0.75 for "all lightweight," and 0.85 for "sand lightweight" concrete.

ϕ = Strength reduction factor = 0.65.

Exception: When *the anchor is attached to or hooked around reinforcing steel or otherwise terminated so as to effectively transfer forces to reinforcing steel that is designed to distribute forces and avert sudden local failure,* $\phi = 0.85$.

When edge distance is less than embedment length, reduce proportionally. For multiple edge distances less than the embedment length, use multiple reductions.

When loaded toward an edge greater than 10 diameters away:

$$V_s = 0.75 \, A_b f'_s$$

and

$$\phi V_c = \phi 800 A_b \lambda \sqrt{f'_c}$$

When loaded toward an edge less than 10 diameters away:

$$\phi V_c = \phi 2\pi d_e^2 \lambda \sqrt{f'_c}$$

where d_e = distance from the anchor axis to the free edge.

For groups of anchors, the concrete design shear strength shall be taken as the smallest of:

1. *The strength of the weakest stud times the number of studs;*
2. *The strength of the row of studs nearest the free edge in the direction of shear times the number of rows; or*
3. *The strength of the row farthest from the free edge in the direction of shear.*

For shear loading toward an edge less than 10 diameters away, or tension or shear not toward an edge less than four diameters away, reinforcing sufficient to carry the load shall be provided to prevent failure of the concrete in tension. In no case shall the edge distance be less than one-third the aforementioned. The bearing area of headed anchors shall be at least one and one-half times the shank area for anchors of not over 120,000 psi yield strength.

When tension and shear act simultaneously, both the following shall be met:

$$\frac{1}{\phi}\left[\left(\frac{P_u}{P_c}\right)^2 + \left(\frac{V_u}{V_c}\right)^2\right] \le 1$$

and

$$\left(\frac{P_u}{P_s}\right)^2 + \left(\frac{V_u}{V_s}\right)^2 \le 1$$

where P_u, V_u = tensile, shear strength required due to factored loads (in pounds).

A.9.6.2.3 Anchor Bolts in Tops of Columns. *Anchor bolts at the top of columns shall have a minimum embedment of 9-bolt diameters and shall be enclosed with not less than two No. 4 ties located within 4 in. of the column top.*

A.9.6.3 Classification of Moment Frames

A.9.6.3.1 Ordinary Moment Frames. Ordinary moment frames are frames conforming to the requirements of [9.6-1] exclusive of Section 21.

A.9.6.3.2 Intermediate Moment Frames. Intermediate moment frames are frames conforming to the requirements of Section 21.8 of [9.6-1] in addition to those requirements for ordinary moment frames.

A.9.6.3.3. Special Moment Frames. Special moment frames are frames conforming to the requirements of Sections 21.2–21.5 of [9.6-1] in addition to those requirements for ordinary moment frames.

A.9.6.4 Seismic Performance Category A. Buildings assigned to Category A shall be of any construction permitted in [9.6-1] and 9.6-2] and these provisions.

A.9.6.5 Seismic Performance Category B. Buildings assigned to Category B shall conform to all the requirements for Category A and to the additional requirements for Category B in other sections of these provisions.

A.9.6.5.1 Ordinary Moment Frames: In flexural members of ordinary moment frames forming part of the seismic-force-resisting system, at least two main flexural reinforcing bars shall be provided continuously top and bottom throughout the beams, through or developed within exterior columns or boundary elements. Columns of ordinary moment frames having a clear height to maximum plan dimension ratio of five or less shall be designed for shear in accordance with section 21.8.3 of [9.6-1].

A.9.6.5.2 Moment Frames: All moment frames that are part of the seismic force resisting system of a building assigned to Category B and founded on Soil Profile Type E or F shall be intermediate moment frames conforming to Section A.9.6.3.2 or special moment frames conforming to Section A.9.6.3.3.

A.9.6.6 Seismic Performance Category C. Buildings assigned to Category C shall conform to all the requirements for Category B and to the additional requirements for Category C in other sections of these provisions as well as to the requirements of this section.

A.9.6.6.1 Moment Frames. All moment frames that are part of the seismic force-resisting system shall be intermediate moment frames conforming to Section A.9.6.3.2 or special moment frames conforming to Section A.9.6.3.3.

A.9.6.6.2 Discontinuous Members. Columns supporting reactions from discontinuous stiff members such as walls shall be provided with transverse reinforcement at the spacing s_o as defined in section 21.8.5.1 of [9.6-1] over their full height beneath the level at which the discontinuity occurs. This transverse reinforcement shall be ex-

tended above and below the column as required in Sec. 21.4.4.5 of [9.6-1.]

A.9.6.6.3 Plain Concrete: Structural members of plain concrete in buildings assigned to Category C shall conform to all requirements for Category B and the additional provisions and limitations of this section.

A.9.6.6.3.1 Walls. Minimum reinforcement shall be provided around windows and door openings in basement, foundation, or other walls below the base shall be reinforced as required by section 7.1.6.5 of [9.6-2]. Other walls shall be reinforced as required by Section 10.5.3.2 of [9.8-1].

A.9.6.6.3.2 Footings. Plain concrete shall not be used in isolated footings supporting pedestals or columns if the projection of the footing beyond the face of the supported member exceeds the footing thickness.

Exception: In detached one- and two-family dwellings three stories or less in height, the projection of the footing beyond the face of the supported member is not limited to the footing thickness.

Plain concrete footings supporting walls shall be provided with not less than two continuous longitudinal reinforcing bars. Bars shall not be smaller than No. 4 and shall have a total area of not less than 0.002 times the gross cross-sectional area of the footing. Continuity of reinforcement shall be provided at corners and intersections.

Exception: In detached one- and two-family dwellings three stories or less in height and constructed with stud bearing walls, plain concrete footings supporting walls are not required to have longitudinal reinforcement.

A.9.6.6.3.3 Pedestals: Plain concrete pedestals shall not be used to resist lateral seismic forces.

A.9.6.7 Seismic Performance Categories D and E. Buildings assigned to Category D or E shall conform to all of the requirements for Category C and to the additional requirements of this section.

A.9.6.7.1 Moment Frames. All moment frames that are part of the seismic force-resisting system, regardless of height, shall be special moment frames conforming to Section A.9.6.3.3.

A.9.6.7.2 Seismic Force-Resisting System. All materials and components in the seismic force-resisting system shall conform to sections 21.2–21.6 of [9.6-1].

A.9.6.7.3 Frame Members Not Proportioned to Resist Forces Induced by Earthquake Motions. All frame components assumed not to contribute to lateral force resistance shall conform to Section 9.2.2.2.4.3 of these provisions and to sections 2.1.7.1.1 or 2.1.7.1.2 and 2.1.7.2 of [9.6-1].

A.9.6.7.4 Plain Concrete: Structural members of plain concrete shall not be used in buildings assigned to Category D or E.

Exceptions:

1. In detached one- and two-family dwellings three stories or less in height and constructed with stud bearing walls, plain concrete footings without longitudinal reinforcement supporting walls and isolated plain concrete footings supporting columns or pedestals.
2. In all other buildings, plain concrete footings supporting walls reinforced longitudinally as specified in Section A.9.6.6.3.2.
3. In detached one- and two-family dwellings three stories or less in height and constructed with stud bearing walls, plain concrete foundation or basement walls if the wall is not less than 7-1/2 in. (190 mm) thick and retains no more than 4 ft (1219 mm) of unbalanced fill.

A.9.9 Supplementary Provisions for Wood Structures

A.9.9.1 General: Dimensions for wood products and associated products designated in this section are nominal dimensions and actual dimensions shall be not less than prescribed by the reference standards. For diaphragms and shear walls, the acceptable types of sheet sheathing listed in Sections A.9.9.9.1.1 and A.9.9.9.1.2 shall have nominal sheet sizes of 4 ft by 8 ft (1,200 mm by 2,400 mm) or larger.

A.9.9.2 Strength of Members and Connections

A.9.9.2.1 Allowable Stress Design. When using the load combinations of Section 2.4.1, the design strength of members and connections shall be as set forth in the reference documents, including the adjustment factor for the duration of load (1.6 in [9.9-1] and the equivalent factor in other References), and as set forth in these supplementary provisions. The load combination adjustment factors of Section 2.4.3 shall not be used.

A.9.9.2.2 Strength Based Design: The design strength of members and connections subjected to seismic forces acting alone or in combination with other prescribed loads shall be determined using a capacity reduction factor, ϕ,

and 2.16 times the stresses permitted in the reference documents and in this chapter. The value of the capacity reduction factor, ϕ, shall be as follows:

Wood members in flexure	$\phi = 1.00$
in compression	$\phi = 0.90$
in tension	$\phi = 1.00$
in shear and torsion	$\phi = 1.00$
Connectors	
bolts, lag bolts, nails, screws, etc.	$\phi = 085$
bolts in single shear members that are part of the seismic force resisting system	$\phi = 0.40$
Shear on diaphragms and shear walls (as given in this chapter)	$\phi = 0.60$

A.9.9.3 Seismic Performance Category A: Buildings assigned to Category A shall be constructed using any of the materials and procedures specified in the reference documents and need only conform to the requirements of Section 9.2.2.5.1. Buildings constructed in compliance with Section A.9.9.10 are assumed to satisfy Section 9.2.2.5.1.

A.9.9.4 Seismic Performance Category B: Buildings assigned to Category B shall be constructed using any of the materials and procedures specified in the reference documents and Section 9.9 except as limited by this section.

A.9.9.4.1 Construction Limitations, Conventional Construction: Buildings not exempted by Section 9.1.2, *shall conform to the requirements of either* Section A.9.9.8 or Section A.9.9.10.

A.9.9.5 Seismic Performance Category C: Buildings assigned to Category C shall conform to all of the requirements for Category B and to the additional requirements of this section.

A.9.9.5.1 Material Limitations, Structural-Use Panel Sheathing: Where structural-use panel sheathing is used as siding on the exterior of outside walls, it shall be of the exterior type. Where structural-use panel sheathing is used elsewhere, it shall be manufactured with intermediate or exterior glue.

A.9.9.5.2 Detailing Requirements: The construction shall comply with the requirements given herein.

A.9.9.5.2.1 Anchorage of Concrete or Masonry Walls: Ties and splices required in Sections 9.2.2.5.1.1 and 9.2.2.5.1.2 shall be provided in buildings within category IV of Table 1-1 at sites with C_a equal to or greater than 0.10 and the diaphragm sheathing shall not be considered for this purpose.

A.9.9.5.2.2 Lag Screws: Washers shall be provided under the heads of lag screws that otherwise bear on wood.

A.9.9.6 Seismic Performance Category D: Buildings assigned to Category D shall conform to all the requirements for Category C and to the additional requirements of this section.

A.9.9.6.1 Framing Systems: The limitations on framing systems used in Category D construction are given below.

A.9.9.6.1.1 Diaphragms: Wood diaphragms shall not be used to resist torsional forces induced by concrete or masonry wall construction in structures over two stories in height.

A.9.9.6.1.2 Anchorage of Concrete and Masonry Walls: Ties and splices required in Sections 9.2.2.5.1.1 and 9.2.2.5.1.2 shall be provided and the diaphragm sheathing shall not be considered for this purpose.

A.9.9.7 Seismic Performance Category E: Buildings assigned to Category E shall conform to all of the requirements for Category D and to the additional requirements of this section.

A.9.9.7.1 Framing Systems: Framing shall be designed in conformance with Section A.9.9.8. Unblocked structural-use panel sheathed diaphragms shall not be considered to be part of the seismic force resisting system.

A.9.9.7.2 Diaphragm and Shear Wall Limitations: Structural-use panel sheathing used for diaphragms and shear walls that are part of the seismic force resisting system shall be applied directly to the framing members.

Exception: Structural-use panel sheathing used as a diaphragm if fastened over solid lumber planking or laminated decking and if the panel joints do not coincide with the lumber planking or laminated decking joints.

The allowable working stress shear for structural-use panel sheathed vertical shear walls used to resist seismic forces in buildings with concrete or masonry walls shall be one-half the values set forth in Table A.9.9.9.1-1B.

A.9.9.8 Engineered Wood Construction: Engineered wood construction is a structural system that is designed in conformance with well established principles of mechanics. When seismic analysis is prescribed for buildings, the proportioning and design of wood systems, members, and connections shall be in accordance with the reference documents and this section.

A.9.9.8.1 Framing Requirements: All wood columns and posts shall be framed to true end bearing. Supports for columns and posts shall be designed to hold them securely in position and to provide protection against deterioration. Positive connections shall be provided to resist uplift and lateral displacement.

A.9.9.8.2 Diaphragm and Shear Wall Requirements. Diaphragm and shear wall framing and detailing shall conform to the requirements of this section. *Diaphragms and shear walls shall also conform to the requirements of Section A.9.9.9.*

A.9.9.8.2.1 Framing: All framing used for shear panel construction shall conform to [9.9-2] for 2-by (actual 1.5 in., 38 mm) or larger members. Boundary members and chords in diaphragms and shear walls, and collectors transferring forces to such elements, shall be designed and detailed for the induced axial forces. Boundary members shall be tied together at all corners.

Openings in diaphragms and shear walls shall be designed and detailed to transfer the shear and axial forces induced by the discontinuity created by the opening and the details shall be shown on the approved plans.

A.9.9.8.2.2 Anchorage and Connections: Connections and anchorages capable of resisting the prescribed forces shall be provided between the diaphragm or shear wall and the attached components. Concrete or masonry wall anchorage shall not be accomplished by use of toe nails or nails subject to withdrawal and wood ledgers shall not be used in cross-grain bending or tension.

A.9.9.8.2.3 Torsion: Buildings with two lines of resistance in either orthogonal direction and having torsional irregularity due to stiffness ratios between the two lines of resistance greater than 4 to 1, or buildings with one line of resistance in either orthogonal direction shall meet the following requirements:

Diaphragm sheathing shall conform to Sections A.9.9.9.1.1–A.9.9.9.1.4. The width of the diaphragm normal to the orthogonal axis about which the torsional irregularity exists shall not exceed 25 ft (7,600 mm) nor shall the l/w ratio be less than 1/1 for one-story buildings or 1.5/1 for buildings over one story in height, where l = the length of a diaphragm and w = the width of a diaphragm.

Exception: Where calculations demonstrate that the diaphragm deflections will be tolerated, the width shall not be limited and the l/w ratio shall not be less than to 1/1.5 when sheathed in conformance with Section A.9.9.9.1.1 or not less

117

than 1/1 when sheathed in conformance with Section A.9.9.9.1.3 or A.9.9.9.1.4.

A.9.9.9 Diaphragms and Shear Walls: The width of a panel sheet in a diaphragm or shear wall shall not be less than 2 ft (600 mm) and the l/w ratio of a diaphragm or h/w ratio of a shear wall shall not be more than permitted in Sections A.9.9.9.1.1–A.9.9.9.1.4 where: l = the length of a diaphragm, h = the height of a shear wall, and w = the width of a diaphragm or shear wall, and h = the sum of story heights for single element cantilevers or the height of the opening in pierced walls when detailed in conformance with Section A.9.9.8.2.1. The h/w ratio shall not be greater than 2.1.

Capacities of diaphragms and shear walls shall be determined from Section A.9.9.9.1 or shall be calculated by principles of mechanics without limitation by using values of fastener strength and sheathing shear strength given in the reference standards. Fastener strength in the sheathing material must be based on verified test data from cyclical tests.

A.9.9.9.1 Shear Panel Requirements: Shear panels in diaphragms and shear walls shall conform to the requirements in this section. All panel sheathing joints in shear walls shall occur over studs or blocking. Where designated as blocked in Table A.9.9.9.1-1A, all joints shall occur over framing members of the width prescribed in the table. Fasteners shall be placed at least 3/8 in. (9.5 mm) from ends of boards or edges of sheets.

The shear values for shear panels of different materials applied to the same wall line are not cumulative. The shear values for the same material applied to both faces of the same wall are cumulative. Adhesives shall not be used to attach wall sheathing.

Sheet type sheathing shall be so arranged at boundaries and changes in direction of framing that no sheet has a minimum dimension less than 2 ft (600 mm).

A.9.9.9.1.1 Structural-Use Shear Panels: When horizontal and vertical shear panels sheathed with structural-use sheets are used to resist earthquake forces, the design values shall be based on the allowable working stress shear set forth in Table A.9.9.9.1-1A for horizontal diaphragms and Table A.9.9.9.1-1B for shear walls.

The edges of all structural-use panel sheets shall be supported by framing or blocking having the minimum width given in the tables for shear walls and blocked diaphragms. The size and spacing of fasteners at structural-use sheathing panel boundaries, structural-use sheathing sheet edges, and intermediate supports shall be as given in Tables A.9.9.9.1-1A and A.9.9.9.1-1B. The l/w ratio and the h/w ratio shall not exceed the limits prescribed in Tables A.9.9.9.1-1A and A.9.9.9.1-1B.

A.9.9.9.1.2 Shear Panels Sheathed with Other Sheet Materials: Sheet materials other than structural-use materials have no recognized capacity for seismic force resistance and shall not be part of the seismic force resisting system except in conventional construction, Section A.9.9.10.

A.9.9.9.1.3 Single Diagonally Sheathed Shear Panels: Single diagonally sheathed shear panels shall consist of 1-by (actual 3/4 in., 19 mm) sheathing boards laid at an angle of approximately 45° (0.8 rad) to supports. Common nails at each intermediate support shall be two 8d for 1 by 6 (actual 3/4 in., 19 mm, by 5-1/2 in., 140 mm) and three 8d for 1 by 8 (actual 3/4 in., 19 mm, by 7-1/2 in., 190 mm) boards. One additional nail shall be provided in each board at shear panel boundaries. For box nails, one additional nail shall be provided in each board at each intermediate support and two additional nails shall be provided in each board at shear panel boundaries. End joints in adjacent boards shall be separated by at least one framing space between supports. Alternatively, single diagonally sheathed shear panels shall consist of 2-by (actual 1-1/2 in., 38 mm) sheathing boards where 16d nails are substituted for 8d nails, end joints are located as above, and the support is not less than 3 in. (actual 2-1/2 in., 63 mm) width or 4 in. (actual 3-1/2 in., 89 mm) depth.

The allowable working stress shear for these panels is 200 plf (2,900 N/m). The l/w ratio shall not be more than 3/1 and the h/w ratio shall not be more than 2/1.

A.9.9.9.1.4 Double Diagonally Sheathed Shear Panels: Double diagonally sheathed shear panels shall conform to the requirements for single diagonally sheathed diaphragms and the requirements of this section.

Double diagonally sheathed shear panels shall be sheathed with two layers of diagonal boards placed perpendicular to each other on the same face of the supports. Each chord shall be designed for the axial force induced and for flexure between supports due to a uniform load equal to 50% of the shear per foot in the shear panel. The allowable working stress shear for these panels is 600 plf (8800 N/m). The l/w ratio shall not be more than 3/1 and the h/w ratio shall not be more than 2/1.

A.9.9.10 Conventional Light Frame Construction: Conventional light frame construction is a system of repetitive horizontal and vertical framing members selected from tabulations prepared to conform to [9.9-1] for residential live loads and common roof loads and conforming to the framing and bracing requirements of [9.9-8] except as modified by the provisions in this section. This system is limited to buildings with bearing wall heights not exceeding 10 feet (3 m) and number of stories as prescribed in Table A.9.9.10.1-1A. The gravity dead load of the construction is limited to 15 psf (750 Pa) for roofs and exterior walls and 10 psf (500 Pa) for floors and partitions and the gravity live load is limited to 40 psf (2,000 Pa).

Exception: Masonry veneer shall be allowed on Category A buildings and on one-story Category B buildings.

A.9.9.10.1 Braced Walls: The following braced wall requirements shall apply as a minimum.

A.9.9.10.1.1 Braced Wall Spacing: Braced exterior walls and braced partitions shall be located at the spacing indicated in Table A.9.9.10.1A.

A.9.9.10.1.2 Braced Wall Sheathing Requirements: All braced walls and partitions shall be effectively and thoroughly braced by one of the types of sheathing prescribed in Table A.9.9.10.1-1B. The length of bracing at each braced line is prescribed in Table A.9.9.10.1-1B. Such bracing shall be distributed along the length of the braced line with sheathing placed at each end of the wall or partition or as near thereto as possible. The sheathing shall be at least 48 in. (1,200 mm) in width covering three 16 in. (400 mm) stud spaces or two 24 in. (600 mm) stud spaces for diagonal boards or structural-use panel sheets and shall be at least 96 in. (2,400 mm) in width covering six 16-in. (400 mm) stud spaces or four 24 in. (600 mm) stud spaces for all other sheathing. All vertical panel sheathing joints shall occur over studs. Sheathing shall be fastened to all studs and plates. All wall framing to which sheathing used for bracing is applied shall conform to [9.9-2] for 2 (actual 1-1/2 in., 38 mm) by or larger members.

Panel sheathing nailing shall be not less than the minimum given in Table A.9.9.9.1-1B or as prescribed in the footnotes of Table A.9.9.10.1-1B. Nailing for diagonal boards shall be as prescribed in Sections A.9.9.9.1.3 and A.9.9.9.1.4. Adhesives shall not be used to attach wall sheathing.

Cripple stud walls shall be braced as required for braced walls or partitions and shall be considered an additional story. Where interior post and girder framing is used, the capacity of the braced panels at exterior cripple stud walls shall be increased to compensate for length of interior braced wall eliminated by increasing the length of the sheathing or increasing the number of fasteners.

A.9.9.10.2 Wall Framing and Connections: The following wall framing and connection details shall apply as a minimum.

A.9.9.10.2.1 Wall Anchorage: Anchorage for braced wall sills to concrete or masonry foundations conforming to the requirements of Sections 9.6 and 9.8 shall be provided. Anchor bolts 1/2 in. (12 mm) diameter having a minimum embedment of 7 bolt diameters spaced at not over 6 ft (1,800 mm) on center for one- and two-story buildings and at not more than 4 ft (1,200 mm) on center for buildings over two stories in height shall be provided. Other anchorage devices having equivalent capacity are not prohibited.

A.9.9.10.2.2 Top Plates: Stud walls shall be capped with double-top plates installed to provide overlapping at corners and intersections. End joints in double-top plates shall be offset at least 4 ft (1,200 mm). Single top plates shall not be used unless they are spliced by framing devices providing capacity equivalent to the lapped splice prescribed for double top plates.

A.9.9.10.2.3 Bottom Plates: Studs shall have full bearing on a plate or sill conforming to [9.9-2] for 2-by (actual 1-1/2 in., 38 mm) or larger members having a width at least equal to the width of the studs.

A.9.9.10.2.4 Roof and Floor to Braced Wall Connection: Provision shall be made to transfer forces from roofs and floors to braced walls and from the braced walls in upper stories to the braced walls in the story below. Such transfer shall be accomplished with toe nailing using three 8d nails per joist or rafter where these elements are spaced at not over 2 ft (600 mm) on center or by blocking and nailing or by metal framing devices capable of transmitting the equivalent lateral force.

Roof to braced wall connections shall be made at the exterior walls and interior bearing walls, except that for buildings with maximum dimensions not over 50 ft (15 m), the connections at interior bearing walls are not required. Floor to braced wall connections shall be made at every braced wall. The connections shall be distributed along the length of the braced wall. Where all wood foundations are used, the transfer force shall be the same as that applicable for the number of stories indicated above.

TABLE A.9.9.1-1A

Allowable Shear in Pound per Foot (at Working Stress) for Seismic Forces for Horizontal Wood Diaphragms with Framing Members of Douglas Fir, Larch, or Southern Pine[a] for Seismic Loading[a]

Panel Grade	Fastener[b] Type	Minimum penetration in framing (in.)	Minimum nominal panel thickness (in.)	Minimum nominal width of framing (in.)	Lines of fasteners	Blocked Diaphragms — Fastener spacing at diaphragm boundaries (all cases), at continuous panel edges parallel to load (Cases 3 and 4) and at all panel edges (Cases 5 and 6)[d]							Unblocked Diaphragms[c] — Fastener spacing at 6 in. centers at supported edges[e]	
						6	4	2-1/2[e]		2[e]			Case 1	Cases 2, 3, 4, 5, and 6
						Spacing per line at other panel edges (in.)								
						6	6	4	4	3	3	2		
Structural I	6d common	1-1/4	5/16	2	1	185	250	—	375	—	420	—	165	125
	common			3	1	210	280	—	420	—	475	—	185	140
	8d common	1-1/2	3/8	2	1	270	360	—	530	—	600	—	240	180
	common			3	1	300	400	—	600	—	675	—	265	200
	10d common	1-5/8	15/32	2	1	320	425	—	640	—	730	—	285	215
	common			3	1	360	480	—	720	—	820	—	320	240
	10d common	1-5/8	23/32	3	2	—	650	870	940	1,230	—	1,200	—	—
	common			4	2	—	755	980	1,080	1,410	1,040	1,800	—	—
	common			4	3	—	940	1,305	1,375	1,800	1,440	—	—	—
	14 gauge staples	2	23/32	3	2	—	600	600	840	900	—	—	—	—
				4	3	—	840	900	1,140	1,350	—	—	—	—
	6d common	1-1/4	5/16	2	1	170	225	—	335	—	380	—	150	110
	common			3	1	190	250	—	380	—	430	—	170	125
Sheathing, single floor and other grades covered in [9-3] and [9-13]	8d common	1-1/2	3/8	2	1	240	320	—	480	—	545	—	215	160
	common			3	1	270	360	—	540	—	610	—	240	180
			7/16	2	1	255	340	—	575	—	575	—	230	170
				3	1	285	380	—	645	—	645	—	255	190
	10d common	1-5/8	15/32	2	1	290	385	—	575	—	655	—	255	190
	common			3	1	325	430	—	650	—	735	—	290	215
			19/32	2	1	320	425	—	640	—	730	—	285	215
				3	1	360	480	—	720	—	820	—	320	240
			23/32	3	2	—	645	870	935	1,225	1,020	1,200	—	—
				4	2	—	750	980	1,075	1,395	1,400	1,510	—	—
				4	3	—	935	1,305	1,390	1,510	—	—	—	—
	14 gauge staples	2	23/32	3	2	—	600	600	820	900	—	—	—	—
				4	3	—	820	900	1,120	1,350	—	—	—	—

NOTE: For conversion to metric, 1 in. = 25.4 mm and 1 lb = 4.45 N; thus 1 lb/ft = 14.6 N/m.

[a] l/w shall not be more than 4/1 for blocked diaphragms or more than 3/1 for unblocked diaphragms. For framing members of other species set forth in [9-1], Table 12A, with the range of specific gravity (SG) noted, allowable shear values shall be calculated for all grades by multiplying the values for Structural I or panel siding, as appropriate, by the following factors: 0.82 for SG equal to or greater than 0.42 but less than 0.49 (0.42 ≤ SG < 0.49) and 0.65 for SG less than 0.42 (SG < 0.42).

[b] Space nails along intermediate framing members at 12-in. centers except where spans are greater than 32 in.; space nails at 6-in. centers.

[c] Blocked values shall be used for 1-1/8-in. panels with tongue-and-groove edges where 1 in. by 3/8 in. crown by No. 16 gauge staples are driven through the tongue-and-groove edges 3/8 in. from the panel edge so as to penetrate the tongue. Staples shall be spaced at one half the boundary nail spacing for Cases 1 and 2 and at one third the boundary nail spacing for Cases 3 through 6.

[d] Maximum shear for Cases 3 through 6 is limited to 1200 pounds per foot.

[e] For values listed for 2-in. nominal framing member width, the framing members at adjoining panel edges shall be 3-in. nominal width. Nails at panel edges shall be placed in two lines at these locations.

[f] The tabulated values are for short term load and shall not be increased by any factor other than the 2.16 φ given for strength based design in Sec. A.9.9.2.2.

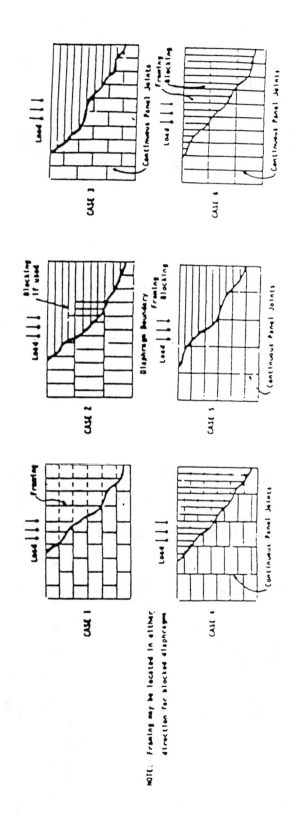

NOTE: Framing may be located in either direction for blocked diaphragm.

121

Table A.9.9.1-1B

Allowable Working Stress Shear in Pounds per Foot (at Working Stress) for Seismic Forces for Structural-Use Panel Shear Walls with Framing of Douglas Fir-Larch or Southern Pine[a]

Panel Grade	Nail Size[b]	Penetration in Framing (in.)	Panel Thickness (in.)	Panel Applied Direct to Framing[c]				Nail Size[b]	Panel Applied Over 1/2-in. Gypsum Sheathing[c]			
				6	4	3[d]	2[d]		6	4	3[d]	2[d]
Structural I	6d	1-1/4	5/16	200	300	390	610	8d	200	300	390	510
	8d	1-1/2	3/8[e]	230	360	460	610	10d	230	360	460	610
	8d	1-1/2	15/32	280	430	550	730	10d	280	430	550	730
	10d	1-5/8	15/32	340	510	665	870	—	—	—	—	—
All other sheathing grades covered in [9-3] and [9-13]	6d	1-1/4	5/16	180	270	350	450	8d	180	270	350	450
	6d	1-1/4	3/8	200	300	390	510	8d	200	300	390	510
	8d	1-1/2	3/8[e]	220	320	410	530	10d	220	320	410	530
	8d	1-1/2	15/32	260	380	490	640	10d	260	380	490	640
	10d	1-5/8	15/32	310	460	600	770	—	—	—	—	—
	10d	1-5/8	15/32	340	510	665	870	—	—	—	—	—
Panel siding in grades covered in [9-3]	6d	1-1/4	5/16	140	210	275	360	8d	140	210	275	360
	8d	1-1/2	3/8[e]	160	240	310	410	10d	160	240	310	410

NOTE: For conversion to metric, 1 in. = 25.4 mm and 1 lb = 4.45 N; thus 1 lb/ft = 14.6 N/m.

[a]h/w ratio shall not be more than 2/1. All panel edges backed with 2-in. nominal or wider framing. Panels installed either horizontally or vertically. Space nails at 6 in. on center along intermediate framing members for 3/8-in. panels installed with face grain parallel to studs spaced 24 in. on center and 12 in. on center for other conditions and panel thicknesses. For framing members of other species set forth in Ref. 9.1, Table 12A, with the range of specific gravity (SG) noted, allowable shear values shall be calculated for all grades using common or galvanized box nails by multiplying the values for Structural I by the following factors: 0.82 for SG equal to or greater than 0.49 ($0.42 \leq SG < 0.49$) and 0.65 for SG less than 0.42 (SG < 0.42). For panel siding using galvanized casing nails, the allowable shear values shall be the values in the table for panel siding multiplied by the same factors.

[b]Nails for values shown for Structural I and all other sheathing grades shall be common nails or galvanized box nails and for values shown for panel siding shall be galvanized casing nails.

[c]Nails spacing at panel edges.

[d]Framing shall be 3-in. nominal or wider and nails shall be staggered where nails are spaced 2 in. on center and where 10d nails having penetration into framing of more than 1-1/5 in. are spaced at 3 in. on center.

[e]the values for 3/8-in. panels applied directly to framing shall be increased 20 percent if the studs are spaced no more than 16 in. on center or if the panel is applied with face grain across studs.

[f]The tabulated values are for short term load and shall not be increased by any factor other than the 2.16 φ given for strength based design in Sec. A.9.9.2.2.

TABLE A.9.9.10.1-1A
Conventional Construction Braced Wall Requirements

Seismic Performance Category	Maximum Distance Between Braced Walls	Maximum Number of Stories Permitted[a]
A[b]	35 ft	3
B	35 ft	3
C	25 ft	2
D	25 ft	1[c]
E	Conventional construction not permitted; conformance with Section 9.8 required.	

NOTE: For conversion to metric, 1 ft = 305 mm.

[a]A cripple wall is considered to be a story; maximum bearing wall height shall not exceed 10 ft.

[b]See exceptions to Section 1.2.

[c]Two stories for detached one- and two-family dwellings.

TABLE A.9.9.10.1-1B
Conventional Construction Braced Wall Requirements in Minimum Length of Wall Bracing per 25 Lineal Feet of Braced Wall Line[a]

Story Location	Sheathing Type[b]	$0.05 \leq C_a < 0.10$	$0.10 \leq C_a < 0.15$	$0.15 \leq C_a < 0.20$	$0.20 \leq C_a < 0.30$	$0.30 \leq C_a^e \leq 0.40$
Top or only story	G-P[d]	8 ft 0 in.	8 ft 0 in.	10 ft 8 in.	14 ft 8 in.	18 ft 8 in.[c]
	S-W	4 ft 0 in.	4 ft 0 in.	5 ft 4 in.	8 ft 0 in.	9 ft 4 in.[c]
Story below top story	G-P[d]	10 ft 8 in.	14 ft 8 in.	18 ft 8 in.[c]	NP	NP
	S-W	5 ft 4 in.	6 ft 8 in.	10 ft 8 in.[c]	13 ft 4 in.[c]	17 ft 4 in.[c]
Bottom story of 3 stories	G-P[d]	14 ft 8 in.	Conventional construction not permitted; conformance with Section 9.8 required.			
	S-W	8 ft 0 in.				

NOTE: For conversion to metric, 1 in. = 25.4 mm and 1 ft = 304.8 mm.

[a]Minimum length of panel bracing of one face of wall for S-W sheathing or both faces of wall for G-P sheathing; h/w ratio shall not exceed 2/1. For S-W panel bracing of the same material on two faces of the wall, the minimum length is one half the tabulated value but the h/w ratio shall not exceed 2/1 and design for uplift is required if the length is less than the tabulated value.

[b]G-P = gypsumboard, particleboard, lath and plaster, or gypsum sheathing boards; S-W structural-use panels and diagonal wood sheathing. NP = not permitted.

[c]Applies to one- and two-family detached dwellings only.

[d]Nailing shall be as follows:

For 1/2-in. gypsum board, 5d (0.113 in. diameter) coolers at 7-in. centers;

For 5/8-in. gypsum board, No. 11 gauge (0.120 in. diameter);

For gypsum sheathing board, 1-3/4-in. long by 7/16-in. head, diamond point galvanized at 4-in. centers;

For gypsum lath, No. 13 gauge (0.092 in.) by 1-1/8-in. long, 19/64 head, plasterboard at 5-in. centers;

For Portland cement plaster, No. 11 gauge by 1-1/2-in. long, 7/16 head at 6-in. centers;

For fiberboard, No. 11 gauge by 1-1/2-in. long, 7/16 head, galvanized at 3-in. centers.

Nailing as specified above shall occur at all panel edges at studs, at top and bottom plates, and, where occurring, at blocking.

[e]Where $C_a > 0.4$, conventional construction is not permitted.

APPENDIX B. SERVICEABILITY CONSIDERATIONS

*B. Serviceability Considerations

This Appendix is not a mandatory part of the standard, but provides guidance for design for serviceability in order to maintain the function of a building and the comfort of its occupants during normal usage. Serviceability limits (e.g., maximum static deformations, accelerations, etc.) shall be chosen with due regard to the intended function of the structure.

Serviceability shall be checked using appropriate loads for the limit state being considered.

B.1 Deflection, Vibration and Drift

*B.1.1 Vertical Deflections. Deformations of floor and roof members and systems due to service loads shall not impair the serviceability of the structure.

*B.1.2 Drift of Walls and Frames. Lateral deflection or drift of structures and deformation of horizontal diaphragms and bracing systems due to wind effects shall not impair the serviceability of the structure.

*B.1.3 Vibrations. Floor systems supporting large open areas free of partitions or other sources of damping, where vibration due to pedestrian traffic might be objectionable, shall be designed with due regard for such vibration.

Mechanical equipment that can produce objectionable vibrations in any portion of an inhabited structure shall be isolated to minimize the transmission of such vibrations to the structure.

Building structural systems shall be designed so that wind-induced vibrations do not cause occupant discomfort or damage to the building, its appurtenances or contents.

*B.2 Design for Long-Term Deflection

Where required for acceptable building performance, members and systems shall be designed to accommodate long-term irreversible deflections under sustained load.

*B.3 Camber

Special camber requirements that are necessary to bring a loaded member into proper relations with the work of other trades shall be set forth in the design documents.

Beams detailed without specified camber shall be positioned during erection so that any minor camber is upward. If camber involves the erection of any member under preload, this shall be noted in the design documents.

*B.4 Expansion and Contraction

Dimensional changes in a structure and its elements due to variations in temperature, relative humidity, or other effects shall not impair the serviceability of the structure.

Provision shall be made either to control crack widths or to limit cracking by providing relief joints.

*B.5 Durability. Buildings and other structures shall be designed to tolerate long-term environmental effects or shall be protected against such effects.

(This Commentary is not a part of American Society of Civil Engineers Standard Design Loads for Buildings and Other Structures. It is included for information purposes.)

Commentary on American Society of Civil Engineers Standard ASCE 7-95

Contents

Commentary to American Society of Civil Engineers Standard ASCE 7-95

This Commentary consists of explanatory and supplementary material designed to assist local building code committees and regulatory authorities in applying the recommended requirements. In some cases it will be necessary to adjust specific values in the standard to local conditions; in others, a considerable amount of detailed information is needed to put the general provisions into effect. This Commentary provides a place for supplying material that can be used in these situations and is intended to create a better understanding of the recommended requirements through brief explanations of the reasoning employed in arriving at them.

The sections of this Commintary are numbered to correspond to the sections of the standard to which they refer. Since it is not necessary to have supplementary material for every section in the standard, there are gaps in the numbering in the Commentary.

1. General

1.1 Scope

The minimum load requirements contained in this standard are derived from research and service performance of buildings and other structures. The user of this standard, however, must exercise judgement when applying the requirements to "other structures." Loads for some structures other than buildings may be found in Sections 3–10 of this standard and additional guidance may be found in the commentary.

Both loads and load combinations are set forth in this document with the intent that they be used together. If one were to use loads from some other source with the load combinations set forth herein or vice versa, the reliability of the resulting design may be affected.

Earthquake loads contained herein are developed for structures that possess certain qualities of ductility and postelastic energy dissipation capability. For this reason, provisions for design, detailing, and construction are provided in Appendix A.

In some cases, these provisions modify or add to provisions contained in design specifications.

1.3 Basic Requirements

1.3.1 Strength. Buildings and other structures must satisfy strength limit states in which members are proportioned to carry the design loads safely to resist buckling, yielding, fracture, etc. It is expected that other standards produced under consensus procedures and intended for use in connection with building code requirements will contain recommendations for resistance factors for strength design methods or allowable stresses (or safety factors) for allowable stress design methods.

1.3.2 Serviceability. In addition to strength limit states, buildings and other structures must also satisfy serviceability limit states which define functional performance and behavior under load and include such items as deflection and vibration. In the United States, strength limit states have traditionally been specified in building codes because they control the safety of the structure. Serviceability limit states, on the other hand, are usually noncatastrophic, define a level of quality of the structure or element and are a matter of judgement as to their application. Serviceability limit states involve the perceptions and expectations of the owner or user and are a contractual matter between the owner or user and the designer and builder. It is for these reasons, and because the benefits themselves are often subjective and difficult to define or quantify, that serviceability limit states for the most part are not included within the three model U.S. Building Codes. The fact that serviceability limit states are usually not codified should not diminish their importance. Exceeding a serviceability limit state in a building or other structure usually means that its function is disrupted or impaired because of local minor damage or deterioration or because of occupant discomfort or annoyance.

1.3.3 Self-Straining Forces. Constrained structures that experience dimensional changes develop self-straining forces. Examples include moments in rigid frames that undergo differential foundation settlements and shears in bearing wall which support concrete slabs that shrink. Unless provisions are made for self-straining forces, stresses in structural elements, either alone or in combination with stresses from external loads, can be high enough to cause structural distress.

In many cases, the magnitude of self-straining forces can be anticipated by analyses of expected shrinkage, temperature fluctuations, foundation movement, etc. However, it is not always practical to calculate the magnitude of self-straining forces. Designers often provide for self-straining forces by specifying relief joints, suitable framing systems, or other details to minimize the effects of self-straining forces.

This section of the standard is not intended to require the designer to provide for self-straining forces that cannot be anticipated during design. An example is settlement resulting from future adjacent excavation.

1.4 General Structural Integrity

Through accident or misuse, properly designed structures may be subject to conditions that could lead to either general or local collapse. Except for specially designed protective systems, it is impractical for a structure to be designed to resist general collapse caused by gross misuse of a large part of the system or severe abnormal loads acting directly on a large portion of it. However, precautions can be taken in the design of structures to limit the effects of local collapse, that is, to prevent progressive collapse, which is the spread of an initial local failure from element to element resulting, eventually, in the collapse of an entire structure or a disproportionately large part of it.

Since accidents and misuse are normally unforeseeable events, they cannot be defined precisely. Likewise, general structural integrity is a quality that cannot be stated in simple terms. It is the purpose of 1.4 and this commentary to direct attention to the problem of local collapse, present guidelines for handling it that will aid the design engineer, and promote consistency of treatment in all types of structures and in all construction materials.

Accidents, Misuse, and Their Consequences. In addition to unintentional or willful misuse, some

---

[1]Numbers in brackets refer to references listed at the ends of the major sections in which they appear (that is, at the end of Section 1, Section 2, and so forth).

of the incidents that may cause local collapse are [1][1]: explosions due to ignition of gas or industrial liquids; boiler failures; vehicle impact; impact of falling objects; effects of adjacent excavations; gross construction errors; and very high winds such as tornadoes. Generally, such abnormal events would not be ordinary design considerations.

The distinction between general collapse and limited local collapse can best be made by example.

The immediate demolition of an entire structure by a high-energy bomb is an obvious instance of general collapse. Also, the failure of one column in a one-, two-, three-, or possibly even four-column structure could precipitate general collapse, because the local failed column is a significant part of the total structure at that level. Similarly, the failure of a major bearing element in the bottom story of a two- or three-story structure might cause general collapse of the whole structure. Such collapses are beyond the scope of the provisions discussed herein. There have been numerous instances of general collapse that have occurred as the result of such abnormal events as wartime bombing, landslides, and floods.

An example of limited local collapse would be the containment of damage to adjacent bays and stories following the destruction of one or two neighboring columns in a multibay structure. The restriction of damage to portions of two or three stories of a higher structure following the failure of a section of bearing wall in one story is another example. A prominent case of local collapse that progressed to a disproportionate part of the whole building (and is thus an example of the type of failure of concern here) was the Ronan Point disaster. Ronan Point was a 22-story apartment building of large, precast-concrete, loadbearing panels in Canning Town, England. In March 1968, a gas explosion in an 18th-story apartment blew out a living room wall. The loss of the wall led to the collapse of the whole corner of the building. The apartments above the 18th story, suddenly losing support from below and being insufficiently tied and reinforced, collapsed one after the other. The falling debris ruptured successive floors and walls below the 18th story, and the failure progressed to the ground. Another example is the failure of a one-story parking garage reported in [2]. Collapse of one transverse frame under a concentration of snow led to the later progressive collapse of the whole roof, which was supported by 20 transverse frames of the same type. Similar progressive collapses are mentioned in [3].

There are a number of factors that contribute to the risk of damage propagation in modern structures [4]. Among them are:

1. There can be a lack of awareness that structural integrity against collapse is important enough to be regularly considered in design.
2. In order to have more flexibility in floor plans and to keep costs down, interior walls and partitions are often nonload bearing and hence may be unable to assist in containing damage.
3. In attempting to achieve economy in structures through greater speed of erection and less site labor, systems may be built with minimum continuity, ties between elements, and joint rigidity.
4. Unreinforced or lightly reinforced load-bearing walls in multistory structures may also have inadequate continuity, ties, and joint rigidity.
5. In roof trusses and arches there may not be sufficient strength to carry the extra loads or sufficient diaphragm action to maintain lateral stability of the adjacent members if one collapses.
6. In eliminating excessively large safety factors, code changes over the past several decades have reduced the large margin of safety inherent in many older structures. The use of higher strength materials permitting more slender sections compounds the problem in that modern structures may be more flexible and sensitive to load variations and, in addition, may be more sensitive to construction errors.

Experience has demonstrated that the principle of taking precautions in design to limit the effects of local collapse is realistic and can be satisfied economically. From a public-safety viewpoint it is reasonable to expect all multistory structures to possess general structural integrity comparable to that of properly designed, conventional framed structures [4],[5].

Design Alternatives. There are a number of ways to obtain resistance to progressive collapse. In [6], a distinction is made between direct and indirect design, and the following approaches are defined:

Direct design: explicit consideration of resistance to progressive collapse during the design process through either:

alternate path method: a method that allows local failure to occur but seeks to provide alternate load paths so that the damage is absorbed and major collapse is averted, or

specific local resistance method: a method that seeks to provide sufficient strength to resist failure from accidents or misuse.

Indirect design: implicit consideration of resistance to progressive collapse during the design process through the provision of minimum levels of strength, continuity, and ductility.

The general structural integrity of a structure may be tested by analysis to ascertain whether alternate paths around hypothetically collapsed regions exist. Alternatively, alternate path studies may be used as guides for developing rules for the minimum levels of continuity and ductility needed in applying the indirect design approach to ensuring general structural integrity. Specific local resistance may be provided in regions of high risk, since it may be necessary for some elements to have sufficient strength to resist abnormal loads in order for the structure as a whole to develop alternate paths. Specific suggestions for the implementation of each of the defined methods are contained in [6].

Guidelines for the Provision of General Structural Integrity. Generally, connections between structural components should be ductile and have a capacity for relatively large deformations and energy absorption under the effect of abnormal conditions. This criterion is met in many different ways, depending on the structural system used. Details that are appropriate for resistance to moderate wind loads and seismic loads often provide sufficient ductility.

Work with large precast panel structures [7]–[9] provides an example of how to cope with the problem of general structural integrity in a building system that is inherently discontinuous. The provision of ties combined with careful detailing of connections can overcome difficulties associated with such a system. The same kind of methodology and design philosophy can be applied to other systems [10]. The ACI Building Code Requirements for Reinforced Concrete [11] includes such requirements in Section 7.13.

There are a number of ways of designing for the required integrity to carry loads around severely damaged walls, trusses, beams, columns, and floors. A few examples of design concepts and details relating particularly, but not solely, to precast and bearing-wall structures are:

1. Good Plan Layout—An important factor in achieving integrity is the proper plan layout of walls (and columns). In bearing-wall structures there should be an arrangement of interior longitudinal walls to support and reduce the span of long sections of crosswall, thus enhancing the stability of individual walls and of the structures as a whole. In the case of local failure this will also decrease the length of wall likely to be affected.

2. Returns on Walls—Returns on interior and exterior walls will make them more stable.

3. Changing Directions of Span of Floor Slab—Where a floor slab is reinforced in order that it can, with a low safety factor, span in another direction if a load-bearing wall is removed, the collapse of the slab will be prevented and the debris loading of other parts of the structure will be minimized. Often, shrinkage and temperature steel will be enough to enable the slab to span in a new direction.

4. Load-Bearing Interior Partitions—The interior walls must be capable of carrying enough load to achieve the change of span direction in the floor slabs.

5. Catenary Action of Floor Slab—Where the slab cannot change span direction, the span will increase if an intermediate supporting wall is removed. In this case, if there is enough reinforcement throughout the slab and enough continuity and restraint, the slab may be capable of carrying the loads by catenary action, though very large deflections will result.

6. Beam Action of Walls—Walls may be assumed to be capable of spanning an opening if sufficient tying steel at the top and bottom of the walls allows them to act as the web of a beam with the slabs above and below acting as flanges (see [7]).

1.5 Classification of Buildings and Other Structures

The categories in Table 1-1 are used to relate the criteria for maximum environmental loads or distortions specified in this standard to the consequence of the loads being exceeded for the structure and its occupants. It should be noted that the category numbering has changed from that in previous revisions of the standard. Classification now reflects a progression of consequence of failure from lowest hazard to human life (Category I) to highest (Category IV).

In Sections 6 and 7, importance factors are presented for the four categories identified. The specific importance factors differ according to the statistical characteristics of the environmental loads and the manner in which the structure responds to the loads. The principle of requiring more stringent loading criteria for situations in which the consequence of failure may be severe has been recognized in previous versions of this standard by the specification of mean recurrence interval maps for wind speed and ground snow load. Table 1-1 makes the classification of buildings and other structures according to failure consequences reasonably consistent for all environmental loads.

The occupancy classifications given in Table 1-1 result from an attempt to reconcile the classifications in the previous edition of the standard (ASCE 7-93) and the Seismic Hazard Exposure Group classifications from the NEHRP Provisions upon which the seismic provisions in this standard are based [12]. The intent was to have only one occupancy classification system which would be independent of load.

Category I contains buildings and other structures that represent a low hazard to human life in the event of failure either because they have a small number of occupants or have a limited period of exposure to extreme environmental loadings. Category II contains all occupancies other than those in Categories I, III and IV and are sometimes referred to as "ordinary" for the purpose of risk exposure. Category III contains those buildings and other structures that have large numbers of occupants, are designated for public assembly or for which the occupants are restrained or otherwise restricted from movement or evacuation. Buildings and other structures in Category III therefore represent a substantial hazard to human life in the event of failure. Category IV contains buildings and other structures that are designated as essential facilities and are intended to remain operational in the event of extreme environmental loadings. Such occupancies include hospitals, fire, rescue and other emergency response facilities.

1.7 Load Tests

No specific method of test for completed construction has been given in this standard, since it may be found advisable to vary the procedure according to conditions. Some codes require the construction to sustain a superimposed load equal to a stated multiple of the design load without evidence of serious damage. Others specify that the superimposed load shall be equal to a stated multiple of the live load plus a portion of the dead load. Limits are set on maximum deflection under load and after removal of the load. Recovery of at least three-quarters of the maximum deflection, within 24 hours after the load is removed, is a common requirement [11].

References

[1] Leyendecker, E.V., Breen, J.E., Somes, N.F., and Swatta, M. Abnormal loading on buildings and progressive collapse—An annotated bibliography. Washington, D.C.: U.S. Dept. of Commerce, National Bureau of Standards. NBS BSS 67, Jan. 1976.

[2] Granstrom, S., and Carlsson, M. Byggfurskningen T3: Byggnaders beteende vid overpaverkningar [The behavior of buildings at excessive loadings]. Stockholm, Sweden: Swedish Institute of Building Research. 1974.

[3] Seltz-Petrash, A. Winter roof collapses: Bad luck, bad construction, or bad design. *Civil Engineering*, Dec. 1979, 42–45.

[4] Breen, J.E., Ed. Progressive collapse of building structures [summary report of a workshop held at the Univ. of Texas at Austin, Oct. 1975]. Washington, D.C.: U.S. Dept. of Housing and Urban Development. Rep. PDR-182, Sept. 1976.

[5] Burnett, E.F.P. The avoidance of progressive collapse: Regulatory approaches to the problem. Washington, D.C.: U.S. Dept. of Commerce, National Bureau of Standards. NBS GCR 75-48, Oct. 1975. [Available from: National Technical Information Service, Springfield, Va.]

[6] Leyendecker, E.V., and Ellingwood, B.R. Design methods for reducing the risk of progressive collapse in buildings. Washington, D.C.: U.S. Dept. of Commerce, National Bureau of Standards. NBS BSS 98, 1977.

[7] Schultz, D.M., Burnett, E.F.P., and Fintel, M. A design approach to general structural integrity, design and construction of large-panel concrete structures. Washington, D.C.: U.S. Dept. of Housing and Urban Development. 1977.

[8] PCI Committee on Precast Bearing Walls. Considerations for the design of precast bearing-wall buildings to withstand abnormal loads. *J. Prestressed Concrete Institute*, 21(2), 46–69, March/April 1976.

[9] Fintel, M., and Schultz, D.M. Structural integrity of large-panel buildings. *J. Am. Concrete Inst.*, 76(5), 583–622, May 1979.

[10] Fintel, M., and Annamalai, G. Philosophy of structural integrity of multistory load-bearing concrete masonry structures. *Concrete Int.*, 1(5), 27–35, May 1979.

[11] Building Code Requirements for Reinforced Concrete, ACI Standard 318-89, American Concrete Institute, Detroit, Mich., 1989.

[12] NEHRP Recommended Provisions for the Development of Seismic Regulations for New Buildings, 1991 Ed., Part 1 Provisions, Building Seismic Safety Council, Washington, D.C., 1991.

2. Combinations of Loads

Loads in this standard are intended for use with design specifications for conventional structural materials, including steel, concrete, masonry, and timber. Some of these specifications are based on allowable stress design, while others employ strength design. In the case of allowable stress design, design specifications define allowable stresses that may not be exceeded by load effects due to unfactored loads, that is, allowable stresses contain a factor of safety. In strength design, design specifications provide load factors and, in some instances, resistance factors. Structural design specifications based on limit states design have been adopted by a number of specification-writing groups. Therefore, it is desirable to include herein common load factors that are applicable to these new specifications. It is intended that these load factors be used by all material-based design specifications that adopt a strength design philosophy in conjunction with nominal resistances and resistance factors developed by individual material-specification-writing groups. Load factors given herein were developed using a first-order probabilistic analysis and a broad survey of the reliabilities inherent in contemporary design practice. References [9],[10],[13] also provide guidelines for materials-specification-writing groups to aid them in developing resistance factors that are compatible, in terms of inherent reliability, with load factors and statistical information specific to each structural material.

2.3 Combining Loads Using Strength Design

2.3.1 Applicability. Load factors and load combinations given in this section apply to limit states or strength design criteria (referred to as "Load and Resistance Factor Design" by the steel and wood industries) and they should not be used with allowable stress design specifications.

2.3.2 Basic Combinations. Unfactored loads to be used with these load factors are the nominal loads of Sections 3–9 of this standard. Load factors are from NBS SP 577 with the exception of the factor 1.0 for E, which is based on the more recent NEHRP research on seismic-resistant design [15]. The basic idea of the load combination scheme is that in addition to dead load, which is considered to be permanent, one of the variable loads takes on its maximum lifetime value while the other variable loads assume "arbitrary point-in-time" values, the latter being loads that would be measured at any instant of time [17]. This is consistent with the manner in which loads actually combine in situations in which strength limit states may be approached. However, nominal loads in Sections 3–9 are substantially in excess of the arbitrary point-in-time values. To avoid having to specify both a maximum and an arbitrary point-in-time value for each load type, some of the specified load factors are less than unity in combinations 2–6.

Load factors in 2.3.2 are based on a survey of reliabilities inherent in existing design practice. Standards governing design of most ordinary buildings permit a one-third increase in allowable stress or a 25% reduction in total factored load effect for load combinations involving wind. These adjustments are reflected in the load factor of 1.3 on wind load in combinations 4 and 6. However, standards governing design of certain nonredundant structures, such as chimneys, and stacks, do not permit such adjustments in allowable stress or total factored load effect. The load factor on wind load in combinations 4 and 6, to be consistent with the latter standards, should be 1.5. Load combination 6 applies specifically to the case in which the structural actions due to lateral forces and gravity loads counteract one another.

Load factors given herein relate only to strength limit states. Serviceability limit states and associated load factors are covered in Appendix B of this standard.

This standard historically has provided specific procedures for determining magnitudes of dead, occupancy live, wind, snow, and earthquake loads. Other loads not traditionally considered by this standard may also require consideration in design. Some of these loads may be important in certain material specifications and are included in the load criteria to enable uniformity to be achieved in the load criteria for different materials. However, statistical data on these loads are limited or nonexistent, and the same procedures used to obtain load factors and load combinations in 2.3.2 cannot be applied at the present time. Accordingly, load factors for fluid load (F), lateral pressure due to soil and water in soil (H), flood load (F_a), and self-straining forces and effects (T) have been chosen to yield designs that would be similar to those obtained with existing specifications, if appropriate adjustments consistent with the load combinations in 2.3.2 were made to the resistance factors. Further research is needed to develop more accurate load factors because the load factors selected for H and F, are probably conservative.

2.4 Combining Loads Using Allowable Stress Design

2.4.1 Basic Combinations. The load combinations listed cover those loads for which specific values are given in other parts of this standard. However, these combinations are not all-inclusive, and designers will need to exercise judgement in some situations. Design should be based on the load combination causing the most unfavorable effect. In some cases this may occur when one or more loads are not acting. No safety factors have been applied to these loads, since such factors depend on the design philosophy adopted by the particular material specification.

Wind and earthquake loads need not be assumed to act simultaneously. However, the most unfavorable effects of each should be considered separately in design, where appropriate. In some instances, forces due to wind might exceed those due to earthquake, while ductility requirements might be determined by earthquake loads.

2.4.3 Load Reduction. Most loads, other than dead loads, vary significantly with time. When these variable loads are combined with dead loads, their combined effect should be sufficient to reduce the risk of unsatisfactory performance to an acceptably low level. However, when more than one variable load is considered, it is extremely unlikely that they will all attain their maximum value at the same time. Accordingly, some reduction in the total of the combined load effects is appropriate. This reduction is accomplished through the 0.75 load combination factor.

The warning "allowable stresses should not be increased to account for these combinations," indicates that some justifications for one-third increases in allowable stresses in some material design standards have been tied to this same concept. Where that is the case, simultaneous use of both the one-third increase in allowable stress and the 25% reduction in combined loads obviously would be unsafe. This is not to be confused with allowable stress increases that are based upon duration of load or loading rate effects, which are independent concepts and could be combined with the reduction factor for combining multiple transient loads.

Stress increases for load duration or load rate effects legitimately apply to the total stress; that is, the stress resulting from the combination of all loads. Load combination reduction factors for combined transient loads are different in that they apply only to the transient loads, and they do not affect the permanent loads nor the stresses caused by permanent loads. This explains the change from the 1993 edition, in which the 0.75 factor applied to the sum of all loads, to this edition, in which the 0.75 factor applies only to the sum of the transient loads, not the dead load.

Certain material design standards permit a one-third increase in allowable stress for load combinations with one transient load where that transient is wind or earthquake load. This standard handles allowable stress design for earthquake loads in a fashion to give results comparable to the strength design basis for earthquake loads as explained in the commentary of Section 9 titled "Use of Allowable Stress Design Standards." The case of wind and dead should be carefully investigated by the user. Where the basis for the stress increase in material design standards is rooted in a concept of load occurrence rather than in material system or system behavior, it may be advisable to forego use of the stress increase, unless shown to give results comparable to the strength design basis.

2.5 Load Combinations for Extraordinary Events

ASCE Standard 7 Commentary 1.4 recommends approaches to providing general structural integrity in building design and construction. Commentary 2.5 explains the basis for the load combinations that the designer should use if the Direct Design alternative in Commentary 1.4 is selected. If the authority having jurisdiction requires the Indirect Design alternative, that authority may use these load requirements as one basis for determining minimum required levels of strength, continuity and ductility. Generally, extraordinary events with a probability of occurrence in the range of 10^{-6}–10^{-4}/yr or greater should be identified, and measures should be taken to ensure that the performance of key load-bearing structural systems and components is sufficient to withstand such events.

Extraordinary events arise from extraordinary service or environmental conditions that traditionally are not considered explicitly in design of ordinary buildings and structures. Such events are characterized by a low probability of occurrence and usually a short duration. Few buildings are ever exposed to such events and statistical data to describe their magnitude and structural effects are rarely available. Included in the category of extraordinary events would be fire, explosions of volatile liquids or natural gas in building service systems, sabotage, vehicular impact, misuse by building occupants, subsidence (not settlement) of subsoil, and tornadoes. The occurrence of any of these events is likely to lead to structural damage or failure. If the structure is not properly designed and detailed, this local failure may initiate a chain reaction of failures that propagates throughout a major portion of the structure and leads to a potentially catastrophic collapse. Approximately 15–20% of building collapses occur in this way [1]. Although all buildings are susceptible to progressive failures in varying degrees, types of construction that lack inherent continuity and ductility are particularly vulnerable [2],[16].

Good design practice requires that structures be robust and that their safety and performance not be sensitive to uncertainties in loads, environmental influences and other situations not explicitly considered in design. The structural system should be designed in such a way that if an extraordinary event occurs, the probability of damage disproportionate to the original event is sufficiently small [7]. The philosophy of designing to limit the spread of damage rather than to prevent damage entirely is different from the traditional approach to designing to withstand dead, live, snow and wind loads, but is similar to the philosophy adopted in modern earthquake-resistant design [15].

In general, structural systems should be designed with sufficient continuity and ductility that alternate load paths can develop following individual member failure so that failure of the structure as a whole does not ensue. At a simple level, continuity can be achieved by requiring development of a minimum tie force—say 20 kN/m—between structural elements [3]. Member failures may be controlled by protective measures that ensure that no essential load-bearing member is made ineffective as a result of an accident, although this approach may be more difficult to implement. Where member failure would inevitably result in a disproportionate collapse, the member should be designed for a higher degree of reliability [14]. In either approach, an enhanced quality assurance and maintenance program may be required.

Design limit states include loss of equilibrium as a rigid body, large deformations leading to significant second-order effects, yielding or rupture of members of connections, formation of a mechanism, instability of members or the structure as a whole. These limit states are the same as those considered for other load events, but the load-resisting mechanisms in a damaged structure may be different and sources of load-carrying capacity that normally would not be considered in ordinary ultimate limit states design, such as a membrane or catenary action, may be included. The use of elastic analysis vastly underestimates the load-carrying capacity of the structure. Materially or geometrically nonlinear or plastic analyses may be used, depending on the response of the structure to the actions.

Specific design provisions to control the effect of extraordinary loads and risk of progressive failure can be developed with a probabilistic basis [8],[11]. One can either attempt to reduce the likelihood of the extraordinary event or design the structure to withstand or absorb damage from the event if it occurs. Let F be the event of failure and A be the event that a structurally damaging event occurs. The probability of failure due to event A is,

$$P_f = P(F \mid A)\, P(A) \qquad (C2.5.1)$$

in which $P(F|A)$ = the conditional probability of failure of a damaged structure; and $P(A)$ = the probability of occurrence of event A. The separation of $P(F|A)$ and $P(A)$ allows one to focus on strategies for reducing risk. $P(A)$ depends on siting, controlling the use of hazardous substances, limiting access, and other actions that are essentially independent of structural design. In contrast, $P(F|A)$ depends on structural design measures ranging from minimum provisions for continuity to a complete postdamage structural evaluation.

The probability, $P(A)$, depends on the specific hazard. Limited data for severe fires, gas explosions, bomb explosions and vehicular collisions indicate that the event probability depends on building size, measured in dwelling units or square footage, and ranges from about 0.23×10^{-6} per dwelling unit per year to about 7.8×10^{-6} per dwelling unit per year [6],[8]. Thus, the probability that a building structure is affected depends on the number of dwelling units (or square footage) in the building. If one were to set the conditional limit state probability, $P(F|A) = 0.1 - 0.2/\text{yr}$, however, the annual probability of structural failure from Eq. (C2.5.1) would be on the order of 10^{-7} to 10^{-6}, placing the risk in the low-magnitude background along with risks from rare accidents [18].

Design requirements corresponding to this desired $P(F|A) = 0.1 - 0.2$ can be developed using first-order reliability analysis if the limit state function describing structural behavior is available [10],[13]. As an alternative, one can leave material and structural behavior considerations to the responsible material specifications and consider only the load combination aspect of the safety check, which is more straightforward.

For checking a structure to determine its residual load-carrying capacity following occurrence of a damaging extraordinary event, selected load-bearing elements should be notionally removed and the capacity of the remaining structure evaluated using the following load combination:

$$(0.9 \text{ or } 1.2)\, D + (0.5L \text{ or } 0.2S) + 0.2W \quad (C2.5.2)$$

For checking the capacity of a structure or structural element to withstand the effect of an extraordinary event, the following load combinations should be used:

$$1.2\, D + A_k + (0.5L \text{ or } 0.2S) \qquad (C2.5.3)$$

$$(0.9 \text{ or } 1.2)\, D + A_k + 0.2W \qquad (C2.5.4)$$

The value of the load or load effect resulting from extraordinary event A used in design is denoted A_k. Only limited data are available to define the frequency distribution of the load, and A_k must be specified by the authority having jurisdiction [4]. The uncertainty in the load due to the extraordinary event is encompassed in the selection of a conservative A_k and thus the load factor on A_k is set equal to 1.0, as is done in the earthquake load combinations in Section 2.3. Load factors less than 1.0 on the companion actions reflect the small probability of a joint occurrence of the extraordinary load and the design live, snow, or wind load. The companion action $0.5L$ corresponds, approximately, to the mean of the yearly maximum load [5]. Companion actions $0.2S$ and $0.2W$ are interpreted similarly. A similar set of load combinations for extraordinary events appears in [12].

References

[1] Allen, D.E. and Schriever, W. Progressive collapse, abnormal loads and building codes. *Structural Failures: Modes, Causes, Responsibilities*, ASCE, 21–48, 1973.

[2] Breen, J.E. and Siess, C.P. Progressive collapse—symposium summary, *ACI Journal*, 76(9):997–1004, 1979.

[3] British standard structural use of steelwork in building (BS 5950: Part 8), British Standards Institution, London, U.K., 1990.

[4] Burnett, E.F.P. "The avoidance of progressive collapse: regulatory approaches to the problem." National Bureau of Standards Report GCR 75-48, Washington, DC., 1975. (Available from NTIS, Springfield, VA.)

[5] Chalk, P.L. and Corotis, R.B. Probability models for design live loads. *J. Str. Div.*, ASCE 106(10):2017–2033, 1980.

[6] CIB W14. A conceptual approach towards a probability based design guide on structural fire safety. *Fire Safety Journal* 6(1):1–79, 1983.

[7] Commentary C Structural Integrity. National Building Code of Canada, National Research Council of Canada, Ottawa, Ontario, 1990.

[8] Ellingwood, B., and Leyendecker, E.V. Approaches for design against progressive collapse, *J. Str. Div.*, ASCE, 104(3):413–423, 1978.

[9] Ellingwood, B., Galambos, T.V., MacGregor, J.G., and Cornell, C.A. Development of a probability-based load criterion for American National Standard A58, Washington, D.C.: U.S. Dept. of Commerce, National Bureau of Standards, NBS SP 577, 1980.

[10] Ellingwood, B., Galambos, T.V., MacGregor, J.G., and Cornell, C.A. Probability-based load criteria: Load factors and load combinations, *J. Str. Div.*, ASCE, 108(5):978–997, 1982.

[11] Ellingwood, B., and Corotis, R.B. Load combinations for buildings exposed to fires, *Eng. J.*, ASIC, 28(1):37–44, 1991.

[12] Eurocode No. 1. "Common unified rules for different types of construction and material." Commission of the European Communities, Brussels, 1990.

[13] Galambos, T.V., Ellingwood, B., MacGregor, J.G., and Cornell, C.A. Probability-based load criteria: assessment of current design practice, *J. Str. Div.*, ASCE, 108(5):959–977, 1982.

[14] NKB. Guidelines for loading and safety regulations for structural design (1987), NKB (Nordic Committee on Building Regulations) Report No. 55E, Copenhagen, Denmark, 1987.

[15] NEHRP recommended provisions for the development of seismic regulations for buildings (1992), FEMA Report 222, Federal Emergency Management Agency, Washington, DC, 1992.

[16] Taylor, D.A. Progressive collapse, *Canadian J. Civ. Engrg.*, 2(4):517–529, 1975.

[17] Turkstra, C.J. and Madsen, H. Load combinations for codified structural design, *J. Str. Div.*, ASCE, 106(12):2527–2543, 1980.

[18] Wilson, R., and Crouch, E.A. Risk assessment and comparisons: An introduction, *Science* 236:267–270.1, 1987.

3. Dead Loads

3.2 Weights of Materials and Constructions

To establish uniform practice among designers, it is desirable to present a list of materials generally used in building construction, together with their proper weights. Many building codes prescribe the minimum weights for only a few building materials, and in other instances no guide whatsoever is furnished on this subject. In some cases the codes are so drawn up as to leave the question of what weights to use to the discretion of the building official, without providing any authoritative guide. This practice, as well as the use of incomplete lists, has been subjected to much criticism. The solution chosen has been to present, in this commentary, an extended list that will be useful to designer and official alike. However, special cases will unavoidably arise, and authority is there-

TABLE C3-1a
Minimum Design Dead Loads*

Component	Load (psf)
CEILINGS	
Acoustical Fiber Board	1
Gypsum board (per 1/8-in. thickness)	0.55
Mechanical duct allowance	4
Plaster on tile or concrete	5
Plaster on wood lath	8
Suspended steel channel system	2
Suspended metal lath and cement plaster	15
Suspended metal lath and gypsum plaster	10
Wood furring suspension system	2.5
COVERINGS, ROOF, AND WALL	
Asbestos-cement shingles	4
Asphalt shingles	2
Cement tile	16
Clay tile (for mortar add 10 lb):	
Book tile, 2-in.	12
Book tile, 3-in.	20
Ludowici	10
Roman	12
Spanish	19
Composition:	
Three-ply ready roofing	1
Four-ply felt and gravel	5.5
Five-ply felt and gravel	6
Copper or tin	1
Corrugated asbestos-cement roofing	4
Deck, metal, 20 gage	2.5
Deck, metal, 18 gage	3
Decking, 2-in. wood (Douglas fir)	5
Decking, 3-in. wood (Douglas fir)	8
Fiberboard, 1/2-in.	0.75
Gypsum sheathing, 1/2-in	2
Insulation, roof boards (per inch thickness)	
Cellular glass	0.7
Fibrous glass	1.1
Fiberboard	1.5
Perlite	0.8
Polystyrene foam	0.2
Urethane foam with skin	0.5
Plywood (per 1/8-in. thickness)	0.4
Rigid insulation, 1/2-in.	0.75
Skylight, metal frame, 3/8-in. wire glass	8
Slate, 3/16-in.	7
Slate, 1/4-in.	10
Waterproofing membranes:	
Bituminous, gravel-covered	5.5
Bituminous, smooth surface	1.5
Liquid applied	1
Single-ply, sheet	0.7
Wood sheathing (per inch thickness)	3
Wood shingles	3

Component	Load (psf)
FLOOR FILL	
Cinder concrete, per inch	9
Lightweight concrete, per inch	8
Sand, per inch	8
Stone concrete, per inch	12
FLOORS AND FLOOR FINISHES	
Asphalt block (2-in.), 1/2-in. mortar	30
Cement finish (1-in.) on stone-concrete fill	32
Ceramic or quarry tile (3/4-in.) on 1/2-in. mortar bed	16
Ceramic or quarry tile (3/4-in.) on 1-in. mortar bed	23
Concrete fill finish (per inch thickness)	12
Hardwood flooring, 7/8-in.	4
Linoleum or asphalt tile, 1/4-in.	1
Marble and mortar on stone-concrete fill	33
Slate (per inch thickness)	15
Solid flat tile on 1-in. mortar base	23
Subflooring, 3/4-in.	3
Terrazzo (1-1/2-in.) directly on slab	19
Terrazzo (1-in.) on stone-concrete fill	32
Terrazzo (1-in.), 2-in. stone concrete	32
Wood block (3-in.) on mastic, no fill	10
Wood block (3-in.) on 1/2-in. mortar base	16
FLOORS, WOOD-JOIST (NO PLASTER)	
DOUBLE WOOD FLOOR	

Joist sizes (inches):	12-in. spacing (lb/ft²)	16-in. spacing (lb/ft²)	24-in. spacing (lb/ft²)
2 × 6	6	5	5
2 × 8	6	5	5
2 × 10	7	6	6
2 × 12	8	7	6

Component	Load (psf)
FRAME PARTITIONS	
Movable steel partitions	4
Wood or steel studs, 1/2-in. gypsum board each side	8
Wood studs, 2 × 4, unplastered	4
Wood studs, 2 × 4, plastered one side	12
Wood studs, 2 × 4, plastered two sides	20
FRAME WALLS	
Exterior stud walls:	
2 × 4 @ 16-in., 5/8-in. gypsum, insulated, 3/8-in. siding	11
2 × 6 @ 16-in., 5/8-in. gypsum, insulated, 3/8-in. siding	12
Exterior stud walls with brick veneer	48
Windows, glass, frame and sash	8

Clay brick wythes:

Component	Load (psf)
4 in.	39
8 in.	79
12 in.	115
16 in.	155

Hollow concrete masonry unit wythes:

Wythe thickness (in inches)	4	6	8	10	12
Density of unit (105 pcf):					
No grout	22	24	31	37	43
48" o.c.		29	38	47	55
40" o.c. grout		30	40	49	57
32" o.c. spacing		32	42	52	61
24" o.c.		34	46	57	67
16" o.c.		40	53	66	79
Full Grout		55	75	95	115
Density of unit (125 pcf):					
No grout	26	28	36	44	50
48" o.c.		33	44	54	62
40" o.c. grout		34	45	56	65
32" o.c. spacing		36	47	58	68
24" o.c.		39	51	63	75
16" o.c.		44	59	73	87
Full Grout		59	81	102	123
Density of unit (135 pcf):					
No grout	29	30	39	47	54
48" o.c.		36	47	57	66
40" o.c. grout		37	48	59	69
32" o.c. spacing		38	50	62	72
24" o.c.		41	54	67	78
16" o.c.		46	61	76	90
Full Grout		62	83	105	127

Solid concrete masonry unit wythes

Wythe thickness (in inches)	4	6	8	10	12
Density of unit (105 pcf):	32	51	69	87	105
Density of unit (125 pcf):	38	60	81	102	124
Density of unit (135 pcf):	41	64	87	110	133

*Weights of masonry include mortar but not plaster. For plaster, add 5 lb/ft² for each face plastered. Values given represent averages. In some cases there is a considerable range of weight for the same construction.

TABLE C3-1b
Minimum Design Dead Loads*

Component	Load (kN/m²)
CEILINGS	
Acoustical Fiber Board	0.05
Gypsum board (per mm thickness)	0.008
Mechanical duct allowance	0.19
Plaster on tile or concrete	0.24
Plaster on wood lath	0.38
Suspended steel channel system	0.10
Suspended metal lath and cement plaster	0.72
Suspended metal lath and gypsum plaster	0.48
Wood furring suspension system	0.12
COVERINGS, ROOF, AND WALL	
Asbestos-cement shingles	0.19
Asphalt shingles	0.10
Cement tile	0.77
Clay tile (for mortar add 0.48 kN/m2)	
Book tile, 51 mm	0.57
Book tile, 76 mm	0.96
Ludowici	0.48
Roman	0.57
Spanish	0.91
Composition:	
Three-ply ready roofing	0.05
Four-ply felt and gravel	0.26
Five-ply felt and gravel	0.29
Copper or tin	0.05
Corrugated asbestos-cement roofing	0.19
Deck, metal, 20 gage	0.12
Deck, metal, 18 gage	0.14
Decking, 51 mm wood (Douglas fir)	0.24
Decking, 76 mm wood (Douglas fir)	0.38
Fiberboard, 13 mm	0.04
Gypsum sheathing, 13 mm	0.10
Insulation, roof boards (per mm thickness)	
Cellular glass	0.0013
Fibrous glass	0.0021
Fiberboard	0.0028
Perlite	0.0015
Polystyrene foam	0.0004
Urethane foam with skin	0.0009
Plywood (per mm thickness)	0.006
Rigid insulation, 13 mm	0.04
Skylight, metal frame, 10 mm wire glass	0.38
Slate, 5 mm	0.34
Slate, 6 mm	0.48
Waterproofing membranes:	
Bituminous, gravel-covered	0.26
Bituminous, smooth surface	0.07
Liquid applied	0.05
Single-ply, sheet	0.03
Wood sheathing (per mm thickness)	0.0057
Wood shingles	0.14

Component	Load (kN/m²)
FLOOR FILL	
Cinder concrete, per mm	0.017
Lightweight concrete, per mm	0.015
Sand, per mm	0.015
Stone concrete, per mm	0.023
FLOORS AND FLOOR FINISHES	
Asphalt block (51 mm), 13 mm mortar	1.44
Cement finish (25 mm) on stone-concrete fill	1.53
Ceramic or quarry tile (19 mm) on 13 mm mortar bed	0.77
Ceramic or quarry tile (19 mm) on 25 mm mortar bed	1.10
Concrete fill finish (per mm thickness)	0.023
Hardwood flooring, 22 mm	0.19
Linoleum or asphalt tile, 6 mm	0.05
Marble and mortar on stone-concrete fill	1.58
Slate (per mm thickness)	0.028
Solid flat tile on 25 mm mortar base	1.10
Subflooring, 19 mm	0.14
Terrazzo (38 mm) directly on slab	0.91
Terrazzo (25 mm) on stone-concrete fill	1.53
Terrazzo (25 mm), 51 mm stone concrete	1.53
Wood block (76 mm) on mastic, no fill	0.48
Wood block (76 mm) on 13 mm mortar base	0.77
FLOORS, WOOD-JOIST (NO PLASTER) DOUBLE WOOD FLOOR	

Joist sizes (mm)	305 mm spacing (kN/m²)	406 mm spacing (kN/m²)	610 mm spacing (kN/m²)
51 × 152	0.29	0.24	0.19
51 × 203	0.29	0.24	0.24
51 × 254	0.34	0.29	0.29
51 × 305	0.38	0.34	0.29

Component	Load (kN/m²)
FRAME PARTITIONS	
Movable steel partitions	0.19
Wood or steel studs, 13 mm gypsum board each side	0.38
Wood studs, 51 × 102, unplastered	0.19
Wood studs, 51 × 102, plastered one side	0.57
Wood studs, 51 × 102, plastered two sides	0.96
FRAME WALLS	
Exterior stud walls:	
51mm × 102mm @ 406mm, 16mm gypsum, insulated, 10mm siding	0.53
51mm × 152mm @ 406mm, 16mm gypsum, insulated, 10mm siding	0.57
Exterior stud walls with brick veneer	2.30
Windows, glass, frame and sash	0.38

Component			Load (kN/m²)		
Clay brick wythes:					
102 mm					1.87
203 mm					3.78
305 mm					5.51
406 mm					7.42

Hollow concrete masonry unit wythes:					
Wythe thickness (in mm)	102	152	203	254	305
Density of unit (16.49 kN/m³)					
No grout	1.05	1.15	1.48	1.77	2.06
1219 mm		1.39	1.82	2.25	2.63
1016 mm grout		1.44	1.92	2.35	2.73
813 mm		1.53	2.01	2.49	2.92
610 mm spacing		1.63	2.20	2.73	3.21
406 mm		1.92	2.54	3.16	3.78
Full Grout		2.63	3.59	4.55	5.51
Density of unit (19.64 kN/m³):					
No grout	1.24	1.34	1.58	1.72	2.11
1,219 mm		1.58	2.11	2.59	2.97
1,016 mm grout		1.63	2.15	2.68	3.11
813 mm		1.72	2.25	2.78	3.26
610 mm spacing		1.87	2.44	3.02	3.59
406 mm		2.11	2.82	3.50	4.17
Full Grout		2.82	3.88	4.88	5.89
Density of unit (21.21 kN/m³):					
No grout	1.39	1.44	1.87	2.25	2.59
1219 mm		1.72	2.25	2.73	3.16
1016 mm grout		1.77	2.30	2.82	3.30
813 mm		1.82	2.39	2.97	3.45
610 mm spacing		1.96	2.59	3.21	3.73
406 mm		2.20	2.92	3.64	4.31
Full Grout		2.97	3.97	5.03	6.08

Solid concrete masonry unit wythes (incl. concrete brick):					
Wythe thickness (in mm)	102	152	203	254	305
Density of unit (16.49 kN/m³)	1.53	2.44	3.30	4.17	5.03
Density of unit (19.64 kN/m³)	1.82	2.87	3.88	4.88	5.94
Density of unit (21.21 kN/m³)	1.96	3.06	4.17	5.27	6.37

*Weights of masonry include mortar but not plaster. For plaster, add 0.24 kN/m² for each face plastered. Values given represent averages. In some cases there is a considerable range of weight for the same construction.

TABLE C3-2a
Minimum Densities for Design Loads from Materials

Material	Load (lb/cu ft)	Material	Load (lb/cu ft)
Aluminum	170	Lead	710
Bituminous products		Lime	
Asphaltum	81	Hydrated, loose	32
Graphite	135	Hydrated, compacted	45
Parafin	56	Masonry, Ashlar Stone	
Petroleum, crude	55	Granite	165
Petroleum, refined	50	Limestone, crystalline	165
Petroleum, benzine	46	Limestone, oolitic	135
Petroleum, gasoline	42	Marble	173
Pitch	69	Sandstone	144
Tar	75	Masonry, Brick	
Brass	526	Hard (low absorbtion)	130
Bronze	552	Medium (medium absorbtion)	115
Cast-stone masonry (cement, stone, sand)	144	Soft (high absorbtion)	100
Cement, portland, loose	90	Masonry, Concrete*	
Ceramic tile	150	Lightweight units	105
Charcoal	12	Medium weight units	125
Cinder fill	57	Normal weight units	135
Cinders, dry, in bulk	45	Masonry Grout	140
Coal		Masonry, Rubble Stone	
Anthracite, piled	52	Granite	153
Bituminous, piled	47	Limestone, crystalline	147
Lignite, piled	47	Limestone, oolitic	138
Peat, dry, piled	23	Marble	156
Concrete, plain		Sandstone	137
Cinder	108	Mortar, cement or lime	130
Expanded-slag aggregate	100	Particleboard	45
Haydite (burned-clay aggregate)	90	Plywood	36
Slag	132	Riprap (Not submerged)	
Stone (including gravel)	144	Limestone	83
Vermiculite and perlite aggregate, nonload-bearing	25-50	Sandstone	90
Other light aggregate, load-bearing	70-105	Sand	
Concrete, Reinforced		Clean and dry	90
Cinder	111	River, dry	106
Slag	138	Slag	
Stone (including gravel)	150	Bank	70
Copper	556	Bank screenings	108
Cork, compressed	14	Machine	96
Earth (not submerged)		Sand	52
Clay, dry	63	Slate	172
Clay, damp	110	Steel, cold-drawn	492
Clay and gravel, dry	100	Stone, Quarried, Piled	
Silt, moist, loose	78	Basalt, granite, gneiss	96
Silt, moist, packed	96	Limestone, marble, quartz	95
Silt, flowing	108	Sandstone	82
Sand and gravel, dry, loose	100	Shale	92
Sand and gravel, dry, packed	110	Greenstone, hornblende	107
Sand and gravel, wet	120	Terra Cotta, Architectural	
Earth (submerged)		Voids filled	120
Clay	80	Voids unfilled	72
Soil	70	Tin	459
River mud	90	Water	
Sand or gravel	60	Fresh	62
Sand or gravel and clay	65	Sea	64
Glass	160	Wood, Seasoned	
Gravel, dry	104	Ash, commercial white	41
Gypsum, loose	70	Cypress, southern	34
Gypsum, wallboard	50	Fir, Douglas, coast region	34
Ice	57	Hem fir	28
Iron		Oak, commercial reds and whites	47
Cast	450	Pine, southern yellow	37
Wrought	48	Redwood	28
		Spruce, red, white, and Stika	29
		Western hemlock	32
		Zinc, rolled sheet	449

*Tabulated values apply to solid masonry and to the solid portion of hollow masonry.

TABLE C3-2b
Minimum Densities for Design Loads from Materials

Material	Load (kN/m³)	Material	Load (kN/m³)
Aluminum	26.7	Lead	111.5
Bituminous products		Lime	
Asphaltum	12.7	Hydrated, loose	5.0
Graphite	21.2	Hydrated, compacted	7.1
Parafin	8.8	Masonry, Ashlar Stone	
Petroleum, crude	8.6	Granite	25.9
Petroleum, refined	7.9	Limestone, crystalline	25.9
Petroleum, benzine	7.2	Limestone, oolitic	21.2
Petroleum, gasoline	6.6	Marble	27.2
Pitch	10.8	Sandstone	22.6
Tar	11.8	Masonry, Brick	
Brass	82.6	Hard (low absorbtion)	20.4
Bronze	86.7	Medium (medium absorbtion)	18.1
Cast-stone masonry (cement, stone, sand)	22.6	Soft (high absorbtion)	15.7
Cement, portland, loose	14.1	Masonry, Concrete*	
Ceramic tile	23.6	Lightweight units	16.5
Charcoal	1.9	Medium weight units	19.6
Cinder fill	9.0	Normal weight units	21.2
Cinders, dry, in bulk	7.1	Masonry Grout	22.0
Coal		Masonry, Rubble Stone	
Anthracite, piled	8.2	Granite	24.0
Bituminous, piled	7.4	Limestone, crystalline	23.1
Lignite, piled	7.4	Limestone, oolitic	21.7
Peat, dry, piled	3.6	Marble	24.5
Concrete, plain		Sandstone	21.5
Cinder	17.0	Mortar, cement or lime	20.4
Expanded-slag aggregate	15.7	Particleboard	7.1
Haydite (burned-clay aggregate)	14.1	Plywood	5.7
Slag	20.7	Riprap (Not submerged)	
Stone (including gravel)	22.6	Limestone	13.0
Vermiculite and perlite aggregate, nonload-bearing	3.9-7.9	Sandstone	14.1
Other light aggregate, load-bearing	11.0-16.5	Sand	
Concrete, Reinforced		Clean and dry	14.1
Cinder	17.4	River, dry	16.7
Slag	21.7	Slag	
Stone (including gravel)	23.6	Bank	11.0
Copper	87.3	Bank screenings	17.0
Cork, compressed	2.2	Machine	15.1
Earth (not submerged)		Sand	8.2
Clay, dry	9.9	Slate	27.0
Clay, damp	17.3	Steel, cold-drawn	77.3
Clay and gravel, dry	15.7	Stone, Quarried, Piled	
Silt, moist, loose	12.3	Basalt, granite, gneiss	15.1
Silt, moist, packed	15.1	Limestone, marble, quartz	14.9
Silt, flowing	17.0	Sandstone	12.9
Sand and gravel, dry, loose	15.7	Shale	14.5
Sand and gravel, dry, packed	17.3	Greenstone, hornblende	16.8
Sand and gravel, wet	18.9	Terra Cotta, Architectural	
Earth (submerged)		Voids filled	18.9
Clay	12.6	Voids unfilled	11.3
Soil	11.0	Tin	72.1
River mud	14.1	Water	
Sand or gravel	9.4	Fresh	9.8
Sand or gravel and clay	10.2	Sea	10.1
Glass	25.1	Wood, Seasoned	
Gravel, dry	16.3	Ash, commercial white	6.4
Gypsum, loose	11.0	Cypress, southern	5.3
Gypsum, wallboard	7.9	Fir, Douglas, coast region	5.3
Ice	9.0	Hem fir	4.4
Iron		Oak, commercial reds and whites	7.4
Cast	70.7	Pine, southern yellow	5.8
Wrought	75.4	Redwood	4.4
		Spruce, red, white, and Stika	4.5
		Western hemlock	5.0
		Zinc, rolled sheet	70.5

*Tabulated values apply to solid masonry and to the solid portion of hollow masonry.

fore granted in the standard for the building official to deal with them.

For ease of computation, most values are given in terms of pounds per square foot (lb/sq ft) (kN/m^2) of given thickness (see Table C3-1). Pounds-per-cubic-foot (lb/cu ft) (kN/m^3) values, consistent with the pounds-per-square foot (kilonewtons per square meter) values, are also presented in some cases (see Table C3-2). Some constructions for which a single figure is given actually have a considerable range in weight. The average figure given is suitable for general use, but when there is reason to suspect a considerable deviation from this, the actual weight should be determined.

Engineers, architects, and building owners are advised to consider factors that result in differences between actual and calculated loads.

Engineers and architects cannot be responsible for circumstances beyond their control. Experience has shown, however, that conditions are encountered which, if not considered in design, may reduce the future utility of a building or reduce its margin of safety. Among them are:

1. Dead Loads. There have been numerous instances in which the actual weights of members and construction materials have exceeded the values used in design. Care is advised in the use of tabular values. Also, allowances should be made for such factors as the influence of formwork and support deflections on the actual thickness of a concrete slab of prescribed nominal thickness.

2. Future Installations. Allowance should be made for the weight of future wearing or protective surfaces where there is a good possibility that such may be applied. Special consideration should be given to the likely types and position of partitions, as insufficient provision for partitioning may reduce the future utility of the building.

Attention is directed also to the possibility of temporary changes in the use of a building, as in the case of clearing a dormitory for a dance or other recreational purpose.

4. Live Loads

4.2 Uniformly Distributed Loads

4.2.1 Required Live Loads. A selected list of loads for occupancies and uses more commonly encountered is given in 4.2.1, and the authority having jurisdiction should approve on occupancies not mentioned. Tables C4-1 and C4-2 are offered as a guide in the exercise of such authority.

In selecting the occupancy and use for the design of a building or a structure, the building owner should consider the possibility of later changes of occupancy involving loads heavier than originally contemplated. The lighter loading appropriate to the first occupancy should not necessarily be selected. The building owner should ensure that a live load greater than that for which a floor or roof is approved by the authority having jurisdiction is not placed, or caused or permitted to be placed, on any floor or roof of a building or other structure.

In order to solicit specific informed opinion regarding the design loads in Table 4-1, a panel of 25 distinguished structural engineers was selected. A Delphi [1] was conducted with this panel in which design values and supporting reasons were requested for each occupancy type. The information was summarized and recirculated back to the panel members for a second round of responses; those occupancies for which previous design loads were reaffirmed, as well as those for which there was consensus for change, were included.

It is well known that the floor loads measured in a live-load survey usually are well below present design values [2, 3, 4, 5]. However, buildings must be designed to resist the maximum loads they are likely to be subjected to during some reference period T, frequently taken as 50 years. Table C4-2 briefly summarizes how load survey data are combined with a theoretical analysis of the load process for some common occupancy types and illustrates how a design load might be selected for an occupancy not specified in Table 4-1 [6]. The floor load normally present for the intended functions of a given occupancy is referred to as the sustained load. This load is modeled as constant until a change in tenant or occupancy type occurs. A live-load survey provides the statistics of the sustained load. Table C4-2 gives the mean, m_s, and standard deviation, σ_x, for particular reference areas. In addition to the sustained load, a building is likely to be subjected to a number of relatively short-duration, high-intensity, extraordinary or transient loading events (due to crowding in special or emergency circumstances, concentrations during remodeling, and the like). Limited survey information and theoretical considerations

141

TABLE C4-1
Minimum Uniformly Distributed Live Loads

Occupancy or use	Live Load lb/ft² (kN/m²)	Occupancy or use	Live Load lb/ft² (kN/m²)
Air-conditioning (machine space)	200* (9.58)	Laboratories, scientific	100 (4.79)
Amusement park structure	100* (4.79)	Laundries	150* (7.18)
Attic, Nonresidential		Libraries, corridors	80* (3.83)
Nonstorage	25 (1.20)	Manufacturing, ice	300 (14.36)
Storage	80* (3.83)	Morgue	125 (6.00)
Bakery	150 (7.18)	Office Buildings	
Exterior	100 (4.79)	Business machine equipment	100* (4.79)
Interior (fixed seats)	60 (2.87)	Files (see file room)	
Interior (movable seats	100 (4.79)	Printing Plants	
Boathouse, floors	100* (4.79)	Composing rooms	100 (4.79)
Boiler room, framed	300* (14.36)	Linotype rooms	100 (4.79)
Broadcasting studio	100 (4.79)	Paper storage	**
Catwalks	25 (1.20)	Press rooms	150* (7.18)
Ceiling, accessible furred	10# (0.48)	Public rooms	100 (4.79)
Cold Storage		Railroad tracks	‡
No overhead system	250† (11.97)	Ramps	
Overhead system		Driveway (see garages)	
Floor	150 (7.18)	Pedestrian (see sidewalks and corridors in Table	
Roof	250 (11.97)	Seaplane (see hangars)	
Computer equipment	150* (7.18)	Rest rooms	60 (2.87)
Courtrooms	50 - 100 (2.40 - 4.79)	Rinks	
Dormitories		Ice Skating	250 (11.97)
Nonpartitioned	80 (3.83)	Roller skating	100 (4.79)
Partitioned	40 (1.92)	Storage, hay or grain	300* (14.36)
Elevator machine room	150* (7.18)	Telephone exchange	150* (7.18)
Fan room	150* (7.18)	Theaters:	
File room		Dressing rooms	40 (1.92)
Duplicating equipment	150* (7.18)	Grid-iron floor or fly gallery:	
Card	125* (6.00)	Grating	60 (2.87)
Letter	80* (3.83)	Well beams, 250 lb/ft per pair (373 kg/m)	
Foundries	600* (28.73)	Header beams, 1,000 lb/ft (1,490 kg/m)	
Fuel rooms, framed	400 (19.15)	Pin rail, 250 lb/ft (373 kg/m)	
Garages - trucks	§	Projection room	100 (4.79)
Greenhouses	150 (7.18)	Toilet rooms	60 (2.87)
Hangars	150§ (7.18)	Transformer rooms	200* (9.58)
Incinerator charging floor	100 (4.79)	Vaults, in offices	250* (11.97)
Kitchens, other than domestic	150* (7.18)		

*Use weight of actual equipment or stored material when greater.

†Plus 150 lb/ft² (7.18 kN/m²) for trucks.

§Use American Association of State Highway and Transportation Officials lane loads. Also subject to not less than 100% maximum axle load.

**Paper storage 50 lb/ft (2.40 kN/m²) of clear story height.

‡As required by railroad company.

#Accessible ceilings normally are not designed to support persons. The value in this table is intended to account for occasional light storage or suspension of items. If it may be necessary to support the weight of maintenance personnel, this shall be provided for.

lead to the means, m_t, and standard deviations, σ_t, of single transient loads shown in Table C4-2.

Combination of the sustained load and transient load processes, with due regard for the probabilities of occurrence, leads to statistics of the maximum total load during a specified reference period T. The statistics of the maximum total load depend on the average duration of an individual tenancy, τ, the mean rate of occurrence of the transient load, v_e, and the reference period, T. Mean values are given in Table C4-2. The mean of the maximum load is similar, in most cases, to the Table 4-1 values of minimum uniformly distributed live loads and, in general, is a suitable design value.

4.3 Concentrated Loads

4.3.1 Accessible Roof-Supporting Members.

The provision regarding concentrated loads supported by roof trusses or other primary roof members is intended to provide for a common situation for which specific requirements are generally lacking.

TABLE C4-2
Typical Live Load Statistics

Occupancy or use	Survey Load		Transient Load		Temporal Constants			Mean maximum load*
	m_s lb/ft² (kN/m²)	σ_s* lb/ft² (kN/m²)	m_t* lb/ft² (kN/m²)	σ_t* lb/ft² (kN/m²)	τ_s† (years)	v_e‡ \(per year)	T§ (years)	lb/ft² (kN/m²)
Office buildings								
offices	10.9 (0.52)	5.9 (0.28)	8.0 (0.38)	8.2 (0.39)	8	1	50	55 (2.63)
Residential								
renter occupied	6.0 (0.29)	2.6 (0.12)	6.0 (0.29)	6.6 (0.32)	2	1	50	36 (1.72)
owner occupied	6.0 (0.29)	2.6 (0.12)	6.0 (0.29)	6.6 (0.32)	10	1	50	38 (1.82)
Hotels								
guest rooms	4.5 (0.22)	1.2 (0.06)	6.0 (0.29)	5.8 (0.28)	5	20	50	46 (2.2)
Schools								
classrooms	12.0 (0.57)	2.7 (0.13)	6.9 (0.33)	3.4 (0.16)	1	1	100	34 (1.63)

*For 200-ft² (18.58 m²) area, except 1000 ft² (92.9 m²) for schools.

†Duration of average sustained load occupancy.

‡Mean rate of occurrence of transient load.

§Reference period.

4.4 Loads on Handrails, Guardrail Systems, Grab Bar Systems, and Vehicle Barrier Systems

4.4.2 Loads

A. Loads that can be expected to occur on hand-rail and guardrail systems are highly dependent on the use and occupancy of the protected area. For cases in which extreme loads can be anticipated, such as long straight runs of guardrail systems against which crowds can surge, appropriate increases in loading shall be considered.

B. When grab bars are provided for use by persons with physical disabilities the design is governed by CABO A117 Accessible and Usable Buildings and Facilities.

C. Vehicle barrier systems may be subjected to horizontal loads from moving vehicles. These horizontal loads may be applied normal to the plane of the barrier system, parallel to the plane of the barrier system, or at any intermediate angle. Loads in garages accommodating trucks and buses may be obtained from the provisions contained in Standard Specifications for Highway Bridges, 1989, The American Association of State Highway and Transportation Officials.

4.6 Partial Loading

It is intended that the full intensity of the appropriately reduced live load over portions of the structure or member be considered, as well as a live load of the same intensity over the full length of the structure or member.

Partial-length loads on a simple beam or truss will produce higher shear on a portion of the span than a full-length load. "Checkerboard" loadings on multistoried, multipanel bents will produce higher positive moments than full loads, while loads on either side of a support will produce greater negative moments. Loads on the half span of arches and domes or on the two central quarters can be critical. For roofs, all probable load patterns should be considered. Cantilevers cannot rely on a possible live load on the anchor span for equilibrium.

4.7 Impact Loads

Grandstands, stadiums, and similar assembly structures may be subjected to loads caused by crowds swaying in unison, jumping to its feet, or stomping. Designers are cautioned that the possibility of such loads should be considered.

4.8 Reduction in Live Loads

4.8.1 Permissible Reduction. The live-load reduction described in 4.8, first introduced in the 1982 standard, was the first such change since the concept was introduced over 40 years ago. The revised formula is a result of more extensive survey data and theoretical analysis [7]. The change in format to a reduction multiplier results in a formula that is simple and more convenient to use. The use of influence area rather than tributary area in a single equation has been shown to give more consistent reliability for the

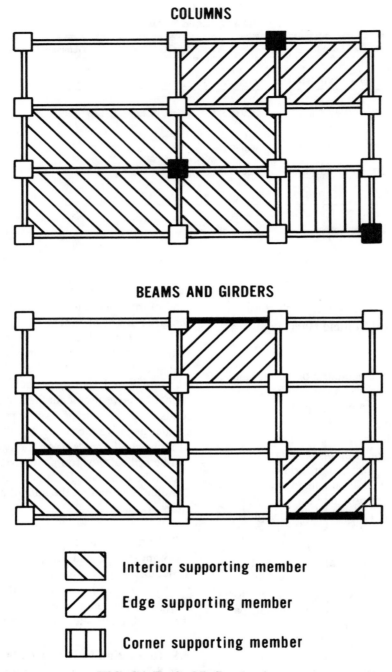

COLUMNS

BEAMS AND GIRDERS

Interior supporting member

Edge supporting member

Corner supporting member

FIG. C4. Typical Influence Areas

various structural effects. The influence area is defined as that floor area over which the influence surface for structural effects is significantly different from zero. For columns this is four times the traditional tributary area, while for flexural members it is two times. For an interior column, for instance, the influence area is the to-tal area of the four surrounding bays, while for an interior girder it is the total area of the two contributing bays. Edge columns and girders have half the influence area of the respective interior members (two bays for columns, one for girders), while a corner column has an influence area of one bay. Fig. C4 illustrates typical influence areas for a structure with regular bay spacing. For unusual shapes, the concept of significant influence effect should be applied. Reductions are permissible for two-way slabs and for beams, but care should be taken in defining the appropriate influence area. For multiple floors, areas for members supporting more than one floor are summed.

The formula provides a continuous transition from unreduced to reduced loads. The smallest allowed value of the reduction multiplier is 0.4 (providing a maximum 60% reduction), but there is a minimum of 0.5 (providing a 50% reduction) for members with a contributory load from just one floor.

4.8.2 Limitations on Live-Load Reduction. In the case of occupancies involving relatively heavy basic live loads, such as storage buildings, several adjacent floor panels may be fully loaded. However, data obtained in actual buildings indicate that rarely is any story loaded with an average actual live load of more than 80% of the average rated live load. It appears that the basic live load should not be reduced for the floor-and-beam design, but that it could be reduced a flat 20% for the design of members supporting more than one floor. Accordingly, this principle has been incorporated in the recommended requirement.

4.9 Minimum Roof Live Loads

4.9.1 Flat, Pitched, and Curved Roofs. The values specified in Eq. 4-1 that act vertically upon the projected area have been selected as minimum roof live loads, even in localities where little or no snowfall occurs. This is because it is considered necessary to provide for occasional loading due to the presence of workers and materials during repair operations.

4.9.2 Special Purpose Roofs. Designers should consider any additional dead loads that may be imposed by saturated landscaping materials. Special purpose or occupancy roof live loads may be reduced in accordance with the requirements of Section 4.8.

4.10 Crane Loads

All support components of moving bridge cranes and monorail cranes, including runway beams, brackets, bracing, and connections, shall be designed to support the maximum wheel load of the crane and the vertical impact, lateral, and longitudinal forces induced by the moving crane. Also, the runway beams shall be designed for crane stop

forces. The methods for determining these loads vary depending on the type of crane system and support. References [8, 9, 10, 11] describe types of bridge cranes and monorail cranes. Cranes described in these references include top running bridge cranes with top running trolley, underhung bridge cranes, and underhung monorail cranes. Reference [12] gives more stringent requirements for crane runway design that are more appropriate for higher capacity or higher speed crane systems.

References

[1] Corotis, R.B., Fox, R.R., and Harris, J.C. Delphi methods: Theory and design load application, *J. Struct. Div.*, ASCE, 107(6), 1095–1105, June 1981.

[2] Peir, J.C., and Cornell, C.A. Spatial and temporal variability of live loads, *J. Struct. Div.*, ASCE, 99(5): 903–922, May 1973.

[3] McGuire, R.K., and Cornell, C.A. Live load effects in office buildings, *J. Struct. Div.*, ASCE, 100(7): 1351–1366, July 1974.

[4] Ellingwood, B.R., and Culver, C.G. Analysis of live loads in office buildings, *J. Struct. Div.*, ASCE. 103(8), 1551–1560, Aug. 1977.

[5] Sentler, L. A stochastic model for live loads on floors in buildings. Lund Institute of Technology, Division of Building Technology, Lund, Sweden, Report 60, 1975.

[6] Chalk, P.L., and Corotis, R.B. A probability model for design live loads, *J. Struct. Div.*, ASCE, 106(10): 2017–2030, Oct. 1980.

[7] Harris, M.E., Corotis, R.B., and Bova, C.J. Area-dependent processes for structural live loads, *J. Struct. Div.*, ASCE, 107(5), 857–872, May 1981.

[8] Specifications for Underhung Cranes and Monorail Systems, ANSI MH 27.1, Material Handling Industry, Charlotte, N.C., 1981.

[9] Specifications for Electric Overhead Traveling Cranes, No. 70, Material Handling Industry, Charlotte, N.C., 1994.

[10] Specifications for Top Running and Under Running Single Girder Electric Overhead Traveling Cranes, No. 74, Material Handling Industry, Charlotte, N.C., 1994.

[11] Metal Building Manufacturers Association.

Low Rise Building Systems Manual, MBMA, Inc., Cleveland, OH, 1986.

[12] Association of Iron and Steel Engineers, Technical Report No. 13, Pittsburgh, Pa., 1979.

5 Soil and Hydrostatic Pressure and Flood Loads

5.1 Pressure on Basement Walls

Table 5-1 includes high earth pressures, 85 psf per foot of depth (13.36 kN/m^2 per meter of depth) or more, to show that certain soils are poor backfill material. In addition, when walls are unyielding the earth pressure is increased from active pressure toward earth pressure at rest, resulting in 60 psf per foot of depth (9.43 kN/m^2 per meter of depth) for granular soils and 100 psf per foot of depth (15.72 kN/m^2 per meter of depth) for silt and clay type soils (see [4]). Examples of light floor systems supported on shallow basement walls mentioned in Table 5-1 are floor systems with wood joists and flooring, and cold formed steel joists without poured cast in place concrete floor attached.

Expansive soils exist in many regions of the United States and may cause serious damage to basement walls unless special design considerations are provided. Expansive soils should not be used as backfill because they can exert very high pressures against walls. Special soil testing is required to determine the magnitude of these pressures. It is preferable to excavate expansive soil and backfill with non-expansive freely-draining sands or gravels. The excavated backslope adjacent to the wall should be no steeper than 45 degrees from the horizontal in order to minimize the transmission of swelling pressure from the expansive soil through the new backfill. Other special details are recommended, such as a cap of non-pervious soil on top of the backfill and provision of foundation drains. Refer to current reference books on geotechnical engineering for guidance.

5.2 Uplift on Floors and Foundations

If expansive soils are present under floors or footings large pressures can be exerted and must be resisted by special design. Alternatively, the expansive soil can be excavated to a depth of at least two feet (0.60 m) and backfilled with nonexpansive freely draining sands or gravel. A geotechnical engineer should make recommendations in these situations.

5.3 Flood Loads

This section presents information for the design of buildings and other structures in areas prone to flooding. Much of the impetus for flood-resistant design has come about from the federal government sponsored initiatives of flood insurance and flood-damage mitigation.

The National Flood Insurance Program (NFIP) is based on an agreement between the federal government and participating communities that have been identified as being floodprone. The Federal Emergency Management Agency (FEMA) through the Federal Insurance Administration (FIA), makes flood insurance available to the residents of communities provided that the community adopts and enforces adequate floodplain management regulations that meet the minimum requirements. Included in the NFIP requirements, found under Title 44 of the U.S. Code of Federal Regulations, are minimum building design and construction standards for buildings and other structures located in Special Flood Hazard Areas (SFHA).

Special Flood Hazards Areas (SFHA) are those identified by FEMA's Mitigation Directorate as being subject to inundation during the 100-year flood. SFHA are shown on Flood Insurance Rate Maps (FIRM), which are produced for floodprone communities. SFHA are identified on FIRM as zones A, A1-30, AE, AR, AO, AH, and coastal high-hazard areas as V1-30, V, and VE. The SFHA is the area in which communities must enforce NFIP-complaint, flood damage resistant design, and construction practices.

Prior to designing a structure in a floodprone area, design professionals should contact the local building official to determine if the site in question is located in a SFHA or other floodprone area that is regulated under the community's floodplain management regulations. If the proposed structure is located within the regulatory floodplain, local building officials can explain the regulatory requirements.

Answers to specific questions on flood-resistant design and construction practices may be directed to the Mitigation Division of each of FEMA's regional offices. FEMA has regional offices that are available to assist design professionals.

5.3.2.1 Design Loads. Wind loads and flood loads may act simultaneously at coastlines, particularly during hurricanes and coastal storms. This may also be true during severe storms at the shorelines of large lakes, and during riverine flooding of long duration.

146

5.3.3.1 Load Basis. Water loads are the loads or pressures on surfaces of buildings and structures caused and induced by the presence of floodwaters. These loads are of two basic types: hydrostatic and hydrodynamic. Impact loads result from objects transported by floodwaters striking against buildings and structures or part thereof. Wave loads can be considered a special type of hydrodynamic load.

5.3.3.2 Hydrostatic Loads. Hydrostatic loads are those caused by water either above or below the ground surface, free or confined, which is either stagnant or moves at velocities less than 5 ft/sec (1.52 m/s). These loads are equal to the product of the water pressure multiplied by the surface area on which the pressure acts.

Hydrostatic pressure at any point is equal in all directions and always acts perpendicular to the surface on which it is applied. Hydrostatic loads can be subdivided into vertical downward loads, lateral loads and vertical upward loads (uplift or buoyancy). Hydrostatic loads acting on inclined, rounded or irregular surfaces may be resolved into vertical downward or upward loads and lateral loads based on the geometry of the surfaces and the distribution of hydrostatic pressure.

5.3.3.3 Hydrodynamic Loads. Hydrodynamic loads are those loads induced by the flow of water moving at moderate to high velocity above the ground level. They are usually lateral loads caused by the impact of the moving mass of water and the drag forces as the water flows around the obstruction. Hydrodynamic loads are computed by recognized engineering methods. In the coastal high hazard area the loads from high velocity currents due to storm surge and overtopping are of particular importance. Reference [1] is one source of design information regarding hydrodynamic loadings.

The magnitude of wave forces (lb/sq ft) (kN/m²) acting against buildings or other structures can be 10 or more times higher than wind forces and other forces under design conditions. Thus, it should be readily apparent that elevating above the wave crest elevation is crucial to the survival of buildings and other structures. Even elevated structures, however, must be designed for large wave forces that can act over a relatively small surface area of the foundation and supporting structure.

It should be pointed out that present NFIP mapping procedures distinguish between A Zones and V Zones by the wave heights expected in each zone.

Generally speaking, A Zones are designated where wave heights less than 3 ft (0.91 m) in height are expected; V Zones are designated where wave heights equal to or greater than 3 ft (0.91 m) are expected. Designers should proceed cautiously, however. Large wave forces can be generated in some A Zones, and wave force calculations should not be restricted to V Zones. Present NFIP mapping procedures do not designate V Zones in all areas where wave heights greater than three feet can occur during base flood conditions. Rather than rely exclusively on flood hazard maps, designers should investigate historical flood damages near a site to determine whether or not wave forces can be significant.

Potential sources of information regarding velocities of floodwaters include local, state and federal government agencies and consulting engineers specializing in coastal engineering, stream hydrology or hydraulics.

5.3.3.4 Impact Loads. Normal impact loads are those which result from isolated occurrences of logs, ice floes and other objects normally encountered striking buildings, structures or parts thereof. Special impact loads are those which result from large objects, such as broken up ice floats and accumulations of debris, either striking or resting against a building, structures, or parts thereof. Extreme impact loads are those that result from very large objects such as boats, barges, or collapsed buildings striking the building, structure or component under consideration [2].

Impact load is calculated as follows:

$$F_i = \text{ma} \qquad\qquad (C5\text{-}1)$$

Where

$\qquad F_i$ = impact load in pounds (kN)

$m = w/g$ = mass in slugs (kN) $\qquad (C5\text{-}2)$
w = weight of object in pounds (kN)
g = acceleration due to gravity 32.2 ft/sec/sec (9.81 m/s²)

$\qquad a = \Delta V/\Delta t \qquad\qquad (C5\text{-}3)$
ΔV = change from V_b to zero velocity
V_b = velocity of object in feet per second (m/s)
Δt = time to decelerate object in seconds

Assume that the velocity of the object is reduced to zero in one second resulting in a minimum impact load:

$$F_i = 31 \times V_b \text{ (in pounds)}$$
$$\text{(in SI } F_i = 0.453 \; V_b \text{ in kN)} \qquad (C5\text{-}4)$$

Where larger than normal impact loads are likely to occur, the minimum impact load presented in this section is inadequate and special consideration in the design of the building or other structure is required. For example, rigid structures of concrete or steel may reduce the velocity of the object to zero within a time interval of 0.1–0.5 sec.

5.3.5 Coastal High Hazards Areas—V Zones.
In riverine flood plains the velocity of flow of the water erodes soil supporting the foundation elements, such as piles, piers, and footings. Adequate embedment must be provided to resist the effects of the base flood as well as the accumulated scour from a number of smaller flood events. Similar design requirements shall be met in other special flood hazard areas, including along coastal areas, and lakefronts.

5.3.5.1 Elevation. Shear walls have not been included as a means of elevating buildings or other structures in coastal high hazard areas. They can be very efficient in resisting loads in the plane of the shear wall from wind, etc. There is concern about serious damage or collapse from wave forces normal to the plane of the shear wall. However, it is possible to design shear walls to resist such wave forces and special impact forces. When shear walls are used, they should be oriented to minimize the total surface area exposed to potential hydrodynamic and impact loads.

5.3.5.3 Erosion and Scour. Scour is an important consideration in the design of foundations in coastal high hazard areas or *V* Zone. In coastal areas, scour can be significant due to area erosion resulting from the effects of storm surge and wave action. Local scour around foundation elements such as a pile or a column, mat foundation or grade beam must also be considered in determining the required depth of embedment or anchorage. Along the coastline the erosion from many small to large storms must be considered through evaluation of historical records. The required embedment of piles and foundations must include consideration of both areal erosion and local scour at the foundation.

References

[1] Shore Protection Manual. U.S. Army Corps of Engineers, Coastal Engineering Research Center, Waterways Experiment Station, 2 Vols., 4th Ed., 1984.

[2] Flood Proofing Regulations. U.S. Army Corps of Engineers, Office of the Chief of Engineers, EP 1165-2-314, March 1992.

[3] National Flood Insurance Program. Federal Emergency Management Agency, 44 CFR, Ch. 1, Parts 59 and 60 (10-1-90 Ed.).

[4] Terzaghi, K. and Peck, R.B., *Soil Mechanics in Engineering Practice*, John Wiley and Sons, 2nd Ed., 1967.

6. Wind Loads

6.1 General
Temporary bracing should be provided to resist wind loading on structural components and structural assemblages during erection and construction phases.

6.2 Definitions
Main wind-force resisting system can consist of a structural frame or an assemblage of structural elements that work together to transfer wind loads acting on the entire structure to the ground. Structural elements such as cross-bracing, shear walls, and roof diaphragms are part of the main wind-force resisting system when they assist in transferring overall loads.

Building, enclosed, open, partially enclosed: These definitions relate to the proper selection of internal pressure coefficients, GC_{pi}. Building, open and Building, partially enclosed are specifically defined. All other buildings are considered to be enclosed by definition, although there may be large openings in two or more walls. An example of this is a parking garage through which the wind can pass. The internal pressure coefficient for such a building would be ± 0.18 and the internal pressures would act on the solid areas of the walls and roof.

Components and cladding: Components receive wind loads directly or from cladding, and transfer the load to the main wind-force resisting system. Cladding receives wind loads directly. Examples of components include fasteners, purlins, girts, studs, roof decking, and roof trusses. Components can be part of the main wind-force resisting system when they act as shear walls or roof diaphragms, but they may also be loaded as individual components. The engineer needs to use appropriate loadings for design of components, which may require certain components to be designed for more than one type of loading, e.g., long-span roof trusses should be designed for loads associated with main wind-force resisting systems, and individual members of trusses should also be designed for component and cladding loads. Examples of cladding include wall coverings, curtain walls, roof coverings, exterior windows and doors, and overhead doors.

Effective wind area is the area of the building surface used to determine GC_p. This area does not necessarily correspond to the area of the building surface contributing to the force being considered. Two cases arise. In the usual case the effective wind area does correspond to the area tributary to the force component being considered. For example, for a cladding panel, the effective wind area may be equal to the total area of the panel; for a cladding fastener, the effective wind area is the area of cladding secured by a single fastener. A mullion may receive wind from several cladding panels; in this case, the effective wind area is the area associated with the wind load that is transferred to the mullion.

The second case arises where components such as roofing panels, wall studs or roof trusses are spaced closely together; the area served by the component may become long and narrow. To better approximate the actual load distribution in such cases, the width of the effective wind area used to evaluate GC_p need not be taken as less than one third the length of the area. This increase in effective wind area has the effect of reducing the average wind pressure acting on the component. Note however that this effective wind area should only be used in determining the GC_p in Figures 6.5 through 6.8. The induced wind load should be applied over the actual area tributary to the component being considered.

For membrane roof systems, the effective wind area for attachment is the area of an insulation board (or deck panel if insulation is not used) if the boards are fully adhered (or the membrane is adhered directly to the deck). If the insulation boards or membrane are mechanically attached or partially adhered, the effective wind area is the area of the board or membrane secured by a single fastener or individual spot or row of adhesive.

Flexible buildings and other structures: A building or other structure is considered flexible if it exhibits a significant dynamic resonant response. Resonant response depends on the gust structure exhibits in the approach wind, on wind loading pressures generated by the wind flow about the building, and on the dynamic properties of the building or structure. The criterion that normally indicates a small resonant response is height to width ratio less than 4. If width varies with height, the horizontal dimension which controls the lowest natural frequency should be used. Gust energy in the wind is smaller at frequencies above about 1 Hz, therefore the resonant response of most buildings and structures with lowest natural frequency above 1 Hz will be sufficiently small that resonant response can often be ignored. When buildings or other structures have a height exceeding four times the least horizontal dimension, their resonant response should be investigated.

6.3 Symbols and Notation

The following additional symbols and notation are used herein:

n = reference period, in years;
P_a = annual probability of wind speed equaling or exceeding a given magnitude [see Eq. (C4)];
P_n = probability of equaling or exceeding the design wind speed during n years [see Eq. (C4)];
V_t = wind speed averaged over t secs (see Fig. C6-1), in miles per hour (meters per second);
$V_{3,600}$ = mean wind speed averaged over 1 h (see Fig. C6-1), in miles per hour (meters per second);
z_g = gradient height (see Table C6-2), in feet (meters);
α = power law coefficient (see Table C6-2);
β = structural damping coefficient (percentage of critical damping);

6.4 Calculation of Wind Loads

6.4.2 Analytical Procedure. The analytical procedure provides wind pressures and forces for the design of main wind-force resisting systems and for the design of components and cladding of buildings and other structures. The procedure involves the determination of a velocity pressure, the selection or determination of an appropriate gust effect factor, and the selection of appropriate pressure or force coefficients. The procedure allows for the level of structural reliability required, the effects of differing wind exposures, the speed-up effects of certain topographic features such as hills and escarpments, and the size and geometry of the building or other structure under consideration.

149

The procedure differentiates between rigid and flexible buildings and other structures, and the results generally envelope the most critical load conditions for the design of main wind-force resisting systems as well as components and cladding.

6.4.2.1 Limitations of Analytical Procedure. The provisions given under 6.4.2 apply to the majority of site locations and buildings and structures, but for some, these provisions may be inadequate. Examples of site locations and buildings and structures (or portions thereof) that require use of recognized literature for documentation pertaining to wind effects, or the use of the wind tunnel procedure of 6.4.3 include:

1. Site locations which have channeling effects or wakes from upwind obstructions. Channeling effects can be caused by topographic features (e.g., mountain gorge) or buildings (e.g., a cluster of tall buildings). Wakes can be caused by hills or by buildings or other structures.
2. Buildings with unusual or irregular geometric shape, including domes, barrel vaults, and other buildings whose shape (in plan or profile) differs significantly from a uniform or series of superimposed prisms similar to those indicated in Figs. 6-3 through 6-8. Unusual or irregular geometric shapes include buildings with multiple setbacks, curved facades, irregular plan resulting from significant indentations or projections, openings through the building, or multi-tower buildings connected by bridges.
3. Buildings with unusual response characteristics, that result in across-wind and/or dynamic torsional loads, loads caused by vortex shedding, or loads resulting from instabilities such as flutter or galloping. Examples of buildings and structures which may have unusual response characteristics include flexible buildings with natural frequencies below 1 Hz, tall slender buildings (building height-to-width ratio exceeds 4), and cylindrical buildings or structures. Note: Vortex shedding occurs when wind blows across a slender prismatic or cylindrical body. Vortices are alternatively shed from one side of the body and then the other side, which results in a fluctuating force acting at right angles to the wind direction (across-wind) along the length of the body.
4. Bridges, cranes, electrical transmission lines, guyed masts, telecommunication towers, and flagpoles.

6.4.2.2 Air-Permeable Cladding. Air-permeable roof or wall claddings allow partial air pressure equalization between their exterior and interior surfaces. Examples include siding, pressure-equalized rain screen walls, shingles, tiles, concrete roof pavers, and aggregate roof surfacing.

The design wind pressures derived from 6.4.2 represent the pressure differential between the exterior and interior surfaces of the exterior envelope (wall or roof system). Because of partial air-pressure equalization provided by air permeable claddings, the pressures derived from 6.4.2 can over estimate the load on air-permeable cladding elements. The designer may elect either to use the loads derived from 6.4.2, or to use loads derived by an approved alternative method. If the designer desires to determine the pressure differential across the air-permeable cladding element, appropriate full-scale pressure measurements should be made on the applicable cladding element, or reference be made to recognized literature [9],[16],[37] for documentation pertaining to wind loads.

6.4.3 Wind-Tunnel Procedure. Wind-tunnel tests are recommended when the building or other structure under consideration satisfies one or more of the following conditions:

1. has a shape which differs significantly from a uniform rectangular prism or "box-like" shape,
2. is flexible with natural frequencies below 1 Hz,
3. is subject to buffeting by the wake of upwind buildings or other structures, or
4. is subject to accelerated flow caused by channeling or local topographic features.

It is common practice to resort to wind-tunnel tests when design data are required for the following wind-induced loads:

1. curtain wall pressures resulting from irregular geometry,
2. across-wind and/or significant torsional loads,
3. periodic loads caused by vortex shedding, and
4. loads resulting from instabilities such as flutter or galloping.

Boundary-layer wind tunnels capable of developing flows that meet the conditions stipulated in 6.4.3.1 typically have test-section dimensions in the following ranges; width of 6–12 ft (2–4 m), height of 6–10 ft (2–3 m), and length of 50–100 ft (15–30 m). Maximum wind speeds are ordinarily in the range of 25–100 mph (10–45 m/s). The wind tunnel may be either an open-circuit or closed-circuit type.

Three basic types of wind-tunnel test models are commonly used. These are designated as follows: (1) rigid pressure model (PM); (2) rigid high-frequency base balance model (H-FBBM), and (3) aeroelastic model (AM). One or more of the models may be employed to obtain design loads for a particular building or structure. The PM provides local peak pressures for design of elements such as cladding and mean pressures for the determination of overall mean loads. The H-FBBM measures overall fluctuating loads (aerodynamic admittance) for the determination of dynamic responses. When motion of a building or structure influences the wind loading, the AM is employed for direct measurement of overall loads, deflections and accelerations. Each of these models, together with a model of the surroundings (proximity model), can provide information other than wind loads such as snow loads on complex roofs, wind data to evaluate environmental impact on pedestrians, and concentrations of air-pollutant emissions for environmental impact determinations. Several references provide detailed information and guidance for the determination of wind loads and other types of design data by wind-tunnel tests [4],[7],[8],[33].

6.5 Velocity Pressure

6.5.1 Procedure for Calculating Velocity Pressure. The basic wind speed is converted to a velocity pressure q_z in pounds per square foot at height z by use of the formula:

$$q_z = 0.00256 K_z K_{zt} V^2 I \text{ (lb/sq ft)}$$
$$[q_z = 0.613 K_z K_{zt} V^2 I \text{ (N/m}^2)] \tag{C1}$$

Numerical constant. The constant 0.00256 (or 0.613 in SI) reflects the mass density of air for the standard atmosphere, i.e., temperature of 59°F (15°C) and sea level pressure of 29.92 in. of mercury (101.325 kPa), and dimensions associated with wind speed in miles per hour (meters per second). The constant is obtained as follows:

$$\begin{aligned} \text{constant} &= 1/2[(0.0765 \text{ lb/cu ft})/(32.2 \text{ ft/s}^2)] \\ &\times [(\text{mi/h})(5280 \text{ ft/mi}) \\ &\times (1\ h/3600\text{ s})]^2 \\ &= 0.00256 \end{aligned} \tag{C2}$$

$$\begin{aligned} \text{constant} &= 1/2[(1.225 \text{ kg/m}^3)/(9.81 \text{ m/s}^2)] \\ &\times [(\text{m/s})]^2[9.81 \text{ N/kg}] \\ &= 0.613 \end{aligned}$$

The numerical constant of 0.00256 should be used except where sufficient weather data are available to justify a different value of this constant for a specific design application. The mass density of air will vary as a function of altitude, latitude, temperature, weather, and season. Average and extreme values of air density are given in Table C6-1.

TABLE C6-1
Ambient Air Density Values for Various Altitudes

Altitude Feet	Altitude Meters	Minimum (lbm/ft³)	Minimum (kg/m³)	Average lbm/ft³	Average kg/m³	Maximum lbm/ft³	Maximum kg/m³
0	0	0.0712	1.1405	0.0765	1.2254	0.0822	1.3167
1000	305	0.0693	1.1101	0.0742	1.1886	0.0795	1.2735
2000	610	0.0675	1.0812	0.0720	1.1533	0.0768	1.2302
3000	914	0.0657	1.0524	0.0699	1.1197	0.0743	1.1902
3281	1000	0.0652	1.0444	0.0693	1.1101	0.0736	1.2222
4000	1219	0.0640	1.0252	0.0678	1.0861	0.0718	1.1501
5000	1524	0.0624	0.9996	0.0659	1.0556	0.0695	1.1133
6000	1829	0.0608	0.9739	0.0639	1.0236	0.0672	1.0764
6562	2000	0.0599	0.9595	0.0629	1.0076	0.0660	1.0572
7000	2134	0.0592	0.9483	0.0620	0.9931	0.0650	1.0412
8000	2438	0.0577	0.9243	0.0602	0.9643	0.0628	1.0060
9000	2743	0.0561	0.8986	0.0584	0.9355	0.0607	0.9723
9843	3000	0.0549	0.8794	0.0569	0.9115	0.0591	0.9467
10,000	3048	0.0547	0.8762	0.0567	0.9082	0.0588	0.9419

Velocity pressure exposure coefficient. The velocity pressure exposure coefficient K_z can be obtained using the equation:

$$K_z = \begin{cases} 2.01\left(\dfrac{z}{z_g}\right)^{2/\alpha} & \text{for } 15 \text{ ft} \leq z \leq z_g \quad \text{(C3a)} \\[2em] 2.01\left(\dfrac{15}{z_g}\right)^{2/\alpha} & \text{for } z < 15 \text{ ft} \quad \text{(C3b)} \end{cases}$$

in which values of α and z_g are given in Table C6-2.

The values of the gradient height, z_g, listed in Table C6-2 are consistent with those values used in ASCE 7-93. However, because the shape of the wind speed profiles changes when the reference wind speed is changed from fastest mile to the 3-sec gust speed, it was necessary to modify the values of α in the power-law representation of the wind speed profile. The new values of α listed in Table C6-2 are based on a comprehensive review of existing data and representations of gust speed profiles. Correspondingly, the multiplier in Eq. (C3) for the exposure coefficient, K_z, changes from 2.58 to 2.01. As with ASCE 7-93, values of K_z are assumed to be constant for heights less than 15 ft (4.6 m), and for heights greater than the gradient height.

The new values of α (Table C6-2) make the wind speed profiles flatter than they are in ASCE 7-93; this is consistent with theory as wind speed averaging time is changed from fastest-mile to 3-sec gust speed [68]. Field data collected recently in flat terrain in 1992 on a 160 ft (48.8 m) high tower with anemometers at several levels also indicated that the value of α changes with the wind speed averaging time. In order to determine α values related to 3-sec gust speeds for exposure categories A, B, C, and D, a published atmospheric boundary layer turbulence model [67] was used. Mean velocity profiles, defined using power-law exponents from ASCE 7-93, were combined with the turbulence profiles to produce profiles of peak gust speed. In the profile calculations, boundary layer

heights were the same ones used for ASCE 7-93 as indicated in Table C6-2. The turbulence profile was fitted to determine α values. As an additional check, log-law profiles were fitted with power-law profiles in the bottom 500 ft (152.4m) to obtain α values. The roughness lengths z_o selected to represent exposure categories A, B, C, and D were 0.3, 0.1, 0.01, and 0.003 m, consistent with gust speed [68]. The α values are rounded for use in the standard. The α values of Table C6-2 increase the K_z values for exposure categories A and B while decreasing the values for exposure category D as compared to values of K_z in ASCE 7-93. In addition, differences in K_z values between exposure categories are reduced; e.g. for exposure category B at 30 ft (9 m) the value of $K_z = 0.7$ in Table 6-3 as compared to the value of $K_z = 0.5$ in ASCE 7-93. The new values of K_z in Table 6-3 are very close to the values specified in the Australian Standard [34], which also uses the 3-second gust speed format; this agreement lends credence to the new values of α listed in Table C6-2.

The effect of applying the various exposure category factors to the velocity pressure, q_z, and the velocity pressure exposure coefficient, K_z, is illustrated in Table C6-3.

Topographic factor. This factor is described in C6.5.5.

Importance factor. The importance factor is used to adjust the level of structural reliability of a building or other structure to be consistent with the building classifications indicated in Table 1-1. The importance factors given in Table 6-2 adjust the velocity pressure for annual probabilities of being exceeded other than the value of 0.02 (50-year mean recurrence interval) on which Fig. 6-1 is based. Importance-factor values of 0.87 and 1.15 are associated, respectively, with annual probabilities of being exceeded of 0.04 and 0.01 (mean recurrence intervals of 25 and 100 years). These values represent the square of the importance factors used in ASCE 7-93, which were applied to the basic wind speed rather than to the velocity pressure, except that the $(0.95)^2 = 0.90$ factor was changed to 0.87 based on new data analysis.

Because the probability distributions of hurricane winds and extratropical winds are different (Weibull versus Fisher-Tippett Type I), it is necessary to apply a hurricane importance factor to ensure the same probability of overload in hurricane-prone regions as in other regions. ASCE 7-93 specified a hurricane importance factor of 1.05 (for a mean recurrence interval of 50 years) to be

TABLE C6-2
Exposure Category Constants

Exposure Category	α	z_g [ft (m)]
A	5.0	1,500 (457)
B	7.0	1,200 (366)
C	9.5	900 (274)
D	11.5	700 (213)

TABLE C6-3
Velocity Pressure, $q = 0.00256K_zV^2$ (psf) for $I = 1.0$ and $K_{zt} = 1.0$
[Velocity Pressure $q = 0.613K_zV^2$ (N/m² for $I = 1.0$ and $K_{zt} = 1.0$)]

Wind Zone	Height, z, Above Ground Level							
	0-15 ft (0–4.6 m)	30 ft (9.1 m)	50 ft (15.2 m)	100 ft (30.5 m)	200 ft (60.9 m)	300 ft (91.4 m)	400 ft (121.9 m)	500 ft (152.4 m)
A 85 (38.0 m/s)	5.9 (283)	7.8 (374)	9.6 (460)	13 (623)	17 (814)	19 (910)	22 (1,054)	24 (1,150)
A 90 (40.2 m/s)	6.6 (316)	8.7 (417)	11 (527)	14 (671)	19 (910)	22 (1,054)	24 (1,150)	27 (1,293)
A110 (49.2 m/s)	10 (479)	13 (623)	16 (766)	21 (1,006)	28 (1,341)	33 (1,581)	37 (1,772)	40 (1,916)
A130 (58.1 m/s)	14 (671)	18 (862)	22 (1,054)	29 (1,389)	39 (1,868)	45 (2,156)	51 (2,443)	56 (2,682)
A150 (67.1 m/s)	18 (862)	24 (1,150)	30 (1,437)	39 (1,868)	52 (2,491)	61 (2,922)	68 (3,257)	74 (3,545)
B 85 (38.0 m/s)	11 (527)	13 (623)	15 (710)	18 (862)	22 (1,054)	25 (1,198)	27 (1,293)	29 (1,389)
B 90 (40.2 m/s)	12 (575)	14 (671)	17 (814)	20 (958)	25 (1,198)	28 (1,341)	30 (1,437)	32 (1,532)
B110 (49.2)	18 (862)	22 (1,054)	25 (1,198)	31 (1,485)	37 (1,772)	42 (2,012)	45 (2,156)	48 (2,299)
B130 (58.1 m/s)	25 (1,198)	30 (1,437)	35 (1,677)	43 (2,060)	52 (2,491)	58 (2,778)	64 (3,066)	67 (3,209)
B150 (67.1 m/s)	33 (1,581)	40 (1,916)	47 (2,251)	57 (2,730)	69 (3,305)	78 (3,736)	85 (4,072)	90 (4,311)
C 85 (38.0 m/s)	16 (766)	18 (862)	20 (958)	23 (1,102)	27 (1,293)	29 (1,389)	31 (1,485)	33 (1,581)
C 90 (40.2 m/s)	18 (862)	20 (958)	23 (1,102)	26 (1,245)	30 (1,437)	33 (1,581)	35 (1,677)	37 (1,772)
C110 (49.2 m/s)	26 (1,245)	30 (1,437)	34 (1,629)	39 (1,868)	45 (2,156)	49 (2,347)	52 (2,491)	55 (2,635)
C130 (58.1 m/s)	37 (1,772)	42 (2,012)	47 (2,251)	55 (2,635)	63 (3,018)	69 (3,305)	73 (3,497)	77 (3,688)
C150 (67.1 m/s)	49 (2,347)	56 (2,682)	63 (3,018)	73 (3,497)	84 (4,024)	92 (4,407)	97 (4,646)	102 (4,886)
D 85 (38.0 m/s)	19 (910)	22 (1,054)	24 (1,150)	26 (1,245)	30 (1,437)	32 (1,533)	34 (1,629)	35 (1,677)
D 90 (40.2 m/s)	21 (1,006)	24 (1,150)	26 (1,245)	30 (1,437)	33 (1,581)	36 (1,724)	38 (1,820)	39 (1,868)
D110 (49.2 m/s)	32 (1,533)	36 (1,724)	39 (1,868)	44 (2,108)	50 (2,395)	54 (2,587)	56 (2,682)	58 (2,778)
D130 (58.1 m/s)	45 (2,156)	50 (2,395)	55 (2,635)	62 (2,970)	70 (3,353)	75 (3,593)	79 (3,784)	82 (3,928)
D150 (67.1 m/s)	59 (2,826)	67 (3,209)	73 (3,496)	82 (3,928)	93 (4,455)	100 (4,790)	105 (5,030)	109 (5,221)

NOTES:
1. Linear interpolation for intermediate values of height z is acceptable.
2. For values of height z greater than 500 ft (152.4 m), q_z shall be calculated using values of K_z from Eq. (C3).
3. Exposure categories are defined in 6.5.3.

applied to the basic wind speed at the hurricane oceanline and which decreased linearly with distance to a value of 1.0 at 100 mi (161 km) inland. Although it is not shown explicitly in this revision of the Standard, this same hurricane importance factor has been incorporated in the wind speeds of Fig. 6-1, along with the difference in gust factor for hurricane and extratropical wind speeds. This adjustment factor decreases linearly to a value of 1.0 at the 90 mph (40 m/s) contour.

The probability P_n that the wind speed associated with a certain annual probability P_a will be equaled or exceeded at least once during an exposure period of n years is given by

$$P_n = 1 - (1 - P_a)^n \tag{C4}$$

and values of P_n for various values of P_a and n are listed in Table C6-4. As an example, if a design wind speed is based upon $P_a = 0.02$ (50 year mean recurrence interval), there exists a probability of 0.40 that this speed will be equaled or exceeded dur-

153

TABLE C6-4
Probability of Exceeding Design Wind Speed During Reference Period

Annual Probability Pa	Reference Period, n (years)					
	1	5	10	25	50	100
0.04	0.04	0.18	0.34	0.64	0.87	0.98
0.02	0.02	0.10	0.18	0.40	0.64	0.87
0.01	0.01	0.05	0.10	0.22	0.40	0.64
0.005	0.005	0.02	0.05	0.10	0.22	0.39

ing a 25-year period, and a 0.64 probability of being equaled or exceeded in a 50-year period.

For applications of serviceability, design using maximum likely events, or other applications, it may be desired to use wind speeds associated with mean recurrence intervals other than 50 years. To accomplish this, the 50-year speeds of Fig. 6-1 are multiplied by the factors listed in Table C6-5.

6.5.2 Selection of Basic Wind Speed

The wind speed map of Fig. 6-1 presents basic wind speeds for the contiguous United States, Alaska and other selected locations. The wind speeds correspond to 3-sec gust speeds at 33 ft (10 m) above ground for exposure category C and are associated with an annual probability of 0.02 that they will be equaled or exceeded (50-year mean recurrence interval). Because the National Weather Service has phased out the measurement of fastest-mile wind speeds, the basic wind speed has been redefined as the peak gust that is recorded and archived for most NWS stations. Given the response characteristics of the instrumentation used, the peak gust is associated with an averaging time of approximately 3 sec. Because the wind speeds of Fig. 6-1 reflect conditions at airports and similar open-country exposures, they do not account for

the effects of significant topographic features such as those described in 6.5.5. Note that the wind speeds shown in Fig. 6-1 are not representative of speeds at which structural failures (ultimate limit states) are expected to occur. Allowable stresses or load factors used in the design equation(s) lead to structural resistances and corresponding wind loads and speeds that are substantially higher than the speeds shown in Fig. 6-1.

The wind speed map of Fig. 6-1 was prepared from peak gust data collected at 485 weather stations where at least five years of data were available [29],[30], and from predictions of hurricane speeds on the U.S. Gulf and Atlantic coasts [5],[15],[54]. For nonhurricane regions, measured gust data were assembled from a number of stations in state-sized areas to decrease sampling error, and the assembled data were fit using a Fisher-Tippett Type I extreme value distribution. This procedure gives the same speed as does area-averaging the 50-year speeds from the set of stations. There was insufficient variation in 50-year speeds over the eastern 3/4 of the lower 48 states to justify contours. The division between the 90 and 85 mph (40.2 and 38.0 m/s) regions, which follows state lines, was sufficiently close to the 85 mph (38.0 m/s) contour that there was no statistical basis for placing the division off political boundaries.

Limited data were available on the Washington and Oregon coast; in this region, existing fastest-mile wind speed data were converted to peak gust speeds using open-country gust factors [13]. This limited data indicates that a speed of 100 mph is appropriate in some portions of the special wind region in Washington and 90 mph in the special wind region in Oregon; these speeds do not include that portion of the special wind region in the Columbia River Gorge where higher speeds may be justified. Speeds in the Aleutian Islands and in the interior of Alaska were established from gust data. Contours in Alaska are modified slightly from ASCE 7-88 based on measured data, but in-

TABLE C6-5
Conversion Factors for Other Mean Recurrence Intervals

	50-yr mean recurrence interval (MRI) Peak gust wind speed, V (mph) (m/s)		
	Continental U.S.		
MRI (years)	$V = 85\text{-}100$ (38-45 m/s)	$V > 100$ (hurricane) (44.7 m/s)	Alaska
500	1.23	1.33	1.18
200	1.14	1.21	1.12
100	1.07	1.105	1.06
50	1.00	1.00	1.00
25	0.93	0.89 (84 mph min.) (37.5 m/s)	0.94
10	0.84	0.73 (76 mph min.) (33.9 m/s)	0.87
5	0.78	0.52 (70 mph min.) (31.3 m/s)	0.81

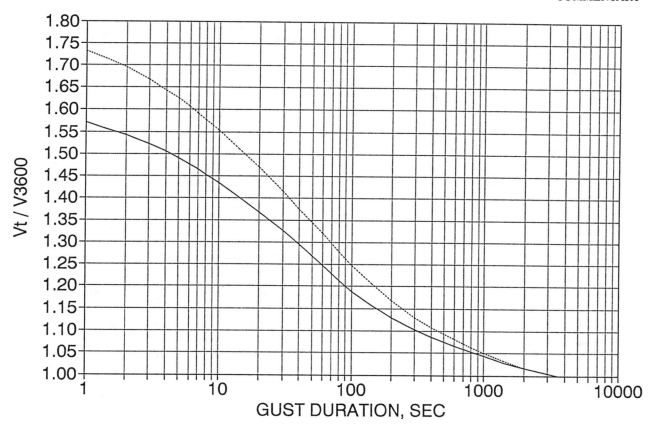

Fig. C6-1. Ratio of Probable Maximum Speed Averaged Over *t* sec to Hourly Mean Speed

sufficient data were available for a detailed coverage of the mountainous regions.

The wind-speed contours in the hurricane-prone region of Fig. 6-1 are based on analyses of hurricane winds [5],[15],[54]. The analyses involved Monte Carlo simulations of hurricanes striking the coastal region. The coastline was divided into discrete points spaced at 50 nautical miles (92.5 km) [5],[15], or at specific locations of interest [54]. The results of the analyses provided wind speeds at each point for various probabilities of being exceeded. Speeds in the three studies were converted from specified time durations to peak gusts using appropriate gust factors as shown in Fig. C6-1 [13],[20]. Hurricane wind speed contours over the Atlantic were placed there only for interpolations and represent values for exposure C over land.

6.5.2.1 Special Wind Regions

Although the wind-speed map of Fig. 6-1 is valid for most regions of the country, there are special re-gions in which wind-speed anomalies are known to exist. Some of these special regions are noted in Fig. 6-1. Winds blowing over mountain ranges or through gorges or river valleys in these special regions can develop speeds that are substantially higher than the values indicated on the map. When selecting basic wind speeds in these special regions, use of regional climatic data and consultation with a wind engineer or meteorologist is advised.

It is also possible that anomalies in wind speeds exist on a micrometeorological scale. For example, wind speed-up over hills and escarpments is addressed in 6.5.5. Wind speeds over complex terrain may be better determined by wind-tunnel studies as described in 6.4.3. Adjustments of wind speeds should be made at the micrometeorological scale on the basis of wind engineering or meteorological advice and used in accordance with the provisions of 6.5.2.2 when such adjustments are warranted.

155

COMMENTARY

6.5.2.2 Estimation of Basic Wind Speeds from Regional Climatic Data.

When using regional climatic data in accordance with the provisions of 6.5.2.2 and in lieu of the basic wind speeds given in Fig. 6-1, the user is cautioned that the gust factors, velocity pressure exposure coefficients, gust effect factors, pressure coefficients, and force coefficients of this Standard are intended for use with the 3-sec gust speed at 33 ft (10 m) above ground in open country. It is necessary, therefore, that regional climatic data based on a different averaging time, for example hourly mean or fastest mile, be adjusted to reflect peak gust speeds at 33 ft (10 m) above ground in open country. The results of statistical studies of wind-speed records, reported by [13] for extratropical winds and by [20] for hurricanes, are given in Fig. C6-1 which defines the relation between wind speed averaged over t seconds, V_t, and over one hour, V_{3600}. This adjustment to reflect peak gust speeds is not always straightforward and advice from a wind engineer or meteorologist may be needed.

In using local data, it should be emphasized that sampling errors can lead to large uncertainties in specification of the 50-year wind speed. Sampling errors are the errors associated with the limited size of the climatological data samples (years of record of annual extremes). It is possible to have a 20 mph (8.9 m/s) error in wind speed at an individual station with a record length of 30 years. It was this type of error that led to the large variations in speed in the non-hurricane areas of the ASCE 7-88 wind map. While local records of limited extent often must be used to define wind speeds in special wind areas, care and conservatism should be exercised in their use.

If meteorological data are used to justify a wind speed lower than 85-mph 50-year peak gust at 10 m, an analysis of sampling error is required to demonstrate that the wind record could not occur by chance. This can be accomplished by showing that the difference between the predicted speed and 85 mph contains two to three standard deviations of sampling error [67]. Other equivalent methods may be used.

6.5.2.3 Limitation.

In recent years, advances have been made in understanding the effects of tornadoes on buildings. This understanding has been gained through extensive documentation of building damage caused by tornadic storms and through analysis of collected data. It is recognized that tornadic wind speeds have a significantly lower probability of occurrence at a point than the probability for basic wind speeds. In addition, it is found that in approximately one-half of the recorded tornadoes, speeds are less than the gust speeds associated with basic wind speeds. In intense tornadoes, wind speeds near the ground are in the range of 150–200 mph (67–89 m/s). Sufficient information is available to implement tornado resistant design for above-ground shelters and for buildings that house essential facilities for postdisaster recovery. This information is in the form of tornado risk probabilities, tornadic wind speeds, and associated forces. Several references provide guidance in developing wind load criteria for tornado-resistant design [1],[2],[24] through [28],[57].

Tornadic gust wind speeds associated with an annual probability of occurrence of 1×10^{-5} (100,000 year mean recurrence interval) are shown in Fig. C6-1A. This map was developed by the American Nuclear Society committee ANS 2.3 in the early 1980s. Tornado occurrence data for the last 15 years can provide a more accurate tornado hazard wind speed for a specific site.

6.5.3 Exposure Categories.

With the exception of Exposure D, the definitions of the four exposure categories are unchanged from ASCE 7-93. For Exposure D, large bodies of water have been defined to mean open water for a distance of at least 1 mi. (1.6 km). In selecting an exposure category, the user of the Standard is cautioned that the terrain representative of the selected exposure must extend the prescribed minimum distance upwind of the building site.

6.5.4 Shielding.

Due to the lack of reliable analytical procedures for predicting the effects of shielding provided by buildings and other structures or by topographic features, reductions in velocity pressure due to shielding are not permitted under the provisions of 6.4.2. However, this does not preclude the determination of shielding effects and the corresponding reductions in velocity pressure by means of the wind tunnel procedure in 6.4.3.

6.5.5 Wind Speed-Up over Hills and Escarpments.

Buildings sited on the upper half of an isolated hill or escarpment may experience significantly higher wind speeds than buildings situated on level ground. To account for these higher wind speeds, the velocity pressure exposure coefficients in Table 6-3 are multiplied by a topographic factor, K_{zt}, defined in Eq. (2) of Section 6.5.5. The topographic feature (two-dimensional ridge or escarpment, or three-dimensional axisymmetrical hill) is described by two parameters, H and L_h. H is the height of the hill

156

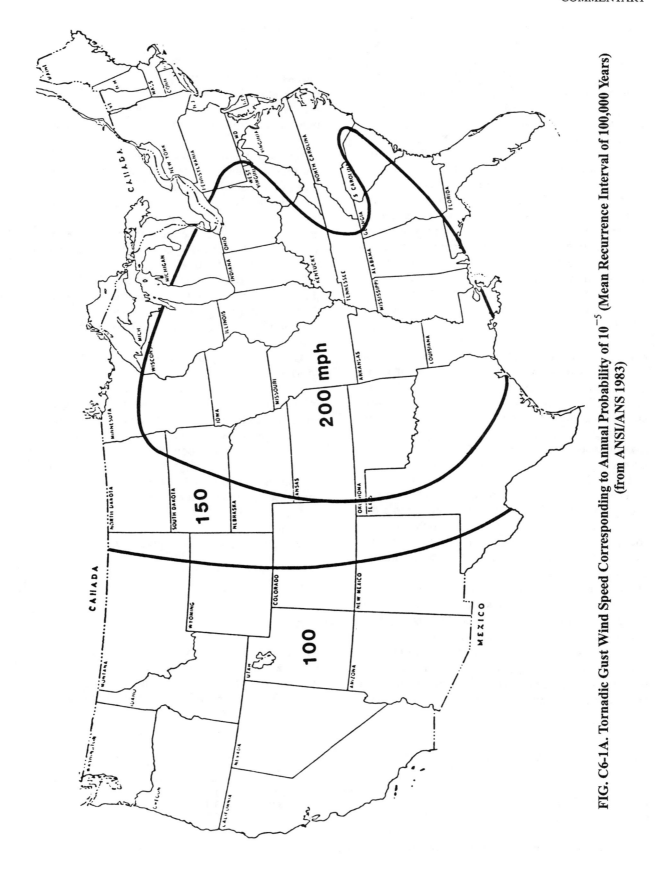

FIG. C6-1A. Tornadic Gust Wind Speed Corresponding to Annual Probability of 10^{-5} (Mean Recurrence Interval of 100,000 Years) (from ANSI/ANS 1983)

or difference in elevation between the crest and that of the upwind terrain. L_h is the distance upwind of the crest to where the ground elevation is equal to half the height of the hill. K_{zt} is determined from three multipliers, K_1, K_2 and K_3, which are obtained from Fig. 6-2, respectively. K_1 is related to the shape of the topographic feature and the maximum speed-up near the crest, K_2 accounts for the reduction in speed-up with distance upwind or downwind of the crest, and K_3 accounts for the reduction in speed-up with height above the local ground surface.

The multipliers listed in Fig. 6-2 are based on the assumption that the wind approaches the hill along the direction of maximum slope, causing the greatest speed-up near the crest. The average maximum upwind slope of the hill is approximately $H/2L_h$, and measurements have shown that hills with slopes of less than about 0.10 ($H/L_h < 0.20$) are unlikely to produce significant speed-up of the wind. For values of $H/L_h > 0.5$ the speed-up effect is assumed to be independent of slope. The speed-up principally affects the mean wind speed rather than the amplitude of the turbulent fluctuations and this fact has been accounted for in the values of K_1, K_2 and K_3 given in Fig. 6-2. Therefore, values of K_{zt} obtained from Table 6-2 are intended for use with velocity pressure exposure coefficients, K_h and K_z, which are based on gust speeds.

The lower bounds placed on the height H for exposure categories B, C and D are intended to aid the user in screening out those situations where speed-up effects can be ignored. The additional restriction that the upwind terrain be free of hills or escarpments for a distance equal to the smaller of $50H$ or 1 mi is intended to limit application of the topographic factor to those situations where the existing information is known to apply. It is not the intent of Section 6.5.5 to address the general case of wind flow over hilly or complex terrain for which engineering judgement, expert advice, or wind tunnel tests as described in Section 6.4.3 may be required. Background material on topographic speed-up effects may be found in the literature [18],[21],[56].

6.6 Gust Effect Factors

The gust effect factor accounts for the loading effects in the along-wind direction due to wind turbulence-structure interaction. It also accounts for along-wind loading effects due to dynamic amplification for flexible buildings and structures. It does not include allowances for across-wind loading effects, vortex shedding, instability due to galloping or flutter, or dynamic torsional effects. For structures susceptible to loading effects that are not accounted for in the gust effect factor, information should be obtained from recognized literature [60]–[65] or from wind-tunnel tests.

The gust effect factor is presented for three major categories namely: (1) Rigid structures—simplified method; (2) rigid structures—complete analysis; and (3) flexible or dynamically sensitive structures.

Category I: Rigid Structures—Simplified Method

For simplification, a gust effect factor, G, given in Section 6.6.1 may be used for rigid structures since the loads are computed corresponding to a 3-sec gust speed. As the size of structure increases the gust effect factor reduces to account for lack of correlation of the wind-induced loads over larger size surfaces. For very large buildings and for more accuracy the next case is appropriate.

Category II: Rigid Structures—Complete Analysis

The gust effect factor is given by

$$G = 0.9 \left(\frac{(1 + 7 I_{\bar{z}} Q)}{1 + 7 I_{\bar{z}}} \right) \qquad \text{(C6-5)}$$

$$I_{\bar{z}} = c \, (33/\bar{z})^{1/6} \qquad \text{(C6-6)}$$

where $I_{\bar{z}}$ = the intensity of turbulence at height $\bar{z}$, where $\bar{z}$ = the equivalent height of the structure (0.6 h but not less than z_{min} listed for each exposure in Table C6-6); c is given in Table C6-6; and

TABLE C6-6

Exp	$\hat{\alpha}$	$\hat{b}$	$\bar{\alpha}$	$\bar{b}$	c	l (ft)	ϵ	z_{min} (ft)
A	1/5	0.64	1/3.0	0.30	0.45	180	1/2.0	60
B	1/7	0.84	1/4.0	0.45	0.30	320	1/3.0	30
C	1/9.5	1.00	1/6.5	0.65	0.20	500	1/5.0	15
D	1/11.5	1.07	1/9.0	0.80	0.15	650	1/8.0	7

*z_{min} = minimum height used to ensure that the equivalent height $\bar{z}$ is greater of 0.6h or z_{min}.

Q represents the background response. Q is given by

$$Q^2 = \frac{1}{1 + 0.63 \left(\dfrac{b + h}{L_{\bar{z}}} \right)^{0.63}} \qquad \text{(C6-7)}$$

where b = structure width; h = structure height; and $L_{\bar{z}}$ = the integral length scale of turbulence at the equivalent height

$$L_{\bar{z}} = l \left(\bar{z} / 33 \right)^{\epsilon} \qquad \text{(C6-8)}$$

in which l and ϵ are as listed in Table C6-6. The factor 0.9 in Eq. C6-5 is used to account for additional size reduction effects as well as to adjust $(K_z G)$ values closer to the ASCE 7-93 values.

Category III—Flexible or Dynamically Sensitive Structures

The gust effect factor is given by

$$G = \frac{1 + 2g I_{\bar{z}} \sqrt{Q^2 + R^2}}{1 + 7 I_{\bar{z}}} \qquad \text{(C6-9)}$$

where R, the resonant response factor, is given by

$$R^2 = \frac{1}{\beta} R_n R_h R_b (0.53 + 0.47 R_d)$$

$$R_n = \frac{7.465 N_1}{(1 + 10.302 N_1)^{5/3}}$$

$$N_1 = \frac{n_1 L_{\bar{z}}}{\bar{V}_{\bar{z}}}$$

$$R_l = \begin{bmatrix} \dfrac{1}{\eta} - \dfrac{1}{2\eta^2}(1 - e^{-2\eta}) & \text{for } \eta > 0 \\[2ex] 1 & \text{for } \eta = 0 \end{bmatrix}$$

$(l = h, b, d)$

$R_l = R_h$ setting $\eta = 4.6 n_1 h / \bar{V}_{\bar{z}}$
$R_l = R_b$ setting $\eta = 4.6 n_1 b / \bar{V}_{\bar{z}}$
$R_l = R_d$ setting $\eta = 15.4 n_1 d / \bar{V}_{\bar{z}}$
β = damping ratio
$\bar{V}_{\bar{z}}$ = mean hourly wind speed at height $\bar{z}$, in ft/sec

$$\bar{V}_{\bar{z}} = \bar{b} \left(\frac{\bar{z}}{33} \right)^{\bar{\alpha}} \hat{V}_{\text{ref}}$$

where $\bar{b}$ and $\bar{\alpha}$ are listed in Table C6-6.

The peak factor, g, may be taken approximately equal to 3.5 in lieu of the calculated values. It is important to note that for $g = 3.5$ and R equal to

zero for a rigid structure, Eq. (C6-9) reduces to the case of G for a rigid structure-complete analysis [Eq. (C6-5)], unreduced by the factor of 0.9.

Along-Wind Response

Based on the preceeding definition of the gust effect factor, predictions of along-wind response, e.g., maximum displacement, rms, and peak acceleration, can be made. These response components are needed for survivability and serviceability limit states. In the following, expressions for evaluating these along-wind response components are given.

Maximum Along-Wind Displacement

The maximum along-wind displacement $X_{\max}(z)$ as a function of height above the ground surface is given by

$$X_{\max}(z) = \frac{\phi(z) \, \rho \, b \, h \, C_{fx} \hat{V}_{\bar{z}}^2}{2 \, m_1 \, (2 \pi n_1)^2} K G \qquad \text{(C6-10)}$$

where $\phi(z)$ = the fundamental mode shape $\phi(z)$ = $(z/h)^{\xi}$; ξ = the mode exponent; ρ = air density; C_{fx} = mean alongwind force coefficient; m_1 = modal mass = $\int_0^h \mu(z) \phi^2(z) \, dz$; $\mu(z)$ = mass per unit height; $K = (1.65)^{\hat{\alpha}} / (\hat{\alpha} + \xi + 1)$; and $\hat{V}_{\bar{z}}$ is the 3-sec gust speed at height $\bar{z}$. This can be evaluated by $\hat{V}_{\bar{z}} = \hat{b} \, (z/33)^{\hat{\alpha}} \, \hat{V}_{\text{ref}}$, where $\hat{V}_{\text{ref}}$ is the 3-sec gust speed in exposure C at the reference height (obtained from Fig. 6-1); $\hat{b}$ and $\hat{a}$ are given in Table C6-6.

RMS Alongwind Acceleration

The rms alongwind acceleration $\sigma_{\ddot{x}}(z)$ as a function of height above the ground surface is given by

$$\sigma_{\ddot{x}}(z) = \frac{0.85 \, \phi(z) \, \rho \, b \, h \, C_{fx} \, \bar{V}_{\bar{z}}^2}{m_1} I_{\bar{z}} K R \qquad \text{(C6-11)}$$

Maximum Alongwind Acceleration

The maximum alongwind acceleration as a function of height above the ground surface is given by

$$\ddot{X}_{\max}(z) = g_{\ddot{x}} \sigma_{\ddot{x}}(z) \qquad \text{(C6-12)}$$

$$g_{\ddot{x}} = \sqrt{2 \ln(n_1 T)} + \frac{0.5772}{\sqrt{2 \ln(n_1 T)}}$$

where T = the length of time over which the minimum acceleration is computed, usually taken to be 3,600 sec to represent 1 hr.

Example

The following example is presented to illustrate the calculation of the gust effect factor. Table C6-7 uses the given information to obtain values from

Table C6-6. Table C6-8 presents the calculated values. Table C6-9 summarizes the calculated displacements and accelerations as a function of the height, z.

Given Values

Basic wind speed at reference height in exposure C = 90 mph

Type of exposure = A

Building height h = 600 ft

Building width b = 100 ft

Building depth d = 100 ft

Building natural frequency n_1 = 0.2 Hz

Damping ratio = 0.01

C_{fx} = 1.3

Mode exponent = 1.0

Building density = 12 lb/cu ft

    = 0.3727 slugs/cu ft

Air density = 0.0024 slugs/cu ft

6.7 Pressure and Force Coefficients

The pressure and force coefficients provided in Figs. 6-3–6-8 and in Tables 6-4–6-10 have been assembled from the latest boundary-layer wind-tunnel and full-scale tests and from previously available literature. Since the boundary-layer wind tunnel results were obtained for specific types of building such as low- or high-rise buildings and buildings having specific types of structural framing systems, the designer is cautioned against indiscriminate interchange of values among the figures and tables.

Loads on Main Wind-Force Resisting Systems Figs. 6-3 and 6-4. The pressure coefficients for main wind-force resisting systems are separated into two categories:

1. Buildings of all heights (Fig. 6-3); and
2. Low-rise buildings having a height less than or equal to 60 ft (18 m) (Fig. 6-4).

In generating these coefficients, two distinctly different approaches were used. For the pressure

TABLE C6-7
Values Obtained from Table C6-6

z_{min}	60 ft
ϵ	0.5
c	0.45
$\bar{b}$	0.3
$\bar{\alpha}$	0.33
$\hat{b}$	0.64
$\hat{\alpha}$	0.2
l	180
C_{fx}	1.3
ξ	1
Height (h)	600 ft
Base (b)	100 ft
Depth (d)	100 ft

TABLE C6-8
Calculated Values

$\hat{V}_{ref}$	132 ft/s		
$\bar{z}$	360 ft		
$I_{\bar{z}}$	0.302		
$L_{\bar{z}}$	594.52 ft		
Q^2	0.589		
$\bar{V}_{\bar{z}}$	87.83 ft/s		
$\hat{V}_{\bar{z}}$	136.24 ft/s		
N_1	1.354		
R_n	0.111		
η	1.047	R_b	0.555
η	6.285	R_h	0.146
η_2	3.507	R_d	0.245
R^2	0.580		
G	1.055		
K	0.502		
m_1	745,400 slugs		
$g\dot{x}$	3.787		

TABLE C6-9
Response Estimate

z (ft)	$\phi(z)$	$X_{max}(z)$	Rms Acc. (ft/sec²)	Rms Acc. (milli-g)	Max. Acc. (ft/sec²)	Max. Acc. (milli-g)
0.0	0.00	0.00	0.00	0.00	0.00	0.00
60.0	0.10	0.08	0.02	0.6	0.07	2.2
120.0	0.20	0.16	0.04	1.2	0.14	4.5
180.0	0.30	0.23	0.06	1.8	0.22	6.7
240.0	0.40	0.31	0.08	2.4	0.29	8.9
300.0	0.50	0.39	0.10	3.0	0.36	11.2
360.0	0.60	0.47	0.11	3.5	0.43	13.4
420.0	0.70	0.55	0.13	4.1	0.50	15.7
480.0	0.80	0.63	0.15	4.7	0.58	17.9
540.0	0.90	0.70	0.17	5.3	0.65	20.1
600.0	1.00	0.78	0.19	5.9	0.72	22.4

coefficients given in Fig. 6-3, the more traditional approach was followed and the pressure coefficients reflect the actual loading on each surface of the building as a function of wind direction; namely, winds perpendicular or parallel to the ridge line.

For low-rise buildings having a height less than or equal to 60 ft (18 m), however, the values of GC_{pf} in Fig. 6-4 represent "pseudo" loading conditions (Case A and Case B) which, when applied to the building, envelope the desired structural actions (bending moment, shear, thrust) independent of wind direction and exposure. To capture all appropriate structural actions, the building must be designed for all wind directions by considering in turn each corner of the building as the windward corner shown in the sketches of Fig. 6-4. Note also that for all roof slopes, load case A and load case

B must be considered individually in order to determine the critical loading for a given structural assemblage or component thereof. These two separate loading conditions are required for each of the windward corners to generate the wind actions, including torsion, to be resisted by the structural systems. Note that the building "end zones" must be aligned in accordance with the assumed windward corner (see Fig. C6-2).

To develop the appropriate "pseudo" values of GC_{pf}, investigators at the University of Western Ontario [11] used an approach which consisted essentially of permitting the building model to rotate in the wind tunnel through a full 360 degrees while simultaneously monitoring the loading conditions on each of the surfaces (see Fig. C6-3). Both exposures B and C were considered. Using influence coefficients for

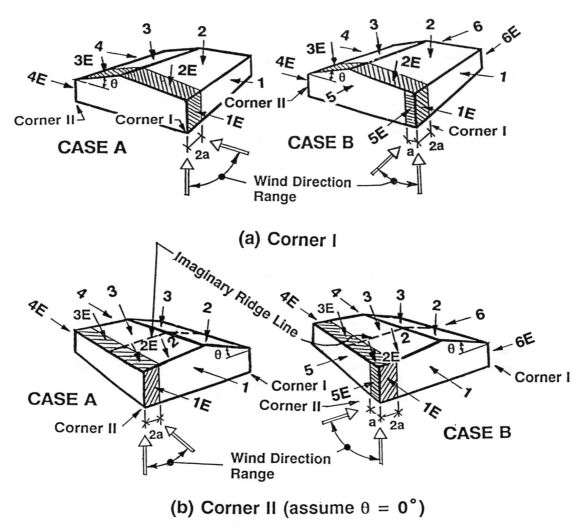

(a) Corner I

(b) Corner II (assume θ = 0°)

FIG. C6-2. Application of Load Cases for Two Windward Corners

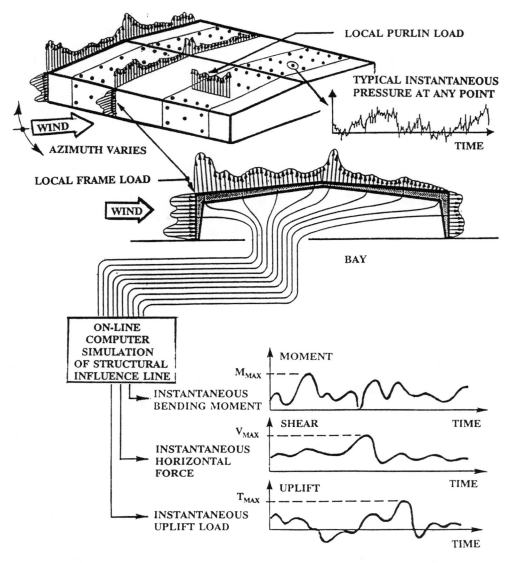

FIG. C6-3. Unsteady Wind Loads on Low Building for Given Wind Direction (after [11])

rigid frames, it was possible to spatially average and time average the surface pressures to ascertain the maximum induced external force components to be resisted. More specifically, the following structural actions were evaluated:

1. total uplift;
2. total horizontal shear;
3. bending moment at knees (two-hinged frame);
4. bending moment at knees (three-hinged frame); and
5. bending moment at ridge (two-hinged frame).

The next step involved developing sets of "pseudo" pressure coefficients to generate loading conditions which would envelope the maximum induced force components to be resisted for all possible wind directions and exposures. Note, for example, that the wind azimuth producing the maximum bending moment at the knee would not necessarily produce the maximum total uplift. The maximum induced external force components determined for each of the above five categories were used to develop the coefficients. The end result was a set of coefficients that represent fictitious loading conditions, but conservatively enve-

162

lope the maximum induced force components (bending moment, shear, and thrust) to be resisted, independent of wind direction.

The original set of coefficients was generated for the framing of conventional pre-engineered buildings, i.e., single story moment-resisting frames in one of the principal directions and bracing in the other principal direction. The approach was later extended to single story moment-resisting frames with interior columns [19].

Subsequent wind tunnel studies [69] have shown that the GC_{pf} values of Fig. 6-4 are also applicable to low-rise buildings with structural systems other than moment-resisting frames. That work examined the instantaneous wind pressures on a low-rise building with a 4:12 pitched gable roof and the resulting wind-induced forces on its main wind-force resisting system. Two (2) different main wind-force resisting systems were evaluated. One consisted of shear walls and roof trusses at different spacings. The other had moment resisting frames in one direction, positioned at the same spacings as the roof trusses, and diagonal wind bracing in the other direction. Wind tunnel tests were conducted for both Exposures B and C. The findings of this study showed that the GC_{pf} values of Fig. 6-4 provided satisfactory estimates of the wind forces for both types of structural systems. This work confirms the validity of Fig. 6-4, which reflects the combined action of wind pressures on different external surfaces of a building and thus takes advantage of spatial averaging.

In the wind tunnel experiments, both B and C exposure terrains were checked. In these experiments, B exposure did not include nearby buildings. In general, the force components, bending moments, etc. were found comparable in both exposures, although GC_{pf} values associated with Exposure B Terrain would be higher than that for Exposure C terrain because of reduced velocity pressure in Exposure B terrain. The GC_{pf} values given in Fig. 6-4 (also in Figs. 6-5 through 6-7) are associated with Exposure C terrain as obtained in the wind tunnel; hence they are required to be used with velocity pressure for Exposure C, irrespective of surrounding terrain.

In recent comprehensive wind tunnel studies conducted at the University of Western Ontario [66], it was determined that when low buildings [$h < 60$ ft (18 m)] are embedded in suburban terrain (Exposure B which included nearby buildings), the pressures in most cases are lower than those currently used in existing standards and

codes, although the values show a very large scatter because of high turbulence and many variables. The results seem to indicate that some reduction in pressures for buildings located in Exposure B is justified; a 15% reduction in calculated pressures is permitted for buildings sited in Exposure B.

Fig. 6-4 is most appropriate for low buildings with width greater than twice their height and a mean roof height that does not exceed 33 ft (10 m). The original data base included low buildings with width no greater than five times their eave height, and eave height did not exceed 33 ft (10 m). In the absence of more appropriate data, Fig. 6-4 may also be used for buildings with mean roof height that does not exceed the least horizontal dimension and is less than or equal to 60 ft (18 m). Beyond these extended limits, Fig. 6-3 should be used.

Internal pressure coefficients (GC_{pi}) to be used for loads on main wind-force resisting systems are given in Table 6-4. The internal pressure load can be critical in one-story moment resisting frames and in the top story of a building where the main wind-force resisting system consists of moment resisting frames. Loading cases with positive and negative internal pressures should be considered. The internal pressure load cancels out in the determination of total lateral load and base shear. The designer should use judgment in the use of internal pressure loading for the main wind-force resisting system of high-rise buildings.

Loads on Components and Cladding

In developing the set of pressure coefficients applicable for the design of components and cladding as given in Figs. 6-5 through 6-7, an envelope approach was followed but using different methods than for the main wind-force resisting systems of Fig. 6-4. Because of the small effective area which may be involved in the design of a particular component (consider, for example, the effective area associated with the design of a fastener), the point-wise pressure fluctuations may be highly correlated over the effective area of interest. Consider the local purlin loads shown in Fig. C6-3. The approach involved spatial averaging and time averaging of the point pressures over the effective area transmitting loads to the purlin while the building model was permitted to rotate in the wind tunnel through 360°. As the induced localized pressures may also vary widely as a function of the specific location on the building, height above ground level, exposure, and more importantly, local geometric discontinuities and location of the element relative to the boundaries in the building surfaces (walls, roof lines), these factors were also enveloped in the wind tunnel tests. Thus, for the pressure coefficients given in Figs. 6-5–6-7, the directionality of the wind and influence of exposure have been removed and the surfaces of the building "zoned" to reflect an envelope of the peak pressures possible for a given design application. Again, the pressure coefficients are all referenced to Exposure C.

As indicated in the discussion for Fig. 6-4, the wind tunnel experiments checked both B and C exposure terrains. Basically GC_p values associated with Exposure B terrain would be higher than those for Exposure C terrain because of reduced velocity pressure in Exposure B terrain. The GC_p values given in Figs. 6-5–6-7 are associated with Exposure C terrain as obtained in the wind tunnel; hence they are required to be used with velocity pressure for Exposure C, irrespective of surrounding terrain.

The wind tunnel studies conducted by Ho [66] determined that when low buildings ($h <$ 60 ft) are embedded in suburban terrain (Exposure B), the pressures on components and cladding in most cases are lower than those currently used in the standards and codes, although the values show a very large scatter because of high turbulence and many variables. The results seem to indicate that some reduction in pressures for components and cladding of buildings located in Exposure B is justified; a 15% reduction in calculated pressures is permitted for buildings sited in Exposure B.

The pressure coefficients given in Fig. 6-8 for buildings with mean height greater than 60 feet were developed following a similar approach, but the influence of exposure was not enveloped. Therefore, exposure categories B, C, or D may be used with the values of GC_p in Fig. 6-8 as appropriate. Exposure A is not to be used with Fig. 6-8 as the orientation of buildings in metropolitan areas can produce increased turbulence and channeling and wake effects that result in higher localized pressures on components and cladding than would be predicted based on K_z values for exposure A.

Fig. 6-5. The pressure coefficient values provided in this figure are to be used for buildings with a mean roof height of 60 ft (18 m) or less. The values were obtained from wind-tunnel tests conducted at the University of Western Ontario

[10],[11], at the James Cook University of North Queensland [6], and at Concordia University [39],[40],[44],[45],[47]. These coefficients have been refined to reflect results of full-scale tests conducted by the National Bureau of Standards [22] and the Building Research Station, England [14]. Pressure coefficients for hemispherical domes on ground or on cylindrical structures have been reported [52]. Some of the characteristics of the values in the figure are as follows:

(1) The values are combined values of GC_p; the gust effect factors from these values should not be separated.
(2) The velocity pressure q_h evaluated at mean roof height should be used with all values of GC_p.
(3) The velocity pressure q_h for exposure category C (smooth terrain) should be used for all terrains.
(4) The values provided in the figure represent the upper bounds of the most severe values for any wind direction. The reduced probability that the design wind speed may not occur in the particular direction for which the worst pressure coefficient is recorded has not been included in the values shown in the figure.
(5) The wind-tunnel values, as measured, were based on the mean hourly wind speed. The values provided in the figures are the measured values divided by $(1.53)^2$ (see Fig. C6-1) to reflect the reduced pressure coefficient values associated with a three-second gust speed.

Each component and cladding element should be designed for the maximum positive and negative pressures (including applicable internal pressures) acting on it. The pressure coefficient values should be determined for each component and cladding element on the basis of its location on the building and the effective area for the element. As recent research has shown [41],[43], the pressure coefficients provided generally apply to facades with architectural features such as balconies, ribs, and various facade textures.

Figs. 6-6 and 6-7A. These figures present values of GC_p for the design of roof components and cladding for buildings with multispan gable roofs and buildings with monoslope roofs. The coefficients are based on wind tunnel studies reported by [46],[47],[51].

Fig. 6-7B. The values of GC_p in this figure are for the design of roof components and cladding for buildings with sawtooth roofs and mean roof height, h, less than or equal to 60 ft (18 m). Note that the coefficients for corner zones on segment A differ from those coefficients for corner zones on the segments designated as B, C and D. Also, when the roof angle is less than or equal to 10 degrees, values of GC_p for regular gabled roofs (Fig. 6-5B) are to be used. The coefficients included in Fig. 6-7B are based on wind tunnel studies reported by [35].

Fig. 6-8. The pressure coefficients shown in this figure have been revised to reflect the results obtained from comprehensive wind tunnel studies carried out by [42]. In general, the loads resulting from these coefficients are lower than those required by ASCE 7-93. However, the area averaging effect for roofs is less pronounced when compared with the requirements of ASCE 7-93. The availability of more comprehensive wind tunnel data has also allowed a simplification of the zoning for pressure coefficients; flat roofs are now divided into three zones, and walls are represented by two zones.

The external pressure coefficients and zones given in Fig. 6-8 were established by wind tunnel tests on isolated "box-like" buildings [2],[31]. Boundary-layer wind tunnel tests on high-rise buildings (mostly in downtown city centers) show that variations in pressure coefficients and the distribution of pressure on the different building facades are obtained [53]. These variations are due to building geometry, low attached buildings, non-rectangular cross sections, setbacks, and sloping surfaces. In addition, surrounding buildings contribute to the variations in pressure. Wind-tunnel tests indicate that pressure coefficients are not distributed symmetrically and can give rise to torsional wind loading on the building.

Boundary-layer wind tunnel tests that include modeling of surrounding buildings permit the establishment of more exact magnitudes and distributions of GC_p for buildings that are not isolated or "box-like" in shape.

Table 6-4. The internal pressure coefficient values provided in this table were obtained from wind-tunnel tests conducted at the University of Western Ontario [38] and from full-scale data obtained at Texas Tech University [59]. Even though the wind-tunnel tests were conducted primarily for low-rise buildings, the internal pressure coefficient values are assumed to be valid for buildings of any height. Because of the great amount of air leakage that often occurs at large hangar doors, designers should consider utilizing the internal pressure coefficient for partially enclosed buildings in Table 6-4.

Openings: Permanent openings in the roof or exterior walls which allow wind to flow into the building. Examples include air intakes/exhausts for air conditioning and/or ventilation systems, gaps around doors, deliberate gaps in cladding, and glazed openings as noted in Table 6-4.

Glazed Openings: An opening which is closed by glass or transparent or translucent plastic sheet (e.g., acrylic or polycarbonate). Examples include windows, skylights, and glass doors. Except as noted in Table 6-4, glazed openings shall be permitted to be considered as nonopenings.

Glazed openings in the bottom 60 ft of buildings that are sited in hurricane-prone regions with a basic wind speed of 110 mph or greater or in Hawaii, are either required to be designed for impact by wind-borne debris (missiles) or the building in that area should use the higher internal pressures in Table 6-4. Because of the nature of hurricane winds [27], glazed openings in buildings sited in hurricane areas are very vulnerable to breakage from missiles, unless the glazing can withstand reasonable missile loads and subsequent wind loading, or the glazing is protected by suitable shutters. Glazing above 60 ft (18 m) is also somewhat vulnerable to missile damage, but because of the greater height, this glazing is typically significantly less vulnerable to damage than glazing at lower levels. When glazed openings are breached by missiles, development of high internal pressure results, which can overload the cladding or structure if the higher pressure was not accounted for in the design. Breaching of glazed openings can also result in a significant amount of water infiltration, which typically results in considerable damage to the building and its contents [33],[49],[50].

If the option of designing for higher internal pressure (versus designing glazing protection) is selected, it should be realized that if glazing is breached, significant damage from overpressurization to interior partitions and ceilings is likely. The influence of compartmentation on the distribution of the increased internal pressure has not been researched. If the space behind breached glazing is separated from the remainder of the building by a sufficiently strong and reasonably air-tight compartment, the increased internal pressure would likely be confined to that compartment. However, if the compartment is breached (e.g., by an open corridor door, or by collapse of the compartment wall), the increased internal pressure will spread beyond the initial compartment quite rapidly. The next compartment may contain the higher pressure, or it too could be breached, thereby allowing the high internal pressure to continue to propagate.

Tables 6-5 to 6-10. With the exception of Table 6-10, the pressure and force coefficient values in these tables are unchanged from ANSI A58.1-1972 and 1982, and ASCE 7-88 and 7-93. The coefficients specified in these tables are based on wind-tunnel tests conducted under conditions of uniform flow and low turbulence, and their validity in turbulent boundary layer flows has yet to be completely established. Additional pressure coefficients for conditions not specified herein may be found in two references [3],[36]. With regard to Table 6-7, local maximum and minimum peak pressure coefficients for cylindrical structures with $h/D < 2$ are $GC_p = 1.1$ and $GC_p = -1.1$, respectively, for Reynolds numbers ranging from 1.1×10^5 to 3.1×10^5 [23]. The latter results have been obtained under correctly simulated boundary layer flow conditions.

With regard to Table 6-10, the force coefficients are a refinement of the coefficients specified in ANSI A58.1-1982 and in ASCE 7-93. The force coefficients specified are offered as a simplified procedure that may be used for trussed towers and are consistent with force coefficients given in ANSI/EIA/TIA-222-E-1991, Structural Standards for Steel Antenna Towers and Antenna Supporting Structures, and force coefficients recommended by Working Group No. 4 (Recommendations for Guyed Masts), International Association for Shell and Spatial Structures (1981).

It is not the intent of the Standard to exclude the use of other recognized literature for the design of special structures such as transmission and telecommunications towers. Recommendations for wind loads on tower guys are not provided as in previous editions of the Standard. Recognized literature should be referenced for the design of these special structures as is noted in C6.4.2.1. For the design of flagpoles, see ANSI/NAAMM FP1001-90, 3rd Ed., Guide Specifications for Design Loads of Metal Flagpoles.

6.8 Full and Partial Loading

General. Tall buildings should be checked for torsional response induced by partial wind loading and by eccentricity of the elastic center with respect to the resultant wind load vector and the center of mass. The load combinations described in Fig. 6-9 reflect surface pressure patterns that have been observed on tall buildings in turbulent wind. Wind tunnel tests have demonstrated that even a 25% selective load reduction can underestimate the wind-induced torsion in buildings with a uniform rectangular cross-section [51]. In some structural systems, more severe effects are observed when the resultant wind load acts diagonally to the building or other structure. To account for this effect and the fact that many structures exhibit maximum response in the across-wind direction, a structure should be capable of resisting 75% of the design wind loads applied simultaneously along the principal axes. Additional information on torsional response due to full and partial loading can be found in the literature [4],[17].

References

[1] Abbey, R.F. Risk probabilities associated with tornado wind speeds, *Proceedings of the Symposium on Tornadoes: Assessment of Knowledge and Implications for Man*, R.E. Peterson, Ed., Institute for Disaster Research, Texas Tech University, Lubbock, TX, 1976.

[2] Akins, R.E. and Cermak, J.E. Wind pressures on buildings, Technical Report CER7677REA-JEC15, Fluid Dynamics and Diffusion Lab, Colorado State University, Fort Collins, CO, 1975.

[3] ASCE Wind forces on structures, *Trans*, ASCE, 126(2), 1124–1198, 1961.

[4] Wind tunnel model studies of buildings and structures, *Manuals and Reports on Engineering Practice*, No. 67, American Society of Civil Engineers, New York, NY, 1987.

[5] Batts, M.E., Cordes, M.R., Russell, L.R., Shaver, J.R., and Simiu, E. Hurricane wind speeds in the United States, NBS Building Science Series 124, National Bureau of Standards, Washington, DC, 1980.

[6] Best, R.J. and Holmes, J.D. Model study of wind pressures on an isolated single-storey house, James Cook University of North Queensland, Australia, Wind Engineering Rep. 3/78, 1978.

[7] Boggs, D.W. and Peterka, J.A. Aerodynamic

model tests of tall buildings, *J. Engrg. Mech.*, 115(3), ASCE, New York, NY, 618–635, 1989.

[8] Cermak, J.E. Wind-tunnel testing of structures. *J. Engrg. Mech. Div.*, 103(6), ASCE, New York, NY, 1125–1140, 1977.

[9] Cheung, J.C.J. and Melbourne, W.H., Wind loadings on porous cladding, Proceedings of the 9th Australian Conference on Fluid Mechanics, pp. 308, 1986.

[10] Davenport, A.G., Surry, D. and Stathopoulos, T. Wind loads on low-rise buildings. Final Report on Phases I and II, BLWT-SS8, University of Western Ontario, London, Ontario, Canada, 1977.

[11] Davenport, A.G., Surry, D. and Stathopoulos, T. Wind loads on low-rise buildings. Final Report on Phase III, BLWT-SS4, University of Western Ontario, London, Ontario, Canada, 1978.

[12] Interim guidelines for building occupants' protection from tornadoes and extreme winds, TR-83A, Defense Civil Preparedness Agency, Washington, DC, 1975. [available from the Superintendent of Documents, U.S. Government Printing Office, Washington, DC 20402].

[13] Durst, C.S. Wind speeds over short periods of time, *Meteor. Mag.*, 89, 181–187, 1960.

[14] Eaton, K.J. and Mayne, J.R. The measurement of wind pressures on two-storey houses at Aylesbury, *J. Industrial Aerodynamics*, 1(1), 67–109, 1975.

[15] Georgiou, P.N., Davenport, A.G. and Vickery, B.J. Design wind speeds in regions dominated by tropical cyclones, *J. Wind Engrg. and Industrial Aerodynamics*, 13, 139–152, 1983.

[16] Haig, J.R. Wind Loads on Tiles For USA, Redland Technology Limited, Horsham, West Sussex, England, June 1990.

[17] Isyumov, N. "The Aeroelastic Modeling of Tall Buildings" *Proceedings of the International Workshop on Wind Tunnel Modeling Criteria and Techniques in Civil Engineering Applications*, Gaithersburg, MD, Cambridge University Press, 373–407, 1982.

[18] Jackson, P.S. and Hunt, J.C.R. "Turbulent Wind Flow Over a Low Hill." *Quarterly Journal of the Royal Meteorological Society*, Vol. 101, 929–955, 1975.

[19] Kavanagh, K.T., Surry, D., Stathopoulos, T. and Davenport, A.G. Wind loads on low-rise buildings: Phase IV, BLWT-SS14, University of Western Ontario, London, Ontario, Canada, 1983.

[20] Krayer, W.R. and Marshall, R.D. Gust factors applied to hurricane winds, *Bulletin of the American Meteorological Society*, Vol. 73, 613–617, 1992.

[21] Lemelin, D.R., Surry, D. and Davenport, A.G. Simple approximations for wind speed-up over hills, *J. Wind Engrg. and Industrial Aerodynamics*, 28, 117–127, 1988.

[22] Marshall, R.D. The measurement of wind loads on a full-scale mobile home. NBSIR 77-1289, National Bureau of Standards, U.S. Dept. of Commerce, Washington, DC, 1977.

[23] Macdonald, P.A., Kwok, K.C.S. and Holmes, J.H. Wind loads on isolated circular storage bins, silos and tanks: Point pressure measurements. Research Report No. R529, School of Civil and Mining Engineering, University of Sydney, Sydney, Australia, 1986.

[24] McDonald, J.R. A methodology for tornado hazard probability assessment, NUREG/CR3058, U.S. Nuclear Regulatory Commission, Washington, DC, 1983.

[25] Mehta, K.C., Minor, J.E. and McDonald, J.R. Wind speed analyses of April 3–4 Tornadoes, *J. Struct. Div.*, ASCE, 102(9), 1709–1724, 1976.

[26] Minor, J.E. Tornado technology and professional practice. *J. Struct. Div.*, ASCE, 108(11), 2411–2422, 1982.

[27] Minor, J.E. and Behr, R.A. Improving the performance of architectural glazing systems in hurricanes, *Proceedings* of Hurricanes of 1992, American Society of Civil Engineers (Dec. 1–3, 1993, Miami, FL), pp. C1–11, 1993.

[28] Minor, J.E., McDonald, J.R. and Mehta, K.C. The tornado: An engineering oriented perspective, TM ERL NSSL-82, National Oceanic and Atmospheric Administration, Environmental Research Laboratories, Boulder, CO, 1977.

[29] Peterka, J.A. Improved extreme wind prediction for the United States, *J. Wind Engrg. and Industrial Aerodynamics*, 41, 533–541, 1992.

[30] Peterka, J.A. and Shahid, S. Extreme gust wind speeds in the U.S., *Proceedings*, 7th U.S. National Conference on Wind Engineering, UCLA, Los Angeles, CA., 2, 503–512, 1993.

[31] Peterka, J.A. and Cermak, J.E. Wind pressures on buildings—Probability densities, *J. Struct. Div.*, ASCE, 101(6), 1255–1267, 1974.

[32] Perry, D.C., Stubbs, N. and Graham, C.W. Responsibility of architectural and engineering communities in reducing risks to life, property and economic loss from hurricanes, *Proceedings*, ASCE Conference on Hurricanes of 1992, Miami, FL, 1993.

[33] Reinhold, T.A. (Ed.). Wind tunnel modeling for civil engineering applications, *Proceedings of the International Workshop on Wind Tunnel Modeling Criteria and Techniques in Civil Engineering Applications*, Gaithersburg, MD, Cambridge University Press, 1982.

[34] Australian Standard SAA Loading Code, Part 2: Wind Loads, published by Standards Australia, Standards House, 80 Arthur St., North Sydney, NSW, Australia, 1989.

[35] Saathoff, P. and Stathopoulos, T. Wind loads on buildings with sawtooth roofs, *J. Struct. Engrg.*, ASCE, 118(2), 429–446, 1992.

[36] *Normen fur die Belastungsannahmen, die Inbetriebnahme und die Uberwachung der Bauten*, SIA Technische Normen Nr 160, Zurich, Switzerland, 1956.

[37] *Standard Building Code*, Southern Building Code Congress International, 1994.

[38] Stathopoulos, T., Surry, D. and Davenport, A.G. "Wind-Induced Internal Pressures in Low Buildings," *Proceedings* of the Fifth International Conference on Wind Engineering, Colorado State University, Fort Collins, CO, 1979.

[39] Stathopoulos, T., Surry, D. and Davenport, A.G. A simplified model of wind pressure coefficients for low-rise buildings, *Fourth Colloquium on Industrial Aerodynamics*, Aachen, West Germany, June 18–20, 1980.

[40] Stathopoulos, T. Wind loads on eaves of low buildings, *J. Struct. Div.*, ASCE, 107(10), 1921–1934, 1981.

[41] Stathopoulos, T. and Zhu, X. "Wind pressures on buildings with appurtenances." *J. Wind Engrg. and Industrial Aerodynamics*, 31, 265–281, 1988.

[42] Stathopoulos, T. and Dumitrescu-Brulotte, M. Design recommendations for wind loading on buildings of intermediate height, *Canadian J. Civ. Engrg*, 16(6), 910–916, 1989.

[43] Stathopoulos, T. and Zhu, X. Wind pressures on buildings with mullions. *J. Struct. Engrg.*, ASCE, 116(8), 2272–2291, 1990.

[44] Stathopoulos, T. and Luchian, H.D. Wind pressures on building configurations with stepped roofs. *Canadian J. Civ. Engrg.*, 17(4), 569–577, 1990.

[45] Stathopoulos, T. and Luchian, H. Wind-induced forces on eaves of low buildings, Wind Engineering Society Inaugural Conference, Cambridge, England, 1992.

[46] Stathopoulos, T. and Mohammadian, A.R. Wind loads on low buildings with mono-sloped roofs, *J. Wind Engrg. and Industrial Aerodynamics*, 23, 81–97, 1986.

[47] Stathopoulos, T. and Saathoff, P. Wind pressures on roofs of various geometries. *J. Wind Engrg. and Industrial Aerodynamics*, 38, 273–284, 1991.

[48] Stubbs, N. and Boissonnade, A. Damage simulation model or building contents in a hurricane environment, *Proceedings*, 7th U.S. National Conference on Wind Engineering, UCLA, Los Angeles, CA, 2, 759–771, 1993.

[49] Stubbs, N. and Perry, D.C. Engineering of the building envelope, *Proceedings*, ASCE Conference on Hurricanes of 1992, Miami, FL, 1993.

[50] Surry, D., Kitchen, R.B. and Davenport, A.G. Design effectiveness of wind tunnel studies for buildings of intermediate height. *Canadian J. Civ. Engrg.*, 4(1), 96–116, 1977.

[51] Surry, D. and Stathopoulos, T. The wind loading of buildings with monosloped roofs. Final Report, BLWT-SS38, University of Western Ontario, London, Ontario, Canada, 1988.

[52] Taylor, T.J. Wind pressures on a hemispherical dome, *J. Wind Engrg. and Industrial Aerodynamics*, 40(2), 199–213, 1992.

[53] Templin, J.T. and Cermak, J.E. Wind pressures on buildings: Effect of mullions, Tech. Rep. CER76-77JTT-JEC24, Fluid Dynamics and Diffusion Lab, Colorado State University, Fort Collins, CO, 1978.

[54] Vickery, P.J. and Twisdale, L.A. Prediction of hurricane wind speeds in the U.S., Proc. 7th Nat. Conf. on Wind Engrg., UCLA, 2, 823–832, 1993.

[55] Vickery, B.J., Davenport, A.G. and Surry, D.

Internal pressures on low-rise buildings, Fourth Canadian Workshop on Wind Engineering, Toronto, Ontario, 1984.

[56] Walmsley, J.L., Taylor, P.A. and Keith, T. A simple model of neutrally stratified boundary-layer flow over complex terrain with surface roughness modulations, *Boundary-Layer Meterology*, 36, 157–186, 1986.

[57] Wen, Y.K. and Chu, S.L. Tornado risks and design wind speed, *J. Struct. Div.*, ASCE, 99(12), 2409–2421, 1973.

[58] Yeatts, B.B., Womble, J.A., Mehta, K.C. and Cermak, J.E. Internal pressures for low rise buildings, *Proceedings* of the Second U.K. Conference on Wind Engineering, Warwick, England, 1994.

[59] Yeatts, B.B. and Mehta, K.C. Field study of internal pressures, *Proceedings*, 7th U.S. National Conference on Wind Engineering, UCLA, Los Angeles, CA, 2, 889–897, 1993.

[60] Gurley, K. and Kareem, A. "Gust Loading Factors for Tension Leg Platforms," 15(3), *Applied Ocean Research*, 1993.

[61] Kareem, A. Dynamic response of high-rise buildings to stochastic wind loads, *J. Wind Engrg. and Industrial Aerodynamics*, 41–44, 1992.

[62] Kareem, A. Lateral-torsional motion of tall buildings to wind loads, *J. Struct. Engrg.*, ASCE, 111(11), 1985.

[63] Solari, G. Gust buffeting I: Peak wind velocity and equivalent pressure, *J. Struct. Engrg.*, ASCE, 119(2), 1993.

[64] Solari, G. Gust buffeting II: Dynamic along-wind response, *J. Struct. Engrg.*, ASCE, 119(2), 1993.

[65] Kareem, A. and Smith, C. Performance of offshore platforms in hurricane Andrew, *Proceedings* of Hurricanes of 1992, ASCE, Miami, FL, Dec., 1993.

[66] Ho, E., "Variability of Low Building Wind Lands," Doctoral Dissertation, University of Western Ontario, London, Ontario, Canada, 1992.

[67] Simiu, E. and Scanlan, R.H. Wind effects on structures, Second Edition, John Wiley & Sons, New York, NY, 1986.

[68] Cook, N. *The designer's guide to wind loading of building structures*, part I, Butterworths Publishers, 1985.

[69] Isyumov, N., and Case, P. "*Evaluation of structural wind loads for low-rise buildings contained in ASCE standard 7-1995.*" BLWT-SS17-1995, Univ. of Western Ontario, London, Ontario, Canada.

7. Snow Loads

Methodology. The procedure established for determining design snow loads is as follows:

1. Determine the ground snow load for the geographic location (7.2 and the Commentary's 7.2).
2. Generate a flat roof snow load from the ground load with consideration given to: (a) roof exposure (7.3.1 and the Commentary's 7.3 and 7.3.1); (b) roof thermal condition (7.3.2 and the Commentary's 7.3 and 7.3.2); and (c) occupancy and function of structure (7.3.3 and the Commentary's 7.3.3).
3. Consider roof slope (7.4–7.4.5 and the Commentary's 7.4).
4. Consider partial loading (7.5 and the Commentary's 7.5).
5. Consider unbalanced loads (7.6–7.6.4 and the Commentary's 7.6).
6. Consider snow drifts: (a) on lower roofs (7.7–7.7.3 and the Commentary's 7.7); and (b) from projections (7.8 and the Commentary's 7.8).
7. Consider sliding snow (7.9 and the Commentary's 7.9).
8. Consider extra loads from rain on snow (7.10 and the Commentary's 7.10).
9. Consider ponding instability (7.11 and the Commentary's 7.11).
10. Consider existing roofs (7.12 and the Commentary's 7.12).
11. Consider other roofs and sites (the Commentary's 7.13)
12. Consider the consequences of loads in excess of the design value (immediately following).

Loads in Excess of the Design Value. The philosophy of the probabilistic approach used in this standard is to establish a design value that reduces the risk of a snow load-induced failure to an acceptably low level. Since snow loads in excess of the design value may occur, the implications of such "excess" loads should be considered. For example, if a roof is deflected at the design snow load so that slope to drain is eliminated, "excess" snow load might cause ponding (as discussed in the Commentary's 7.11) and perhaps progressive failure.

The snow load/dead load ratio of a roof structure is an important consideration when assessing the implications of "excess" loads. If the design snow load is exceeded, the percentage increase in total load would be greater for a lightweight structure (that is, one with a high snow load/dead load ratio) than for a heavy structure (that is, one with a low snow load/dead load ratio). For example, if a 40-lb/sq ft (1.92 kN/m^2) roof snow load is exceeded by 20 lb/sq ft (0.96 kN/m^2) for a roof having a 25-lb/sq ft (1.19 kN/m^2) dead load, the total load increases by 31% from 65 to 85 lb/sq ft (3.11 to 4.07 kN/m^2). If the roof had a 60-lb/sq ft (2.87 kN/m^2) dead load, the total load would increase only by 20% from 100 to 120 lb/sq ft (4.79 to 5.75 kN/m^2).

7.2 Ground Snow Loads

The snow load provisions were developed from an extreme-value statistical analysis of weather records of snow on the ground [1]. The log normal distribution was selected to estimate ground snow loads, which have a 2% annual probability of being exceeded (50-year mean recurrence interval).

Maximum measured ground snow loads and ground snow loads with a 2% annual probability of being exceeded are presented in Table C7-1 for 204 National Weather Service (NWS) "first-order" stations at which ground snow loads have been measured for at least 11 years during the period 1952–1992.

Concurrent records of the depth and load of snow on the ground at the 204 locations in Table C7-1 were used to estimate the ground snow load and the ground snow depth having a 2% annual probability of being exceeded for each of these locations. The period of record for these 204 locations, where both snow depth and snow load have been measured, averages 33 years up through the winter of 1991–1992. A mathematical relationship was developed between the 2% depths and the 2% loads. The nonlinear best-fit relationship between these extreme values was used to estimate 2% (50-year mean recurrence interval) ground snow loads at about 9,200 other locations at which only snow depths were measured. These loads, as well as the extreme-value loads developed directly from snow load measurements at 204 first-order locations, were used to construct the maps.

In general, loads from these two sources were in agreement. In areas where there were differences,

loads from the 204 first-order locations were considered to be more valuable when the map was constructed. This procedure ensures that the map is referenced to the NWS observed loads and contains spatial detail provided by snow-depth measurements at about 9,200 other locations.

The maps were generated from data current through the 1991–1992 winter. Where statistical studies using more recent information are available, they may be used to produce improved design guidance.

However, adding a big snow year to data developed from periods of record exceeding 20 years will usually not change 50-year values much. As examples, the data bases for Boston and Chattanooga were updated to include the winters of 1992–1993 and 1993–1994 since record snows occurred there during that period. In Boston, 50-year loads based on water equivalent measurements only increased from 34 to 35 lb/sq ft (1.63 to 1.68 kN/m^2) and loads generated from snow depth measurements remained at 25 lb/sq ft (1.20 kN/m^2). In Chattanooga, loads generated from water equivalent measurements increased from 6 to 7 lb/sq ft (0.29 to 0.34 kN/m^2) and loads generated from snow depth measurements remained at 6 lb/sq ft (0.29 kN/m^2).

The following additional information was also considered when establishing the snow load zones on the map of the United States (Fig. 7-1).

1. The number of years of record available at each location.
2. Additional meteorological information available from NWS, Soil Conservation Service (SCS) snow surveys and other sources.
3. Maximum snow loads observed there.
4. Regional topography.
5. The elevation of each location.

The map is an updated version of those in the 1993 edition of this Standard.

In much of the south, infrequent but severe snowstorms disrupted life in the area to the point that meteorological observations were missed. In these and similar circumstances more value was given to the statistical values for stations with complete records. Year-by-year checks were made to verify the significance of data gaps.

The mapped snow loads cannot be expected to represent all the local differences that may occur within each zone. Because local differences exist, each zone has been positioned so as to encompass

Ground Snow Loads at 204 National Weather Service Locations at Which Load Measurements are Made
(Note: To convert lb/sq ft to kN/m^2, multiply by 0.0479)

Location	Ground Snow Load (lb/sq ft)			Location	Ground Snow Load (lb/sq ft)		
	Years of Record	Maximum observed	2% Annual probability		Years of Record	Maximum observed	2% Annual probability
ALABAMA				KENTUCKY			
Birmingham	40	4	3	Covington	40	22	13
Huntsville	33	7	5	Jackson	11	12	18
Mobile	40	1	1	Lexington	40	15	13
ARIZONA				Louisville	39	11	12
Flagstaff	38	88	48	LOUISIANA			
Tucson	40	3	3	Alexandria	17	2	2
Winslow	39	12	7	Shreveport	40	4	3
ARKANSAS				MAINE			
Fort Smith	37	6	5	Caribou	34	68	95
Little Rock	24	6	6	Portland	39	51	60
CALIFORNIA				MARYLAND			
Bishop	31	6	8	Baltimore	40	20	22
Blue Canyon	26	213	242	MASSACHUSETTS			
Mt. Shasta	32	62	62	Boston	39	25	34
Red Bluff	34	3	3	Nantucket	16	14	24
COLORADO				Worcester	33	29	44
Alamosa	40	14	14	MICHIGAN			
Colorado Springs	39	16	14	Alpena	31	34	48
Denver	40	22	18	Detroit City	14	6	10
Grand Junction	40	18	16	Detroit Airport	34	27	18
Pueblo	33	7	7	Detroit-Willow	12	11	22
CONNECTICUT				Flint	37	20	24
Bridgeport	39	21	24	Grand Rapids	40	32	36
Hartford	40	23	33	Houghton Lake	28	33	48
New Haven	17	11	15	Lansing	35	34	36
DELAWARE				Marquette	16	44	53
Wilmington	39	12	16	Muskegon	40	40	51
GEORGIA				Sault Ste. Marie	40	68	77
Athens	40	6	5	MINNESOTA			
Atlanta	39	4	3	Duluth	40	55	63
Augusta	40	8	7	International Falls	40	43	44
Columbus	39	1	1	Minneapolis-St. Paul	40	34	51
Macon	40	8	7	Rochester	40	30	47
Rome	28	3	3	St. Cloud	40	40	53
IDAHO				MISSISSIPPI			
Boise	38	8	9	Jackson	40	3	3
Lewiston	37	6	9	Meridian	39	2	2
Pocatello	40	12	10	MISSOURI			
ILLINOIS				Columbia	39	19	20
Chicago-O'Hare	32	25	17	Kansas City	40	18	18
Chicago-Midway	26	37	22	St. Louis	37	28	21
Moline	39	21	19	Springfield	39	14	14
Peoria	39	27	15	MONTANA			
Rockford	26	31	19	Billings	40	21	15
Springfield	40	20	21	Glasgow	40	18	19
INDIANA				Great Falls	40	22	15
Evansville	40	12	17	Havre	26	22	24
Fort Wayne	40	23	20	Helena	40	15	17
Indianapolis	40	19	22	Kalispell	29	27	45
South Bend	39	58	41	Missoula	40	24	22
IOWA				NEBRASKA			
Burlington	11	15	17	Grand Island	40	24	23
Des Moines	40	22	22	Lincoln	20	15	22
Dubuque	39	34	32	Norfolk	40	28	25
Sioux City	38	28	28	North Platte	39	16	13
Waterloo	33	25	32	Omaha	25	23	20
KANSAS				Scottsbluff	40	10	12
Concordia	30	12	17	Valentine	26	26	22
Dodge City	40	10	14	NEVADA			
Goodland	39	12	15	Elko	12	12	20
Topeka	40	18	17	Ely	40	10	9
Wichita	40	10	14	Las Vegas	39	3	3

Ground Snow Loads at 204 National Weather Service Locations at Which Load Measurements are Made
(Note: To convert lb/sq ft to kN/m^2, multiply by 0.0479)

Location	Ground Snow Load (lb/sq ft)			Location	Ground Snow Load (lb/sq ft)		
	Years of Record	Maximum observed	2% Annual probability		Years of Record	Maximum observed	2% Annual probability
Reno	39	12	11	Columbia	38	9	8
Winnemucca	39	7	7	Florence	23	3	3
NEW HAMPSHIRE				Greenville-Spartanburg	24	6	7
Concord	40	43	63	SOUTH DAKOTA			
NEW JERSEY				Aberdeen	27	23	43
Atlantic City	35	12	15	Huron	40	41	46
Newark	39	18	15	Rapid City	40	14	15
NEW MEXICO				Sioux Falls	39	40	40
Albuquerque	40	6	4	TENNESSEE			
Clayton	34	8	10	Bristol	40	7	9
Roswell	22	6	8	Chattanooga	40	6	6
NEW YORK				Knoxville	40	10	9
Albany	40	26	27	Memphis	40	7	6
Binghamton	40	30	35	Nashville	40	6	9
Buffalo	40	41	39	TEXAS			
NYC - Kennedy	18	8	15	Abilene	40	6	6
NYC - LaGuardia	40	23	16	Amarillo	39	15	10
Rochester	40	33	38	Austin	39	2	2
Syracuse	40	32	32	Dallas	23	3	3
NORTH CAROLINA				El Paso	38	8	8
Asheville	28	7	14	Fort Worth	39	5	4
Cape Hatteras	34	5	5	Lubbock	40	9	11
Charlotte	40	8	11	Midland	38	4	4
Greensboro	40	14	11	San Angelo	40	3	3
Raleigh-Durham	36	13	14	San Antonio	40	9	4
Wilmington	39	14	7	Waco	40	3	2
Winston-Salem	12	14	20	Wichita Falls	40	4	5
NORTH DAKOTA				UTAH			
Bismark	40	27	27	Milford	23	23	14
Fargo	39	27	41	Salt Lake City	40	11	11
Williston	40	28	27	Wendover	13	2	3
OHIO				VERMONT			
Akron-Canton	40	16	14	Burlington	40	43	36
Cleveland	40	27	19	VIRGINIA			
Columbus	40	11	11	Dulles Airport	29	15	23
Dayton	40	18	11	Lynchburg	40	13	18
Mansfield	30	31	17	National Airport	40	16	22
Toledo	36	10	10	Norfolk	38	9	10
Youngstown	40	14	10	Richmond	40	11	16
OKLAHOMA				Roanoke	40	14	20
Oklahoma City	40	10	8	WASHINGTON			
Tulsa	40	5	8	Olympia	40	23	22
OREGON				Quillayute	25	21	15
Astoria	26	2	3	Seattle-Tacoma	40	15	18
Burns	39	21	23	Spokane	40	36	42
Eugene	37	22	10	Stampede Pass	36	483	516
Medford	40	6	6	Yakima	39	19	30
Pendleton	40	9	13	WEST VIRGINIA			
Portland	39	10	8	Beckley	20	20	30
Salem	39	5	7	Charleston	38	21	18
Sexton Summit	14	48	64	Elkins	32	22	18
PENNSYLVANIA				Huntington	30	15	19
Allentown	40	16	23	WISCONSIN			
Erie	32	20	18	Green Bay	40	37	36
Harrisburg	19	21	23	La Crosse	16	23	32
Philadelphia	39	13	14	Madison	40	32	35
Pittsburgh	40	27	20	Milwaukee	40	34	29
Scranton	37	13	18	WYOMING			
Williamsport	40	18	21	Casper	40	9	10
RHODE ISLAND				Cheyenne	40	18	18
Providence	39	22	23	Lander	39	26	24
SOUTH CAROLINA				Sheridan	40	20	23
Charleston	39	2	2				

172

TABLE C7-2
Comparison of Some Site-Specific Values and Zoned Values in Fig. 7-1

State	Location	Elev. ft (m)	Zoned value lb/sq ft (kN/m²)	Case Study Value* lb/sq ft (kN/m²)
California	Mount Hamilton	4,210 (1283)	0 to 2400 ft (732 m)	30 (1.44)
Arizona	Palisade Ranger Station	7,950 (2423)	0 to 3500 ft (1067 m)	120 (5.75)
			5 to 4600 ft (0.24 to 1402 m)	
			10 to 5000 ft (0.48 to 1524 m)	
Tennessee	Monteagle	1940 (591)	10 to 1800 ft (0.48 to 549 m)	15 (0.72)
Maine	Sunday River Ski Area	900 (274)	90 to 700 ft (4.31 to 213 m)	100 (4.79)

*Based on a detailed study of information in the vincity of each location.

essentially all the statistical values associated with normal sites in that zone. Although the zones represent statistical values, not maximum observed values, the maximum observed values were helpful in establishing the position of each zone.

For sites not covered in Fig. 7-1 design values should be established from meteorological information, with consideration given to the orientation, elevation, and records available at each location. The same method can also be used to improve upon the values presented in Fig. 7-1. Detailed study of a specific site may generate a design value lower than that indicated by the generalized national map. It is appropriate in such a situation to use the lower value established by the detailed study. Occasionally a detailed study may indicate that a higher design value should be used than the national map indicates. Again, results of the detailed study should be followed.

The area covered by a site-specific case study will vary depending on local climate and topography. In some places, a single case study will suffice for an entire community, but in others, varying local conditions limit a "site" to a much smaller area. The area of applicability usually becomes clear as information in the vicinity is examined for the case study.

It is not appropriate to use only the site-specific information in Table C7-1 for design purposes. It lacks an appreciation for surrounding station information and, in a few cases, is based on rather short periods of record. The map or a site-specific case study provide more valuable information.

The importance of conducting detailed studies for locations not covered in Fig. 7-1 is shown in Table C7-2.

For some locations within the CS areas of the northeast (Fig. 7-1), ground snow loads exceed 100 lb/sq ft (4.79 kN/m²). Even in the southern portion of the Appalachian Mountains, not far

from sites where a 15-lb/sq ft (0.72 kN/m²) ground snow load is appropriate, ground loads exceeding 50 lb/sq ft (2.39 kN/m²) may be required. Lake-effect storms create requirements for ground loads in excess of 75 lb/sq ft (3.59 kN/m²) along portions of the Great Lakes. In some areas of the Rocky Mountains, ground snow loads exceed 200 lb/sq ft (9.58 kN/m²).

Local records and experience should also be considered when establishing design values.

The values in Table 7-1 are for specific Alaskan locations only and generally do not represent appropriate design values for other nearby locations. They are presented to illustrate the extreme variability of snow loads within Alaska. This variability precludes statewide mapping of ground snow loads there.

Valuable information on snow loads for the Rocky Mountain states is contained in references [2]–[12].

Most of these references for the Rocky Mountain states use annual probabilities of being exceeded that are different from the 2% value (50-year mean recurrence interval) used in this standard. Reasonable, but not exact, factors for converting from other annual probabilities of being exceeded to the value herein are presented in Table C7-3.

For example, a ground snow load based on a 3.3% annual probability of being exceeded (30-

TABLE C7-3
Factors for Converting from Other Annual Probabilities of Being Exceeded and Other Mean Recurrence Intervals, to That Used in This Standard

Annual Probability of being exceeded (%)	Mean recurrence interval (years)	Multiplication factor
10	10	1.82
4	25	1.20
3.3	30	1.15
1	100	0.82

173

year mean recurrence interval) should be multiplied by 1.15 to generate a value of p_g for use in Eq. (7-1).

The snow load provisions of several editions of the National Building Code of Canada served as a guide in preparing the snow load provisions in this standard. However, there are some important differences between the Canadian and the United States data bases. They include:

1. The Canadian ground snow loads are based on a 3.3% annual probability of being exceeded (30-year mean recurrence interval) generated by using the extreme-value, Type-I (Gumbel) distribution, while the normal-risk values in this standard are based on a 2% annual probability of being exceeded (50-year mean recurrence interval) generated by a log-normal distribution.

2. The Canadian loads are based on measured depths and regionalized densities based on 4 or less measurements per month. Because of the infrequency of density measurements, an additional weight of rain is added [13]. In this Standard the weight of the snow is based on many years of frequently measured weights obtained at 204 locations across the United States. Those measurements contain many rain-on-snow events and thus a separate rain-on-snow surcharge load is not needed except for some roofs with a slope less than 1/2 in./ft (2.38°).

7.3 Flat-Roof Snow Loads, p_f

The minimum allowable values of p_f presented in 7.3 acknowledge that in some areas a single major storm can generate loads that exceed those developed from an analysis of weather records and snow load case studies.

The factors in this standard that account for the thermal, aerodynamic, and geometric characteristics of the structure in its particular setting were developed using the National Building Code of Canada as a point of reference. The case study reports in references [14]–[22] were examined in detail.

In addition to these published references, an extensive program of snow load case studies was conducted by eight universities in the United States, by the Corps of Engineers' Alaska District, and by the U.S. Army Cold Regions Research and Engineering Laboratory (CRREL) for the Corps of En-

gineers. The results of this program were used to modify the Canadian methodology to better fit United States conditions. Measurements obtained during the severe winters of 1976–1977 and 1977–1978 are included. A statistical analysis of some of that information is presented in [23]. The experience and perspective of many design professionals, including several with expertise in building failure analysis, have also been incorporated.

7.3.1 Exposure Factor, C_e. Except in areas of "aerodynamic shade," where loads are often increased by snow drifting, less snow is present on most roofs than on the ground. Loads in unobstructed areas of conventional flat roofs average less than 50% of ground loads in some parts of the country. The values in this standard are above-average values, chosen to reduce the risk of snow load-induced failures to an acceptably low level. Because of the variability of wind action, a conservative approach has been taken when considering load reductions by wind.

The effects of exposure are handled on two scales. First Eq. (7-1) contains a basic exposure factor of 0.7. Second, the type of terrain and the exposure of the roof are handled by exposure factor C_e. This two-step procedure generates ground-to-roof load reductions as a function of exposure that range from 0.49 to 0.91.

Table 7-2 has been changed from what appeared in the prior (1988) version of this Standard to separate regional wind issues associated with terrain from local wind issues associated with roof exposure. This was done to better define categories without significantly changing the values of C_e.

The adjective "windswept" is used in the "mountainous areas" terrain category to preclude use of this category in those high mountain valleys that receive little wind.

The normal, combined exposure reduction in this standard is 0.70 as compared to a normal value of 0.80 for the ground-to-roof conversion factor in the 1990 National Building Code of Canada. The decrease from 0.80 to 0.70 does not represent decreased safety but arises due to increased choices of exposure and thermal classification of roofs (that is, six terrain categories, three roof exposure categories and three thermal categories in this standard versus three exposure categories and no thermal distinctions in the Canadian code).

It is virtually impossible to establish exposure definitions that clearly encompass all possible exposures that exist across the country. Because individuals may interpret exposure categories somewhat differently, the range in exposure has been divided into several categories rather than just two or three. A difference of opinion of one category results in about a 10% "error" using these several categories and an "error" of 25% or more if only three categories are used.

7.3.2 Thermal Factor, C_t. Usually, more snow will be present on cold roofs than on warm roofs. (An exception to this is discussed in 7.3.2.) The thermal condition selected from Table 7-3 should represent that which is likely to exist during the life of the structure. Although it is possible that a brief power interruption will cause temporary cooling of a heated structure, the joint probability of this event and a simultaneous peak snow load event is very small. Brief power interruptions and loss of heat are acknowledged in the $C_t = 1.0$ category. Although it is possible that a heated structure will subsequently be used as an unheated structure, the probability of this is rather low. Consequently, heated structures need not be designed for this unlikely event.

Some dwellings are not used during the winter. Although their thermal factor may increase to 1.2 at that time, they are unoccupied, so their importance factor reduces to 0.8. The net effect is to require the same design load as for a heated, occupied dwelling.

Discontinuous heating of structures may cause thawing of snow on the roof and subsequent refreezing in lower areas. Drainage systems of such roofs have become clogged with ice, and extra loads associated with layers of ice several inches thick have built up in these undrained lower areas. The possibility of similar occurrences should be investigated for any intermittently heated structure.

Similar icings may build up on cold roofs subjected to meltwater from warmer roofs above. Exhaust fans and other mechanical equipment on roofs may also generate meltwater and icings.

Icicles and ice dams are a common occurrence on cold eaves of sloped roofs. They introduce problems related to leakage and to loads. Large ice dams that can prevent snow from sliding off roofs are generally produced by heat losses from within buildings. Icings associated with solar melting of snow during the day and refreezing along eaves at night are often small and transient. Although icings can occur on cold or warm roofs, roofs that are well insulated and ventilated are not commonly subjected to serious icings at their eaves. Because ice dams can prevent load reductions by sliding on some warm ($C_t = 1.0$) roofs, the "unobstructed

slippery surface" curve in Fig. 7-2a now only applies to unventilated roofs with a thermal resistance equal to or greater than 30 °F·h·sq ft/Btu (5.3 K·m²/W) and to ventilated roofs with a thermal resistance equal to or greater than 20 °F·h·sq ft/Btu (3.5 K·m²/W). Roofs that are well insulated and ventilated have been given a $C_t = 1.1$ in Table 7-3. This increases their flat roof snow load p_f. Methods of minimizing eave icings are discussed in [24, 25, 26, 27, 28, 29].

Glass, plastic, and fabric roofs of continuously heated structures are seldom subjected to much snow load because their high heat losses cause snow melt and sliding. For such specialty roofs, knowledgeable manufacturers and designers should be consulted. The National Greenhouse Manufacturers Association [30] recommends use of $C_t = 0.83$ for continuously heated greenhouses and $C_t = 1.00$ for unheated or intermittently heated greenhouses. They suggest a value of $I = 1.0$ for retail greenhouses and $I = 0.8$ for all other greenhouses. To qualify as a continuously heated greenhouse, a production or retail greenhouse must have a constantly maintained temperature of 50°F (10°C) or higher during winter months. In addition it must also have a maintenance attendant on duty at all times or an adequate temperature alarm system to provide warning in the event of a heating system failure. Finally, the greenhouse roof material must have a thermal resistance, R-value, less than 2 °F·h·sq ft/Btu (0.4 K·m²/W). An unheated or intermittently heated greenhouse is any greenhouse that does not meet the requirements of a continuously heated single or double glazed greenhouse. Greenhouses should be designed so that the structural supporting members are stronger than the glazing. If this approach is used, any failure caused by heavy snow loads will be localized and in the glazing. This should avert progressive collapse of the structural frame. Higher design values should be used where drifting or sliding snow is expected.

Little snow accumulates on warm air-supported fabric roofs because of their geometry and slippery surface. However, the snow that does accumulate is a significant load for such structures and should be considered. Design methods for snow loads on air structures are discussed in [31] and [32].

The combined consideration of exposure and thermal conditions generates ground-to-roof factors that range from a low of 0.49 to a high of 1.09. The equivalent ground-to-roof factors in the 1990 National Building Code of Canada are 0.8

for sheltered roofs, 0.6 for exposed roofs and 0.4 for exposed roofs in exposed areas north of the tree line, all regardless of their thermal condition.

References [3] and [33] indicate that loads exceeding those calculated using this Standard can occur on roofs that receive little heat from below.

7.3.3 Importance Factor, I. The importance factor I has been included to account for the need to relate design loads to the consequences of failure. Roofs of most structures having normal occupancies and functions are designed with an importance factor of 1.0, which corresponds to unmodified use of the statistically determined ground snow load for a 2% annual probability of being exceeded (50-year mean recurrence interval).

A study of the 204 locations in Table C7-1 showed that the ratio of the values for 4% and 2% annual probabilities of being exceeded (the ratio of the 25–50-year mean recurrence interval values) averaged 0.80 and had a standard deviation of 0.06. The ratio of the values for 1% and 2% annual probabilities of being exceeded (the ratio of the 100-year to 50-year mean recurrence interval values) averaged 1.22 and had a standard deviation of 0.08. On the basis of the nationwide consistency of these values it was decided that only one snow load map need be prepared for design purposes and that values for lower and higher risk situations could be generated using that map and constant factors.

Lower and higher risk situations are established using the importance factors for snow loads in Table 7-4. These factors range from 0.8 to 1.2. The factor 0.8 bases the average design value for that situation on an annual probability of being exceeded of about 4% (about a 25-year mean recurrence interval). The factor 1.2 is nearly that for a 1% annual probability of being exceeded (about a 100-year mean recurrence interval).

7.3.4 Minimum Allowable Values of p_f for Low Slope Roofs. These minimums account for a number of situations that develop on low slope roofs. They are particularly important considerations where p_g is 20 lb/sq ft (0.96 kN/m²) or less. In such areas, single storms accompanied by high winds have created loads in excess of the balanced snow load. These minimums provide a way of considering such loads.

7.4 Sloped-Roof Snow Loads, p_s

Snow loads decrease as the slopes of roofs increase. Generally, less snow accumulates on a sloped roof because of wind action. Also, such roofs may shed some of the snow that accumulates

on them by sliding and improved drainage of meltwater. The ability of a sloped roof to shed snow load by sliding is related to the absence of obstructions not only on the roof but also below it, the temperature of the roof, and the slipperiness of its surface. It is difficult to define "slippery" in quantitative terms. For that reason a list of roof surfaces that qualify as slippery and others that do not, are presented in the Standard itself. Most common roof surfaces are on that list. The slipperiness of other surfaces is best determined by comparisons with those surfaces. Some tile roofs contain built-in protrusions or have a rough surface which prevents snow from sliding. However, snow will slide off other smooth-surfaced tile roofs. When a surface may or may not be slippery the implications of treating it either as a slippery or nonslippery surface should be determined.

Discontinuous heating of a building may reduce the ability of a sloped roof to shed snow by sliding, since meltwater created during heated periods may refreeze on the roof's surface during periods when the building is not heated, thereby 'locking' the snow to the roof.

All these factors are considered in the slope reduction factors presented in Fig. 7-2, which are supported by references [33]–[36]. The thermal resistance requirements have been added to the "unobstructed slippery surfaces" curve in Fig. 7-2A to prevent its use for roofs on which ice dams often form since ice dams prevent snow from sliding. Mathematically the information in Fig. 7-2 can be represented as follows:

1. Warm roofs ($C_t = 1.0$):
   a. Unobstructed slippery surfaces with $R \geq$ 30 °F·h·sq ft /Btu (5.3 K·m²/W) if unventilated and $R \geq 20$ °F·h·sq ft /Btu (3.5 K·m²/W) if ventilated:

0–5° slope	$C_s = 1.0$
5–70° slope	$C_s = 1.0 - (\text{slope} - 5°)/65°$
>70° slope	$C_s = 0$

   b. All other surfaces:

0–30° slope	$C_s = 1.0$
30–70° slope	$C_s = 1.0 - (\text{slope} - 30°)/40°$
>70° slope	$C_s = 0$

2. Cold Roofs ($C_t > 1.0$):
   a. Unobstructed slippery surfaces:

0–15° slope	$C_s = 0$
15–70° slope	$C_s = 1 - (\text{slope} - 15°)/55°$
>70° slope	$C_s = 0$

b. All other surfaces:

$0–45°$ slope $\quad C_s = 1.0$
$45–70°$ slope $\quad C_s = 1.0 - (slope - 45°)/25°$
$>70°$ slope $\quad C_s = 0$

If the ground (or another roof of less slope) exists near the eave of a sloped roof, snow may not be able to slide completely off the sloped roof. This may result in the elimination of snow loads on upper portions of the roof and their concentration on lower portions. Steep A-frame roofs that nearly reach the ground are subject to such conditions. Lateral as well as vertical loads induced by such snow should be considered for such roofs.

7.4.3 Roof Slope Factor for Curved Roofs. These provisions have been changed from those in the 1993 edition of this Standard to cause the load to diminish along the roof as the slope increases.

7.4.4 Roof Slope Factor for Multiple Folded Plate, Sawtooth, and Barrel Vault Roofs. Because these types of roofs collect extra snow in their valleys by wind drifting and snow creep and sliding, no reduction in snow load should be applied because of slope.

7.4.5 Ice Dams and Icicles Along Eaves. The intent is to consider heavy loads from ice that forms along eaves only for structures where such loads are likely to form. It is also not considered necessary to analyze the entire structure for such loads, just the eaves themselves.

7.5 Unloaded Portions

In many situations a reduction in snow load on a portion of a roof by wind scour, melting, or snow-removal operations will simply reduce the stresses in the supporting members. However, in some cases a reduction in snow load from an area will induce heavier stresses in the roof structure than occur when the entire roof is loaded. Cantilevered roof joists are a good example; removing half the snow load from the cantilevered portion will increase the bending stress and deflection of the adjacent continuous span. In other situations adverse stress reversals may result.

The word "one" has been added so the phrase in this section now reads "any one portion of the loaded area." This was done to clarify that the intent is not to require consideration of multiple "checkerboard" loadings. Also the intent of this provision (i.e., load removal to produce the great-

est effects on members being analysed) has been added.

Separate, simplified provisions have been added for continuous beams to provide specific partial loading requirements for that common structural system.

7.6 Unbalanced Roof Snow Loads

Unbalanced snow loads may develop on sloped roofs because of sunlight and wind. Winds tend to reduce snow loads on windward portions and increase snow loads on leeward portions. Since it is not possible to define wind direction with assurance, winds from all directions should generally be considered when establishing unbalanced roof loads.

The exposure factor C_e appears in the denominator of all the equations used to establish unbalanced loads. Dividing by C_e acknowledges that the exposure will affect the amount of leeside drifting.

7.6.1 Unbalanced Snow Loads on Hip and Gable Roofs. The unbalanced uniform snow load on the downwind side has been reduced from 1.5 p_s/C_e to 1.3 p_s/C_e to limit the total unbalanced load in most situations to that of a uniformly distributed ground snow load.

A few recent failures in the South indicate that unbalanced snow loads have occurred on large gable roofs with a slope less than 15°. Thus in areas where p_g is equal to or less than 10 lb/sq ft (0.48 kN/m²), it may be appropriate to consider unbalanced snow loads for large, gable roofs with slopes down to 5°.

7.6.2 Unbalanced Snow Loads for Curved Roofs. The method of determining roof slope has been changed to eliminate inconsistencies in loads. Now C_s is based on the actual slope not an equivalent slope. These provisions do not apply to roofs that are concave upward. For such roofs, see Section 7.13.

7.6.3 Unbalanced Snow Loads for Multiple Folded Plate, Sawtooth, and Barrel Vault Roofs. A minimum slope of 3/8 in./ft (1.79°) has been established to preclude the need to determine unbalanced loads for most internally-drained, membrane roofs which slope to internal drains. Case studies indicate that significant unbalanced loads can occur when the slope of multiple gable roofs is as low as 1/2 in./ft (2.38°).

The unbalanced snow load in the valley has been reduced from 3 p_f/C_e to 2 p_f/C_e to create a total unbalanced load that does not exceed a uniformly distributed ground snow load in most situations.

The requirement that snow above the valley not be at an elevation higher than the snow above the ridge may limit the unbalanced load to less than $2\,p_f/C_e$.

Sawtooth roofs and other "up-and-down" roofs with significant slopes tend to be vulnerable in areas of heavy snowfall for the following reasons:

1. They accumulate heavy snow loads and are therefore expensive to build.
2. Windows and ventilation features on the steeply sloped faces of such roofs may become blocked with drifting snow and be rendered useless.
3. Meltwater infiltration is likely through gaps in the steeply sloped faces if they are built as walls, since slush may accumulate in the valley during warm weather. This can promote progressive deterioration of the structure.
4. Lateral pressure from snow drifted against clerestory windows may break the glass.

7.6.4 Unbalanced Snow Loads for Dome Roofs.
This is a new provision based on a similar provision in the 1990 National Building Code of Canada.

7.7 Drifts on Lower Roofs (Aerodynamic Shade)

When a rash of snow-load failures occurs during a particularly severe winter, there is a natural tendency for concerned parties to initiate across-the-board increases in design snow loads. This is generally a technically ineffective and expensive way of attempting to solve such problems, since most failures associated with snow loads on roofs are caused not by moderate overloads on every square foot (square meter) of the roof but rather by localized significant overloads caused by drifted snow.

It is extremely important to consider localized drift loads in designing roofs. Drifts will accumulate on roofs (even on sloped roofs) in the wind shadow of higher roofs or terrain features. Parapets have the same effect. The affected roof may be influenced by a higher portion of the same structure or by another structure or terrain feature nearby if the separation is 20 ft (6.1 m) or less. When a new structure is built within 20 ft (6.1 m) of an existing structure, drifting possibilities should also be inves-

tigated for the existing structure. The snow that forms drifts may come from the roof on which the drift forms, from higher or lower roofs or, on occasion, from the ground.

The leeward drift load provisions are based on studies of snow drifts on roofs [37]–[40]. Drift size is related to the amount of driftable snow as quantified by the upwind roof length and the ground snow load. Drift loads are now considered for ground snow loads as low as 5 lb/sq ft (0.24 kN/m²). This change was made since recent case studies show that, in regions with low ground snow loads, drifts 3 to 4 ft (0.9 to 1.2 m) high can be caused by a single storm accompanied by high winds.

Another change from the prior (1988) edition of this Standard involves the width w when the drift height h_d from Fig. 7-9, exceeds the clear height h_c. In this situation the width of the drift is taken as $4\,h_d^2/h_c$ with a maximum value of $8\,h_c$. This drift width relation is based upon equating the cross-sectional area of this drift (i.e., $1/2\,h_c \times w$) with the cross-sectional area of a triangular drift where the drift height is not limited by h_c (i.e., $1/2\,h_d \times 4\,h_d$) [41]. The upper limit of drift width is based on studies by Finney [42] and Tabler [43], which suggest that a "full" drift has a rise-to-run of about 1:6.5, and case studies [41] that show observed drifts with a rise-to-run greater than 1:10.

The drift height relationship in Fig. 7-9 is based on snow blowing off a high roof upwind of a lower roof. The change in elevation where the drift forms is called a "leeward step." Drifts can also form at "windward steps." An example is the drift that forms at the downwind end of a roof that abuts a higher structure there. Fig. 7-7 shows "windward step" and "leeward step" drifts.

For situations having the same amount of snow available (i.e., upper and lower roofs of the same length) the height of drifts that form in leeward steps is about twice the height of those that form in windward steps [44]. It is for this reason that the height of windward drifts is taken as $1/2\,h_d$ with h_d determined from Fig. 7-9 using the length of the lower roof for l_u.

Depending on wind direction, any change in elevation between roofs can be either a windward or leeward step. Thus the height of each drift is determined twice as shown in Example 3, and the larger of the two heights is used to size the design drift.

The drift load provisions cover most, but not all, situations. References [45] and [46] document a larger drift than would have been expected based on the length of the upper roof. The larger drift was caused when snow on a somewhat lower roof, upwind of the upper roof, formed a drift between those two roofs allowing snow from the upwind lower roof to be carried up onto the upper roof then into the drift on its downwind side. It was suggested that the sum of the lengths of both roofs could be used to calculate the size of the leewind drift.

In another situation [47] a long "spike" drift was created at the end of a long skylight with the wind about 30 degrees off the long axis of the skylight. The skylight acted as a guide or deflector that concentrated drifting snow. This caused a large drift to accumulate in the lee of the skylight. This drift was replicated in a wind tunnel.

Tests in wind tunnels [48] and [49] and flumes [44] have proven quite valuable in determining patterns of snow drifting and drift loads. For roofs of unusual shape or configuration, wind tunnel or water-flume tests may be needed to help define drift loads.

7.8 Roof Projections

Drifts around penthouses, roof obstructions and parapet walls are also of the "windward step" type since the length of the upper roof is small or no upper roof exists.

Solar panels, mechanical equipment, parapet walls, and penthouses are examples of roof projections that may cause "windward" drifts on the roof around them. The drift-load provisions in 7.7 and 7.8 cover most of these situations adequately, but flat-plate solar collectors may warrant some additional attention. Roofs equipped with several rows of them are subjected to additional snow loads. Before the collectors were installed, these roofs may have sustained minimal snow loads, especially if they were windswept. Since a roof with collectors is apt to be somewhat "sheltered" by the collectors, it seems appropriate to set $C_e = 1.1$ and calculate a uniform snow load for the entire area as though the collectors did not exist. Second, the extra snow that might fall on the collectors and then slide onto the roof should be computed using the "cold roofs-all other surfaces" curve in Fig. 7-2b. This value should be applied as a uniform load on the roof at the base of each collector over an area about 2 ft (0.6 m) wide along the length of the collector. The uniform load combined with the load at the base of each collector probably represents a reasonable design load for such situations, except in very windy areas where extensive snow drifting is to be expected among the collectors. By elevating collec-

tors several feet (a meter or more) above the roof on an open system of structural supports, the potential for drifting will be diminished significantly. Finally, the collectors themselves should be designed to sustain a load calculated by using the 'unobstructed slippery surfaces' curve in Fig. 7-2a. This last load should not be used in the design of the roof itself, since the heavier load of sliding snow from the collectors has already been considered. The influence of solar collectors on snow accumulation is discussed in [50] and [51].

7.9 Sliding Snow

Situations that permit snow to slide onto lower roofs should be avoided [52]. Where this is not possible, the extra load of the sliding snow should be considered. Roofs with little slope have been observed to shed snow loads by sliding. Consequently, it is prudent to assume that any upper roof sloped to an unobstructed eave is a potential source of sliding snow.

The dashed lines in Figs. 7-2a and 7-2b should not be used to determine the total load of sliding snow available from an upper roof, since those lines assume that unobstructed slippery surfaces will have somewhat less snow on them than other surfaces because they tend to shed snow by sliding. To determine the total sliding load available from the upper roof, it is appropriate to use the solid lines in Figs. 7-2a and 7-2b. The final resting place of any snow that slides off a higher roof onto a lower roof will depend on the size, position, and orientation of each roof [35]. Distribution of sliding loads might vary from a uniform load 5 ft (1.5 m) wide, if a significant vertical offset exists between the two roofs, to a 20-ft-wide (6.1 m-wide) uniform load, where a low-slope upper roof slides its load onto a second roof that is only a few feet (about a meter) lower or where snow drifts on the lower roof create a sloped surface that promotes lateral movement of the sliding snow.

In some instances a portion of the sliding snow may be expected to slide clear of the lower roof. Nevertheless, it is prudent to design the lower roof for a substantial portion of the sliding load in order to account for any dynamic effects that might be associated with sliding snow.

7.10 Rain on Snow Surcharge Load

The ground snow-load measurements on which this standard is based contain the load effects of light rain on snow. However, since heavy rains percolate down through snowpacks and may drain away, they might not be included in measured values. Where p_g is greater than 20 lb/sq ft (0.96 kN/m²), it is assumed that the full rain-on-snow effect has been measured and a separate rain-on-snow surcharge is not needed. The temporary roof load contributed by a heavy rain may be significant. Its magnitude will depend on the duration and intensity of the design rainstorm, the drainage characteristics of the snow on the roof, the geometry of the roof, and the type of drainage provided. Loads associated with rain on snow are discussed in [53] and [54].

Water tends to remain in snow much longer on relatively flat roofs than on sloped roofs. Therefore, slope is quite beneficial, since it decreases opportunities for drain blockages and for freezing of water in the snow.

For a roof with a 1/4-in./ft (1.19°) slope, where p_g = 20 lb/sq ft (0.96 kN/m²), p_f = 18 lb/sq ft (0.86 kN/m²), and the minimum allowable value of p_f is 20 lb/sq ft (0.96 kN/m²), the rain-on-snow surcharge of 5 lb/sq ft (0.24 kN/m²) would be added to the 18-lb/sq ft (0.86 kN/m²) flat roof snow load to generate a design load of 23 lb/sq ft (1.10 kN/m²).

7.11 Ponding Instability

Where adequate slope to drain does not exist, or where drains are blocked by ice, snow meltwater and rain may pond in low areas. Intermittently heated structures in very cold regions are particularly susceptible to blockages of drains by ice. A roof designed without slope or one sloped with only 1/8 in./ft (0.6°) to internal drains probably contains low spots away from drains by the time it is constructed. When a heavy snow load is added to such a roof, it is even more likely that undrained low spots exist. As rainwater or snow meltwater flows to such low areas, these areas tend to deflect increasingly, allowing a deeper pond to form. If the structure does not possess enough stiffness to resist this progression, failure by localized overloading can result. This mechanism has been responsi-

ble for several roof failures under combined rain and snow loads.

It is very important to consider roof deflections caused by snow loads when determining the likelihood of ponding instability from rain-on-snow or snow meltwater.

Internally drained roofs should have a slope of at least 1/4 in./ft (1.19°) to provide positive drainage and to minimize the chance of ponding. Slopes of 1/4 in./ft (1.19°) or more are also effective in reducing peak loads generated by heavy spring rain on snow. Further incentive to build positive drainage into roofs is provided by significant improvements in the performance of waterproofing membranes when they are sloped to drain.

Rain loads and ponding instability are discussed in detail in Section 8 of this standard.

7.12 Existing Roofs

Numerous existing roofs have failed when additions or new buildings nearby caused snow loads to increase on the existing roof. The prior (1988) edition of this Standard mentioned this issue only in its Commentary where it was not a mandatory provision. This edition moves this issue to the Standard.

The addition of a gable roof alongside an existing gable roof as shown in Fig. C7-1 most likely explains why many such metal buildings failed in the South during the winter of 1992–1993. The change from a simple gable roof to a multiple folded plate roof increased loads on the original roof as would be expected from Section 7.6.3. Unfortunately, the original roofs were not strengthened to account for these extra loads and they collapsed.

If the eaves of the new roof in Fig. C7-1 had been somewhat higher than the eaves of the existing roof, the exposure factor C_e, for the original roof may have increased thereby increasing snow loads on it. In addition, drift loads and loads from sliding snow would also have to be considered.

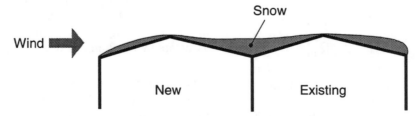

FIG. C7-1. Valley in Which Snow will Drift is Created when New Gable Roof is Added Alongside Existing Gable Roof

7.13 Other Roofs and Sites

Wind tunnel model studies, similar tests employing fluids other than air, for example water flumes, and other special experimental and computational methods have been used with success to establish design snow loads for other roof geometries and complicated sites [44], [48] and [49]. To be reliable, such methods must reproduce the mean and turbulent characteristics of the wind and the manner in which snow particles are deposited on roofs then redistributed by wind action. Reliability should be demonstrated through comparisons with situations for which full-scale experience is available.

EXAMPLES

The following three examples illustrate the method used to establish design snow loads for most of the situations discussed in this standard.

Example 1: Determine balanced and unbalanced design snow loads for an apartment complex in a suburb of Boston, Massachusetts. Each unit has an 8-on-12 slope gable roof. Composition shingles clad the roofs. Trees will be planted among the buildings.

Flat-roof snow load:

$$p_f = 0.7 C_e C_t I p_g$$

where p_g = 30 lb/sq ft (1.44 kN/m²) (from Fig. 7-1); C_e = 1.0 (from Table 7-2 for Terrain Category B and a partially exposed roof); C_t = 1.0 (from Table 7-3); and I = 1.0 (from Table 7-4). Thus

$$p_f = (0.7)(1.0)(1.0)(1.0)(30)$$
$$= 21 \text{ lb/sq ft (balanced load)}$$
$$[\text{in SI}: p_f = (0.7)(1.0)(1.0)(1.0)(1.44)$$
$$= 1.01 \text{ kN/m}^2]$$

Since the slope exceeds 15°, the minimum allowable values of p_f do not apply. Use p_f = 21 lb/sq ft (1.01 kN/m²), see Section 7.3.4.

Sloped-roof snow load:

$$p_s = C_s p_f$$

where C_s = 0.88 (from solid line, Fig. 7-2a). Thus p_s = 0.88 (21) = 18 lb/sq ft
[in SI: p_s = 0.88(1.01) = 0.89 kN/m²]

Finally:

Unbalanced snow load = $1.3 p_s/C_e$
$$= 1.3 (18)/1.0 = 23 \text{ lb/sq ft}$$
$$[\text{in SI} = 1.3(0.89)/1.0 = 1.16 \text{ kN/m}^2]$$

A rain-on-snow surcharge load need not be considered, since the slope is greater than 1/2 in./ft (2.38°) (see Section 7.10). See Fig. C7-2 for both loading conditions.

Example 2: Determine the roof snow load for a vaulted theater which can seat 450 people, planned for a suburb of Chicago, Illinois. The building is the tallest structure in a recreation-shopping complex surrounded by a parking lot. Two large deciduous trees are located in an area near the entrance. The building has an 80-ft (24.4-m) span and 15-ft (4.6-m) rise circular arc structural concrete roof covered with insulation and aggregate surfaced built-up roofing. The roofing system has a thermal resistance of 20 °F·h·sq ft/Btu (3.5 K·m²/W). It is expected that the structure will be exposed to winds during its useful life.

Flat-roof snow load:

$$p_f = 0.7 C_e C_t I p_g$$

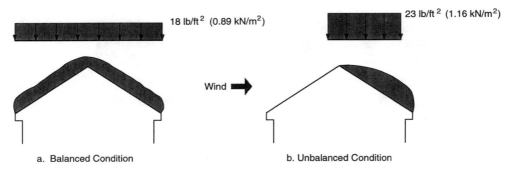

a. Balanced Condition   b. Unbalanced Condition

FIG. C7-2. Design Snow Loads for Example 1

COMMENTARY

where
p_g = 25 lb/sq ft (1.20 kN/m²) (from Fig. 7-1)
C_e = 0.9 (from Table 7-2 for Terrain Category B and a fully exposed roof)
C_t = 1.0 (from Table 7-3)
I = 1.1 (from Table 7-4). Thus
p_f = (0.7)(0.9)(1.0)(1.1)(25) = 17 lb/sq ft
[In SI: p_f = (0.7)(0.9)(1.0)(1.1)(1.19) = 0.83 kN/m²]

Tangent of vertical angle from eaves to crown = 15/40 = 0.375. Angle = 21°.

Since the vertical angle exceeds 10°, the minimum allowable values of p_f do not apply. Use p_f = 17 lb/sq ft (0.83 kN/m²), see Section 7.3.4.

Sloped-roof snow load:

$$p_s = C_s p_f$$

From Fig. 7-2a, C_s = 1.0 until slope exceeds 30° which (by geometry) is 30 ft (9.1 m) from the centerline. In this area p_s = 17(1) = 17 lb/sq ft [in SI: p_s = 0.83(1) = 0.83 kN/m²]. At the eaves, where the slope is (by geometry) 41°, C_s = 0.72 and p_s = 17(0.72) = 12 lb/sq ft [in SI: p_s = 0.83(0.72) = 0.60 kN/m²]. Since slope at eaves is 41°, Case II loading applies.

Unbalanced snow load: Since the vertical angle from the eaves to the crown is greater than 10° and less than 60°, unbalanced snow loads must be considered.

Unbalanced load at crown = 0.5 p_f = 0.5(17)
= 9 lb/sq ft
[in SI = 0.5(0.83) = 0.41 kN/m²]

Unbalanced load at 30° point = 2 $p_f C_s/C_e$
= 2(17)(1.0)/0.9
= 38 lb/sq ft
[in SI = 2(0.83)(1.0)/0.9 = 1.84 kN/m²]

Unbalanced load at eaves = 2(17)(0.72)/0.9
= 27 lb/sq ft
[in SI = 2(0.83)(0.72)/0.9 = 1.33 kN/m²]

A rain-on-snow surcharge load need not be considered, since the slope is greater than 1/2in./ft (2.38°) (see 7.10).
See Fig. C7-3 for both loading conditions.

Example 3. Determine design snow loads for the upper and lower flat roofs of a building located where p_g = 40 lb/sq ft (1.92 kN/m²). The elevation difference between the roofs is 10 ft (3 m). The 100 × 100-ft (30.5 m × 30.5-m) high portion is heated and the 200-ft-wide (60.9 m-wide), 100-ft-long (30.5 m-long) low portion is an unheated storage area. The building is in an industrial park in flat open country with no trees or other structures offering shelter.
High roof:

$$p_f = 0.7 C_e C_t I p_g$$

where p_g = 40 lb/sq ft (1.92 kN/m²) (given); C_e = 0.9 (from Table 7-2); C_t = 1.0 (from Table 7-3); and I = 1.0 (from Table 7-4). Thus

p_f = 0.7 (0.9) (1.0) (1.0) (40) = 25 lb/sq ft
[in SI: p_f = 0.7(0.9)(1.0)(1.0)(1.92) = 1.21 kN/m²]

Since the slope is less than 15°, the minimum allowable value of p_f must be considered (see Section 7.3.4). p_f(min) = 20I where p_g ≥ 20 lb/sq ft = 20(1.0) = 20 lb/sq ft. Use p_f= 25 lb/sq ft. [in SI: p_f(min) = 0.96I where p_g ≥ 0.96 kN/m² = 0.96(1.0) = 0.96 kN/m². Use p_f = 1.21 kN/m²].

Low roof:

$$p_f = 0.7 C_e C_t I p_g$$

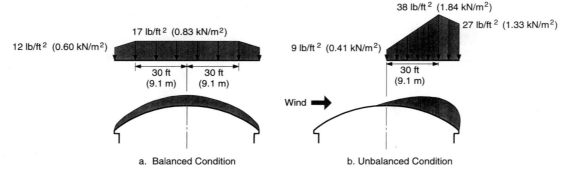

FIG. C7-3. Design Snow Loads for Example 2

182

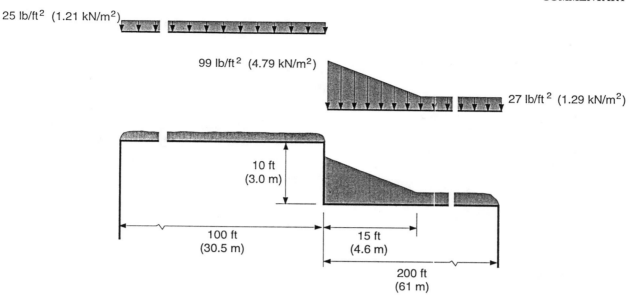

25 lb/ft² (1.21 kN/m²)

99 lb/ft² (4.79 kN/m²)

27 lb/ft² (1.29 kN/m²)

10 ft
(3.0 m)

100 ft
(30.5 m)

15 ft
(4.6 m)

200 ft
(61 m)

FIG. C7-4. Design Snow Loads for Example 3

where
p_g = 40 lb/sq ft (1.92 kN/m²) (given)
C_e = 1.0 (from Table 7-2);
C_t = 1.2 (from Table 7-3)
I = 0.8 (from Table 7-4).

Thus

p_f = 0.7(1.0) (1.2) (0.8) (40) = 27 lb/sq ft
[in SI: p_f = 0.7(1.0)(1.2)(0.8)(1.92) = 1.29 kN/m²]

Since the slope is less than 15°, the minimum allowable value of p_f must be considered (see Section 7.3.4). p_f (min.) = 20I where p_g ≥ 20 lb/sq ft, thus p_f (min) = 20(0.8) = 16 lb/sq ft. Use p_f = 27 lb/sq ft [in SI: p_f (min) = 0.96I where p_g ≥ 0.96 kN/m², thus p_f (min) = 0.96(0.8) = 0.77 kN/m². Use p_f = 1.29 kN/m²]

Drift load calculation

γ = 0.13(40) + 14 = 19 lb/cu ft (Eq. 7-3)
[in SI: γ = 43.5(1.92) + 224 = 308 kg/m³]
h_b = p_f/19 = 27/19 = 1.4 ft
[in SI: h_b = 102(1.29)/308 = 0.43 m]
h_c = 10-1.4 = 8.6 ft
[in SI: h_c = 3.05 − 0.43 = 2.62 m]
h_c/h_b = 8.6/1.4 = 6.1[in SI h_c/h_b = 2.62/0.43 = 6.1]

Since h_c/h_b ≥ 0.2 drift loads must be considered (see Section 7.7.2).

h_d (leeward step) = 3.8 ft (1.16 m)
[Fig. 7-9 with p_g = 40 lb/sq ft (1.92. kN/m²) and l_u = 100 ft (30.5 m)]

h_d (windward step) = 1/2 × 5.2 ft (1.6 m)
= 2.6 ft (0.8 m)
[5.2 ft (1.6 m) from Fig. 7-9 with p_g = 40 lb/sq ft (1.92 kN/m²) and l_u = length of lower roof = 200 ft (60.9 m)]

Leeward drift governs, use h_d = 3.8 ft (1.16 m)

Since h_d < h_c,
h_d = 3.8 ft (1.16 m)
w = 4 h_d = 15.2 ft (4.64 m), say 15 ft (4.6 m)
p_d = $h_d\gamma$ = 3.8(19) = 72 lb/sq ft
[in SI: p_d = 1.16(308/102) = 3.50 kN/m²]

A rain-on-snow surcharge load need not be considered even though the slope is less than 1/2 in./ft (2.38°), since p_g is greater than 20 lb/sq ft (0.96 kN/m²).

See Fig. C7-4 for snow loads on both roofs.

References

[1] Ellingwood, B., and Redfield, R. Ground snow loads for structural design. *J. Struct. Engrg.*, ASCE, 109 (4), 950–964, 1983.

[2] MacKinlay, I., and Willis, W.E. Snow country design. Washington, D.C.: National Endowment for the Arts. 1965.

[3] Sack, R.L., and Sheikh-Taheri, A. *Ground and roof snow loads for Idaho.* Moscow, Idaho: Dept.

of Civil Engineering, University of Idaho. ISBN 0-89301-114-2. 1986.

[4] Structural Engineers Association of Arizona. Snow load data for Arizona. Tempe, Ariz.: Univ. of Arizona. 1973.

[5] Structural Engineers Association of Colorado. Snow load design data for Colorado. Denver, Colo.: 1971. [Available from: Structural Engineers Association of Colorado, Denver, Colo.]

[6] Structural Engineers Association of Oregon. Snow load analysis for Oregon. Salem, Or.: Oregon Dept. of Commerce, Building Codes Division. 1971.

[7] Structural Engineers Association of Washington. Snow loads analysis for Washington, Seattle, Wash., 1981.

[8] USDA Soil Conservation Service. Lake Tahoe basin snow load zones. Reno, Nev.: U.S. Dept. of Agriculture, Soil Conservation Service. 1970.

[9] Videon, F.V., and Stenberg, P. Recommended snow loads for Montana structures. Bozeman, Mt.: Montana State Univ. 1978.

[10] Structural Engineers Association of Northern California. Snow load design data for the Lake Tahoe area. San Francisco, Calif., 1964.

[11] Placer County Building Division. Snow Load Design, *Placer County Code*, Chapter 4, Section 4.20(V). Auburn, Calif. 1985.

[12] Brown, J. An approach to snow load evaluation. *Proceedings 38th Western Snow Conference.* 1970.

[13] Newark, M. A new look at ground snow loads in Canada. In *Proceedings 41st Eastern Snow Conference*, Washington, D.C., 37–48, 1984.

[14] Elliott, M. Snow load criteria for western United States, case histories and state-of-the-art. *Proceedings of the first western states conference of structural engineer associations.* Sun River, Or., June 1975.

[15] Lorenzen, R.T. Observations of snow and wind loads precipitant to building failures in New York State, 1969–1970. American Society of Agricultural Engineers North Atlantic Region meeting; Newark, Del., August 1970. [Available from: American Society of Agricultural Engineers, St. Joseph, Missouri.]

[16] Lutes, D.A., and Schriever, W.R. Snow accumulation in Canada: Case histories: II. Ottawa, Ontario, Canada: National Research Council of Canada. DBR Tech. Paper 339, NRCC 11915. March 1971.

[17] Meehan, J.F. Snow loads and roof failures. 1979 Structural Engineers Association of California convention proceedings. [Available from Structural Engineers Association of California, San Francisco, Calif.]

[18] Mitchell, G.R. Snow loads on roofs—An interim report on a survey. *Wind and snow loading.* Lancaster, England: The Construction Press Ltd., 177–190. 1978.

[19] Peter, B.G.W., Dalgliesh, W.A., and Schriever, W.R. Variations of snow loads on roofs. *Trans. Eng. Inst. Can.* 6(A-1), 8 p. April 1963.

[20] Schriever, W.R., Faucher, Y., and Lutes, D.A. Snow accumulation in Canada: Case histories: I. Ottawa, Ontario, Canada; National Research Council of Canada, Division of Building Research. NRCC 9287, January 1967.

[21] Taylor, D.A. A survey of snow loads on roofs of arena-type buildings in Canada. *Can. J. Civil Eng.*, 6(1), 85–96, March 1979.

[22] Taylor, D.A. Roof snow loads in Canada. *Can. J. Civil Eng.* 7(1), 1–18, March 1980.

[23] O'Rourke, M., Koch, P., and Redfield, R. Analysis of roof snow load case studies: Uniform loads. Hanover, NH: U.S. Dept. of the Army, Cold Regions Research and Engineering Laboratory, CRREL Report 83-1, 1983.

[24] Grange, H.L., and Hendricks, L.T. Roof-snow behavior and ice-dam prevention in residential housing. St. Paul, Minn.: Univ. of Minnesota, Agricultural Extension Service. Extension Bull. 399, 1976.

[25] Klinge, A.F. Ice dams. *Popular Science*, 119–120, Nov. 1978.

[26] Mackinlay, I. Architectural design in regions of snow and ice. *Proc. First Int. Conf. on Snow Eng.*, 441–455, Santa Barbara, CA, July, 1988.

[27] Tobiasson, W. Roof design in cold regions. *Proc. First Int. Conf. on Snow Eng.*, 462–482, Santa Barbara, CA, July 1988.

[28] de Marne, H. Field experience in control and prevention of leaking from ice dams in New Eng-

land. *Proc. First Int. Conf. on Snow Eng.*, 473–482, Santa Barbara, CA, July 1988.

[29] Tobiasson, W. and Buska J. Standing seam metal roofs in cold regions, *Proc. 10th Conf. Roofing Tech.*, 34–44, Gaithersburg, MD, April, 1993.

[30] National Greenhouse Manufacturers Association, Design loads in greenhouse structures, Taylors, South Carolina, 1988.

[31] Air Structures Institute. Design and standards manual. ASI-77. Available from the Industrial Fabrics Assn. International, St. Paul, MN, 1977.

[32] American Society of Civil Engineers, Air supported structures, New York, 1994.

[33] Sack, R.L. Snow loads on sloped roofs. *J. Struct. Engrg.*, ASCE, 114(3), 501–517, March 1988.

[34] Sack, R., Arnholtz, D., and Haldeman, J. Sloped roof snow loads using simulation. *J. Struct. Engrg.*, ASCE, 113(8), 1820–1833, Aug. 1987.

[35] Taylor, D. Sliding snow on sloping roofs. *Canadian Building Digest 228*. National Research Council of Canada, Ottawa, Ontario, Canada, Nov. 1983

[36] Taylor, D. Snow loads on sloping roofs: Two pilot studies in the Ottawa area. Division of Building Research Paper 1282, *Can. J. Civil Engrg.*, (2), 334–343, June 1985.

[37] O'Rourke, M., Tobiasson, W., and Wood, E. Proposed code provisions for drifted snow loads. *J. Struct. Engrg.*, ASCE, 112 (9), 2080–2092, Sept. 1986.

[38] O'Rourke, M., Speck, R., and Stiefel, U. Drift snow loads on multilevel roofs. *J. Struct. Engrg.*, ASCE, 111 (2), 290–306, Feb. 1985.

[39] Speck, R., Jr. Analysis of snow loads due to drifting on multilevel roofs. Thesis, Rensselaer Polytechnic Institute, Troy, N.Y.

[40] Taylor, D.A. Snow loads on two-level flat roofs. *Proc. Eastern Snow Conference.* 29, 41st Annual Meeting. Washington, D.C., June 7–8, 1984.

[41] Zallen, R. Roof collapse under snow drift loading and snow drift design criteria. *J. Perform Constr. Fac.*, ASCE, 2(2), 80–98, May 1988.

[42] Finney, E. Snow drift control by highway design, Bulletin 86, Michigan State College Engineering Station, Lansing, MI, 1939.

[43] Tabler, R. Predicting profiles of snow drifts in topographic catchments, Western Snow Conf., Coronado, CA, 1975.

[44] O'Rourke, M. and Weitman, N. Laboratory studies of snow drifts on multilevel roofs, Proc. 2nd International Conf. Snow Engrg., Santa Barbara, CA, June, 1992.

[45] O'Rourke, M. and El Hamadi, K. Roof snow loads; Drifting against a higher wall, Proc. 55th Western Snow Conf., Vancouver, B.C., April, 1987, pp. 124–132.

[46] O'Rourke, M. Discussion of "Roof collapse under snow drift loading and snow drift design criteria," J. Perform. Const. Fac., ASCE, Nov. 1989, pp. 266–268.

[47] Kennedy, D., Isyumov, M. and Mikitiuk, M. The Effectiveness of code provisions for snow accumulations on stepped roofs, Proc. 2nd Int. Conf. Snow Engrg., Santa Barbara, CA, June 1992.

[48] Isyumou, N. and Mikitiuk, M. "Wind tunnel modeling of snow accumulation on large roofs, Proc. 2nd International Conf. Snow Engrg., Santa Barbara, CA, June 1992.

[49] Irwin, P., Williams, C., Gamble, S. and Retziaff, R. Snow prediction in Toronto and the Andes Mountains; FAE simulation capabilities, Proc. 2nd International Conf. Snow Engrg., Santa Barbara, CA, June 1992.

[50] O'Rourke, M.J. Snow and ice accumulation around solar collector installations. Washington, D.C.: U.S. Dept. of Commerce, National Bureau of Standards. NBS-GCR-79 180, Aug. 1979.

[51] Corotis, R.B., Dowding, C.H., and Rossow, E.C. Snow and ice accumulation at solar collector installations in the Chicago metropolitan area. Washington, D.C.: U.S. Dept. of Commerce, National Bureau of Standards. NBS-GCR-79 181, Aug. 1979.

[52] Paine, J.C. Building design for heavy snow areas, *Proc. First Int. Conf. on Snow Engrg.*, 483–492, Santa Barbara, CA, July 1988.

[53] Colbeck, S.C. Snow loads resulting from rain-on-snow. Hanover, N.H.: U.S. Dept. of the Army, Cold Regions Research and Engineering Laboratory. CRREL Rep. 77-12, 1977.

[54] Colbeck, S.C. Roof loads resulting from rain-on-snow: Results of a physical model. *Can. J. Civil Engrg.*, 4, 482–490, 1977.

8. Rain Loads

8.1 Symbols and Notations

A = roof area serviced by a single drainage system, in square feet (square meters).

i = design rainfall intensity as specified by the code having jurisdiction, in inches per hour (millimeters per hour).

Q = flow rate out of a single drainage system, in gallons per minute (cubic meters per second)

8.2 Roof Drainage

Roof drainage systems are designed to handle all the flow associated with intense, short-duration rainfall events. (For example, the 1993 BOCA National Plumbing Code [1], and Factory Mutual Loss Prevention Data 1-54, "Roof Loads for New Construction" [2] use a 1-hr duration event with a 100-year return period; the 1994 Standard Plumbing Code [3] uses 1-hr and 15-min duration events with 100-year return periods for the primary and secondary drainage systems, respectively and the 1990 National Building Code [4] of Canada uses a 15-min event with a 10-year return period.) A very severe local storm or thunderstorm may produce a deluge of such intensity and duration that properly designed primary drainage systems are temporarily overloaded. Such temporary loads are adequately covered in design when blocked drains (see 8.3) and ponding instability (see 8.4) are considered.

Roof drainage is a structural, architectural and mechanical (plumbing) issue. The type and location of secondary drains and the hydraulic head above their inlets at the design flow must be known in order to determine rain loads. Design team coordination is particularly important when establishing rain loads.

8.3 Design Rain Loads

The amount of water that could accumulate on a roof from blockage of the primary drainage system is determined and the roof is designed to withstand the load created by that water plus the uniform load caused by water that rises above the inlet of the secondary drainage system at its design flow. If parapet walls, cant strips, expansion joints, and other features create the potential for deep water in an area, it may be advisable to install in that area secondary (overflow) drains with separate drain

lines rather than overflow scuppers to reduce the magnitude of the design rain load. Where geometry permits, free discharge is the preferred form of emergency drainage.

When determining these water loads, it is assumed that the roof does not deflect. This eliminates complexities associated with determining the distribution of water loads within deflection depressions. However, it is quite important to consider this water when assessing ponding instability in Section 8.4.

The depth of water, d_h, above the inlet of the secondary drainage system (i.e., the hydraulic head) is a function of the rainfall intensity at the site, the area of roof serviced by that drainage system and the size of the drainage system.

The flow rate through a single drainage system is as follows:

$$Q = 0.0104\, Ai$$
$$(\text{In SI: } Q = 0.278 \times 10^{-6} Ai) \qquad \text{(Eq. C8-1)}$$

The hydraulic head, d_h, is related to flow rate, Q, for various drainage systems in Table C8-1. That table indicates that d_h can vary considerably depending on the type and size of each drainage system and the flow rate it must handle. For this reason the single value of 1 inch (25 mm) [i.e., 5 lb/sq ft (0.24 kN/m²)] used in ASCE 7-93 has been eliminated.

The hydraulic head, d_h, is zero when the secondary drainage system is simply overflow all along a roof edge.

8.4 Ponding Instability

Water may accumulate as ponds on relatively flat roofs. As additional water flows to such areas, the roof tends to deflect more, allowing a deeper pond to form there. If the structure does not possess enough stiffness to resist this progression, failure by localized overloading may result. References [1]–[16] contain information on ponding and its importance in the design of flexible roofs. Rational design methods to preclude instability from ponding are presented in references [5] and [6].

By providing roofs with a slope of 1/4 in./ft (1.19°) or more, ponding instability can be avoided. If the slope is less than 1/4 in./ft (1.19°) the roof structure must be checked for ponding instability because construction tolerances and long-term deflections under dead load can result in flat portions susceptible to ponding.

8.5 Controlled Drainage

In some areas of the country, ordinances are in effect that limit the rate of rainwater flow from roofs into storm drains. Controlled-flow drains are often used on such roofs. Those roofs must be capable of sustaining the storm water temporarily stored on them. Many roofs designed with controlled-flow drains have a design rain load of 30 lb/sq ft (1.44 kN/m^2) and are equipped with a secondary drainage system (for example, scuppers) that prevents water depths ($d_s + d_h$) greater than 5.75 in. (145 mm) on the roof.

References

[1] Building Officials and Code Administrators International. The BOCA National Plumbing Code/1993. Country Club Hills, Illinois, BOCA Inc., Jan. 1993.

[2] Factory Mutual Engineering Corp. Loss Prevention Data 1-54, Roof Loads for New Construction, Norwood, Mass. FM. Aug. 1991.

[3] Southern Building Code Congress International. Standard Plumbing Code, 1991 Edition. Birmingham, Alabama, SBCCI Inc., 1991.

[4] Associate Committee on the National Building Code. National Building Code of Canada 1990, Ottawa, Ontario, National Research Council of Canada, Jan. 1990.

[5] American Institute of Steel Construction. Specification for structural steel for buildings, allowable stress design and plastic design. New York: AISC. June 1989.

[6] American Institute of Steel Construction. Load and resistance factor design specification for structural steel buildings. New York: AISC, Sept. 1986.

[7] American Institute of Timber Construction. Roof slope and drainage for flat or nearly flat roofs. Englewood, Colo.: AITC. Tech. Note No. 5, Dec. 1978.

[8] Burgett, L.B. Fast check for ponding. *Eng. J. Am. Inst. Steel Construction.* 10(1), 26–28, first quarter, 1973.

TABLE C8-1
Flow Rate, Q, in Gallons per Minute of Various Drainage Systems at Various Hydraulic Heads, d_h in inches [2]

Drainage System	Hydraulic Head d_h (in.)									
	1	2	2.5	3	3.5	4	4.5	5	7	8
4-in.-diameter drain	80	170	180							
6-in.-diameter drain	100	190	270	380	540					
8-in.-diameter drain	125	230	340	560	850	1100	1170			
6-in.-wide, channel scupper**	18	50	*	90	*	140	*	194	321	393
24-in.-wide, channel scupper	72	200	*	360	*	560	*	776	1,284	1,572
6-in.-wide, 4-in.-high, closed scupper**	18	50	*	90	*	140	*	177	231	253
24-in.-wide, 4-in.-high, closed scupper	72	200	*	360	*	560	*	708	924	1,012
6-in.-wide, 6-in.-high, closed scupper	18	50	*	90	*	140	*	194	303	343
24-in.-wide, 6-in.-high, closed scupper	72	200	*	360	*	560	*	776	1,212	1,372

In SI, Flow Rate, Q, in cubic meters per Second of Various Drainage Systems at Various Hydraulic Heads, d_h in millimeters [2]

Drainage Provision	Hydraulic Head d_h (mm)									
	25	51	64	76	89	102	114	127	178	203
102-mm-diameter drain	0.0051	0.0107	0.0114							
152-mm-diameter drain	0.0063	0.0120	0.0170	0.0240	0.0341					
203-mm-diameter drain	0.0079	0.0145	0.0214	0.0353	0.0536	0.0694	0.0738			
152-mm-wide, channel scupper**	0.0011	0.0032	*	0.0057	*	0.0088	*	0.0122	0.0202	0.0248
610-mm-wide, channel scupper	0.0045	0.0126	*	0.0227	*	0.0353	*	0.0490	0.0810	0.0992
152-mm-wide, 102-mm-high, closed scupper**	0.0011	0.0032	*	0.0057	*	0.0088	*	0.0112	0.0146	0.0160
610-mm-wide, 102-mm-high, closed scupper	0.0045	0.0126	*	0.0227	*	0.0353	*	0.0447	0.0583	0.0638
152-mm-wide, 152-mm-high, closed scupper	0.0011	0.0032	*	0.0057	*	0.0088	*	0.0122	0.0191	0.0216
610-mm-wide, 152-mm-high, closed scupper	0.0045	0.0126	*	0.0227	*	0.0353	*	0.0490	0.0765	0.0866

*Interpolation is appropriate, including between widths of each scupper.

**Channel scuppers are open topped (i.e., three sided). Closed scuppers are four sided.

[9] Chinn, J., Mansouri, A.H., and Adams, S.F. Ponding of liquids on flat roofs. *J. Struct. Div.*, ASCE, 95(ST 5), 797–808, May 1969.

[10] Chinn, J. Failure of simply-supported flat roofs by ponding of rain. *Eng. J. Am. Inst. Steel Construction.* 3(2): 38–41, April 1965.

[11] Haussler, R.W. Roof deflection caused by rainwater pools. *Civ. Engrg.*, 32, 58–59, Oct., 1962.

[12] Heinzerling, J.E. Structural design of steel joist roofs to resist ponding loads. Tech. Dig. No. 3, Arlington, Va.: Steel Joist Institute, May 1971.

[13] Marino, F.J. Ponding of two-way roof systems. *Eng. J. Am. Inst. Steel Construction*, 3(3), 93–100, July 1966.

[14] Salama, A.E., and Moody, M.L. Analysis of beams and plates for ponding loads. *J. Struct. Div.*, ASCE. 93(1): 109–126, Feb. 1967.

[15] Sawyer, D.A. Ponding of rainwater on flexible roof systems. *J. Struct. Div.*, ASCE. 93(1): 127–148, Feb. 1967.

[16] Sawyer, D.A. Roof-structural roof-drainage interactions. *J. Struct. Div.*, ASCE. 94(1), 175–198, Jan. 1969.

9. Earthquake Loads

The 1995 edition incorporates several new topics and includes several revisions of the 1993 edition. New topics include nonbuilding structures, seismic base isolation, soil-structure interaction, and composite steel-concrete structures. Major revisions include provisions for the effect of soft soils and the design of nonstructural components.

The 1993 edition was a sweeping change from the 1988 and prior editions. The 1993 provisions are taken from the *NEHRP Recommended Provisions for the Development of Seismic Regulations for New Buildings* (1), which is prepared by the Building Seismic Safety Council (BSSC) under sponsorship of the Federal Emergency Management Agency (FEMA). NEHRP stands for the National Earthquake Hazard Reduction Program, which is managed by FEMA. These provisions are a direct descendent of the *Tentative Provisions for the Development of Seismic Regulations for Buildings* (2), developed by the Applied Technology Council (ATC) under sponsorship of the National Science Foundation and the National Bureau of Standards (now the National Institute for Standards and Technology).

The ATC and BSSC efforts had their origin in the 1971 San Fernando valley earthquake, which demonstrated that design rules of that time for seismic resistance had some serious shortcomings. ATC began their effort with two concepts: (1) The resulting provisions should embody, to the extent possible, the state of knowledge in earthquake engineering research as applicable to design and construction regulations; and (2) the provisions should be applicable nationwide. BSSC has endeavored to maintain these concepts while keeping the provisions up to date, evaluating their effect, and building a nationwide consensus. The natural evolution of this process has led the BSSC's *NEHRP Provisions* into ASCE 7 and some of the model building codes.

Content Of Commentary. This commentary does not explain the earthquake loading provisions in great detail. The reader is referred to two excellent resources:

Part 2, Commentary, of the *NEHRP Recommended Provisions for the Development of Seismic Regulations for New Buildings*. Building Seismic Safety Council, Federal Emergency Management Agency, 1994.

Recommended Lateral Force Requirements and Commentary. Seismology Committee, Structural Engineers Association of California, 1990.

Section 9 is organized such that the BSSC Commentary is easily used; simply remove the first "9" (or "A.9") from the section number in this standard to find the corresponding section in the BSSC Commentary. Most of this commentary is primarily devoted to noting and explaining the differences of major substance between Section 9 of ASCE 7-95 and the 1994 edition of the *NEHRP Recommended Provisions*.

Nature of Earthquake "Loads." The 1988 edition of ASCE 7 and the 1982 edition of ANSI A58.1 contained seismic provisions based upon those in the *Uniform Building Code* (UBC) of 1985 and earlier. The UBC provisions for seismic safety have been based upon recommendations of the Structural Engineers Association of California (SEAOC) and predecessor organizations. Until 1988, the UBC and SEAOC provisions had not yet been fully influenced by the ATC and BSSC efforts. The 1972 and 1955 editions of A58.1 contained seismic provisions based upon much earlier versions of SEAOC and UBC recommendations.

The two most far reaching differences between the 1993 (and 1995) editions and these prior editions are that the 1993 edition is based upon a strength level limit state rather than an equivalent loading for use with allowable stress design and that it contains a much larger set of provisions that are not directly statements of loading. The intent is to provide a more reliable and consistent level of seismic safety in new building construction.

Earthquakes "load" structures indirectly. As the ground displaces, a building will follow and vibrate. The vibration produces deformations, strains, and stresses in the structure. Computation of dynamic response to earthquake ground shaking is complex. As a simplification, this standard is based upon the concept of a response spectrum. A response spectrum for a specific earthquake ground motion does not reflect the total time history of response, but only approximates the maximum value of response for simple structures to that ground motion. The design response spectrum is a smoothed and normalized approximation for many different ground motions, adjusted at the extremes for characteristics of larger structures. The *BSSC NEHRP Commentary*, Section 1.4.1, contains a much fuller description of the development of the design response spectrum and the maps that index the design spectrum for various levels of seismic hazard and various ground conditions.

The provisions of Section 9 are stated in terms of forces and loads; however, the user should always bear in mind that there are no external forces applied to the above-ground portion of a structure during an earthquake. The design forces are intended only as approximations to produce the same deformations, when multiplied by the Deflection Amplification factor C_d, as would occur in the same structure should an earthquake ground motion at the design level occur.

The design limit state for resistance to an earthquake is unlike that for any other load within the scope of ASCE 7. The earthquake limit state is based upon system performance, not member performance, and considerable energy dissipation through repeated cycles of inelastic straining is anticipated. The reason is the large demand exerted by the earthquake and the high cost of providing enough strength to maintain linear elastic response in ordinary buildings.

This unusual limit state means that several conveniences of elastic behavior, such as the principle of superposition, are not applicable, and makes it difficult to separate design provisions for loads from those for resistance. This is the reason the *NEHRP Provisions* contains so many provisions that modify customary requirements for proportioning and detailing structural members and systems. It is also the reason for the construction quality assurance requirements. All these "non-load" provisions are presented in the seismic safety appendix to Section 9.

It is anticipated that the volume of provisions in the seismic safety appendix will decrease with time as the concepts of detailing for inelastic energy dissipation find expression in the customary standards for design of structural materials. Consider the provisions for reinforced concrete and structural steel as examples: when the ATC report was published in 1978, the supplemental provisions for design in reinforced concrete were much more extensive than in the present standard, because the standard for reinforced concrete (*Building Code Requirements for Reinforced Concrete, ACI 318*) has adopted many of the provisions in the interim; likewise, the supplemental provisions for steel structures grew very large under the BSSC activity until the appearance of an industry standard for seismic design of steel buildings in 1992 (*Seismic Provisions for Structural Steel Buildings*, AISC). As new editions of design standards for wood and masonry are prepared, it is anticipated that they will incorporate much of the appropriate supplementary provisions. The committee is searching for a standard that may be referenced for appropriate quality assurance provisions. Although seismic resistant design will always need to be practiced with simultaneous considerations of load and resistance, it may be possible at some future time for the earthquake provisions of ASCE 7 to return to their traditional emphasis on only the loading issues. The reader should be aware that there is some opposition to the inclusion of non-load provisions, as well as the treatment of allowable stress design by this standard.

Use of Allowable Stress Design Standards. The conventional design of nearly all masonry and wood structures and many steel structures is accomplished using allowable stress design (ASD) standards. Although the fundamental basis for the earthquake loads in Section 9 is a strength limit state beyond first yield of the structure, the provisions are written such that the conventional ASD standards can be used by the design engineer. Conventional ASD standards may be used in one of two fashions:

1. the earthquake load as defined in Sec. 9 may be used directly in allowable stress load combinations and the resulting stresses compared directly with conventional allowable stresses, or
2. the earthquake load may be used in strength design load combinations and resulting stresses compared with amplified allowable stresses.

At first glance, the first method appears to be conservative. However, if one sets the following design criteria:

Strength:
$$1.2D + 0.5L + 1.0E \leq \phi \cdot \text{Strength}$$

ASD:
$$1.0D + 1.0L + \alpha E \leq \text{Allowable Stress} \cdot \text{Increase Factor}$$

where α is set to give the same structural property required by the two equations and evaluates steel in bending or tension, one finds:

$$\alpha = 0.89 + 0.067 \, D/E - 0.56 \, L/E$$

Repeating the exercise for the following design criteria

Strength: $0.9D - 1.0E \leq \phi \cdot \text{Strength}$

ASD: $1.0D - \alpha E \leq \text{Allowable Stress} \cdot \text{Increase Factor}$

one finds:

$$\alpha = 0.89 + 0.2 \, D/E$$

Similar results can be derived for other types of stress and for other materials. For normal conditions the factor on E in the ASD equations would be less than one for both additive and counteracting effects, however, it is possible for the factor to exceed 1.0 for counteracting effects. Considering the approximate nature of the prediction of earthquake loads, the use of a uniform factor of 1.0 is reasonable for those circumstances where ASD is preferred. However, this demonstrates another reason why strength-based design load combinations are the preferred method for earthquake-resistant design.

The amplification for the second method is accomplished by the introduction of two sets of factors to amplify conventional allowable stresses to approximate the equivalent yield strength: One is a stress increase factor (1.7 for steel, 2.16 for wood, and 2.5 for masonry) and the second is a resistance or strength reduction factor (less than or equal to 1.0) that varies depending on the type of stress resultant and component. The 2.16 factor is selected for conformance with a proposed new design standard for wood and with an existing ASTM standard; it should not be taken to imply an accuracy level for earthquake engineering.

Although the modification factors just described accomplish a transformation of allowable stresses to the earthquake strength limit state, it is not conservative to ignore the provisions in the standard as well as the supplementary provisions in the appendix that deal with design or construction issues that do not appear directly related to computation of equivalent loads, because **the specified loads are derived assuming certain levels of damping and ductile behavior**. In many instances this behavior is not necessarily delivered by designs conforming to conventional standards, which is why there are so many seemingly "non-load" provisions in this standard and appendix.

Other design procedures (the current SEAOC and UBC requirements) for earthquake loads produce loads intended for use with allowable stress design methods. Such procedures generally appear very similar to this standard, but a coefficient R_w is used in place of the response modification factor R. R_w is always larger than R, generally by a factor of about 1.5, thus the loads produced are smaller, much as allowable stresses are smaller that nominal strengths. However, the other procedures contain as many, if not more, seemingly "non-load" provisions for seismic design to assure the assumed performance.

Occupancy Importance Factor. Prior editions of this standard as well as other current design procedures for earthquake loads make use of an occupancy importance factor I in the computation of the total seismic force. This standard does include a classification of buildings by occupancy, but this classification does not affect the total seismic force. It does strongly affect the permissible story drift (see Section 9.2.2.7) and the Seismic Performance Category (see Section 9.1.4), and the Seismic Performance Category affects many other considerations.

Occupancy also affects the requirements for non-structural components.

Federal Government Construction. The Interagency Committee on Seismic Safety in Construction has prepared an order executed by the President that all federally owned or leased building construction, as well as federally regulated and assisted construction, should be constructed to mitigate seismic hazards and that the *NEHRP Provisions* are deemed to be the suitable standard. The ICSSC has also issued a report that the current (1992) editions of the three model building codes are equivalent standards. It is expected that this standard would also be deemed equivalent, but the reader should bear in mind that there are certain differences, which are summarized in this Commentary.

9.1.1 Purpose

The BSSC *NEHRP Provisions* state that their purposes are to minimize the hazard to life for all buildings, to increase the expected performance of higher occupancy structures as compared to ordinary structures, and to improve the capability of essential facilities to function during and after an earthquake. They provide the minimum criteria considered to be prudent and economically justified for the protection of life safety in buildings subject to earthquakes at any location in the United States. The "design earthquake" ground motion levels (and design forces) specified in the provisions may result in both structural and nonstructural damage, but such damage is expected to be repairable. For ground motions larger than the design levels, the intent of these provisions is that there be a low likelihood of building collapse.

9.1.4.1 Seismic Ground Acceleration Maps

Maps 9-1 and 9-2 are based upon maps 3 and 4 of the 1991 NEHRP *Recommended Provisions for the Development of Seismic Regulations for New Buildings* prepared by the Building Seismic Safety Council. The maps are different in the Pacific northwest, and they have point values added within areas bounded by a single contour to aid interpolation. These revisions of the BSSC maps were determined by consideration of two other references: Maps 5 and 7 from the same publication, which are in terms of *response acceleration*, and plates 2 and 5 from U. S. Geological Survey Open File Report 82-1033, *Probabilistic Estimates of Maximum Acceleration and Velocity in Rock in the Contiguous United States*. Both references require conversions to obtain the parameters on maps 9-1 and 9-2. All these maps are based nominally on the same

probability of occurrence. The references do not have contours in the same locations as the base maps, however. With the exception of the Pacific northwest, the contours of *NEHRP* maps 3 and 4 were not shifted, only the point values were added. The point values selected were generally the highest obtained by consideration of the references. The reason for the changes in the Pacific northwest is the revised assessment of the overall seismicity of the region between the preparation of the ATC 3 maps in the mid-1970s and the Open File Report 82-1033.

The maps for earthquake ground motion are based upon a 90% chance of not being exceeded in a 50-year period, which is equivalent to a 475-year mean recurrence interval for events that can be modeled as independent from one another. In contrast, other loads in this standard are specified based upon a 50-year mean recurrence interval. Obviously, the difference is partly explained by the use of a load factor of 1.0 on the earthquake load for strength design, whereas load factors greater than 1.0 are used for other loads. However, the difference is even more profound, because the design limit state is quite different. As described previously, substantial yielding is assumed in prescribing the earthquake load effects on the structure.

It should be realized that the ground motion maps do not present the largest feasible event. Substantially larger events can occur, and supplementary maps are available (refer to the NEHRP *Recommended Provisions for the Development of Seismic Regulations for New Buildings*) that present accelerations for more extreme probabilities.

9.2.2.3.2 Vertical Irregularity

This section provides criteria for effects of vertical irregularities of story mass, strength and stiffness. Significant effect on the path for seismic force can be created by irregularities in the stiffness of individual elements that do not change the overall story stiffness, such as braced frames that change location. Conventional analysis utilizing rigid diaphragm may incorrectly assess these effects. The designer should be aware that the provisions do not directly address these circumstances.

9.2.3.7 *P-Delta Effects*

Note that θ computed from Eq. (9.4-12) when the deformations include *P*-delta amplification is slightly higher than the value that would be computed without *P*-delta. Dividing the higher ϕ by $(1 + \theta)$ gives the value that would be computed before the amplification.

9.3 Architectural, Mechanical, and Electrical Components and Systems

Additional industry standards that are useful references include:

Ceilings and Interior Systems Construction Association (CISCA), *Recommendations for Direct Hung Acoustical Tile and Lay-in Panel Ceilings, Seismic Zones 0-2*, 1991, and *Recommendations for Direct Hung Accoustical Tile and Lay-in Panel Ceilings, Seismic Zones 3–4*, 1990.

HVAC Duct Construction Standards, Metal and Flexible. Sheet Metal and Air Conditioning Contractors National Association (SMACNA), 1985.

Rectangular Industrial Duct Construction Standards, SMACNA, 1980.

Various standards on electrical cabinets from the Nat. Electrical Manufacturers Association (NEMA).

"Recommended Practice for Seismic Qualification of Class 1E Equipment for Nuclear Power Generating Stations." Standard 344, IEEE, 1987.

9.6 Concrete

There are several technical differences between the seismic provisions of [9.6-1] (ACI 318) and the 1991 NEHRP *Recommended Provisions* that are not included in the appendix (Section A.9.11). The items not included here are limited in scope and in their effect on overall performance. Briefly, they:

- Permit the use of posttensioned and prestressed members for seismic resisting members under limited circumstances.
- Require special transverse reinforcement over the full height of certain columns with high axial forces from seismic deformations.
- Permit the use of precast concrete members as diaphragms and establish a strength reduction factor for the connections of the precast units.
- Encourage the use of diagonal reinforcement in the coupling beams of couple shear walls.

These provisions are currently under consideration by the committee that prepares the concrete standard (ACI 318).

9.7 Composite Structures

The 1994 NEHRP *Recommended Provisions* have included a new set of provisions for the design of composite steel and concrete structural components and systems as primary seismic force resisting systems. It is anticipated that these new provisions will be carefully reviewed over the next

few years and that standards will develop to include them. Future editions of this standard will then include appropriate portions of the new provisions, such as the response modification factors and restrictions on use.

9.8 Masonry Structures

The 1994 NEHRP *Recommended Provisions* include a set of provisions for limit states design of masonry as the primary method; the modified allowable stress provisions referenced in this standard are included as an alternative method. Strength-based design methods are superior for seismic-resistant design, and it is anticipated that this standard would make reference to such a procedure once the limit states design method for masonry is adopted as a standard.

9.9 Wood Structures

Additional industry standards that are useful references include:

Plywood Design Specifications (1986), *Diaphragms* (1987), and *Design Capacities of APA Performance Rated Structural Use Panels*. APA N375, American Plywood Association, 1988.

10. Ice Loads—Atmospheric Icing

Much of the material in this Commentary is adapted from the *ASCE Guidelines for Transmission Line Structural Loading* [2].

10.1 Definitions

Accreted ice can be classified by its process of formation or its physical characteristics. Freezing rain or drizzle is the most common icing mechanism in the United States. The glaze ice that forms in these conditions is usually clear but may appear opaque because of included air bubbles. Severe ice loads may also result from snow which can accrete to large radial thicknesses by adhering to wires, cables, conductors and guys. In-cloud icing is caused by the collision of supercooled cloud or fog droplets with a structure. The resulting rime ice ranges from hard, clear ice to softer, lower density white ice containing entrapped air. Hoarfrost is a deposit of ice crystals formed by the deposition of water vapor. It does not usually impose significant loads on structures because the amount of ice accreted by vapor deposition is small.

In a general sense, the meteorological parameters that influence the mass, density and shape of an ice accretion are well known. Wind speed and liquid water content or precipitation intensity control the amount of water available for ice formation. The density and shape of an ice accretion are influenced by the air temperature, wind speed, droplet size, and liquid water content or precipitation intensity. The density of snow accretions depends on the wetness of the snow. Because it is important to understand the meteorological conditions that result in their formation, what follows is a more detailed description of the various types of ice accretions.

Freezing Rain. Freezing rain (or drizzle) is a common icing mechanism. Freezing rain occurs when warm moist air is forced over a layer of subfreezing air at the earth's surface. The precipitation usually begins as snow which melts as it falls through the layer of warm air aloft. The drops cool as they fall through the cold surface air layer and freeze on contact with structures or the ground. As freezing rain is often associated with frontal systems it usually does not last more than a day or two. Precipitation associated with slowly moving frontal systems can alternate between snow and freezing rain to form a composite snow-glaze accretion on structures. The density of glaze is usually assumed to be 57 pcf (910 kg/m³). Bennett [3], quoting a number of Russian publications, gives glaze densities between 19 and 56 pcf (300 and 900 kg/m³), while Tattelman and Gringorten [24] state that glaze densities are usually above 50 pcf (800 kg/m³).

In freezing rain the water impingement rate is usually greater than the freezing rate. The excess water drips off and may freeze as icicles resulting in a wide variety of accretion shapes ranging from a smooth cylindrical sheath, through a crescent on the windward side with icicles hanging on the bottom, to large irregular protuberances. The shape of a glaze accretion depends on a combination of varying meteorological factors and the cross-sectional shape of the structural member, its spatial orientation and flexibility.

Snow. The snow that falls on a round cross-sectional structural member, component or appurtenance (such as a wire, cable, conductor or guy) may deform and/or slide around it, as a result of either its own weight or aerodynamic lift. Because of the shear and tensile strength of the snow resulting from capillary forces, interparticle freezing [5] and/or sintering [12], the accreting snow may not fall off the structural member during this process. Ultimately the snow forms a cylindrical sleeve, even around bundled conductors and wires. The formation of the snow sleeve is enhanced by torsional rotation of flexible structural members, components or appurtenances because of the eccentric weight of the snow. The density of accreted snow ranges from below 5 up to 50 pcf (80 up to 800 kg/m³) and may be much higher than the density of the same snowfall on the ground.

Damaging snow accretions have been observed at surface air temperatures ranging from the low 20s up to about 36°F (−5 to 2°C). Snow with a high moisture content appears to stick more readily than drier snow. Snow falling at a surface air temperature above 32°F (0°C) may accrete even at wind speeds above 25 mph (10 m/s) producing dense [37 to 50 pcf (600 to 800 kg/m³)] accretions. Snow with a lower moisture content is not as sticky, blowing off the structure in high winds. These accreted snow densities are typically between 12 and 25 pcf (200 and 400 kg/m³) [13]. Even apparently dry snow can accrete on structures [8]. The cohesive strength of the dry snow is initially supplied by the interlocking of the flakes and ultimately by sintering, as molecular diffusion increases the bond area between adjacent snowflakes. These dry snow accretions appear to form only in very low winds and have densities estimated at between 5 and 10 pcf (80 and 150 kg/m³) [19], [23].

In-Cloud Icing. This icing condition occurs when supercooled cloud or fog water droplets, 100 μm or less in diameter, collide with a structure. It occurs in mountainous areas where adiabatic cooling causes saturation of the atmosphere to occur at temperatures below freezing, in free air in supercooled clouds, and in supercooled fogs produced by a stable air mass with a strong temperature inversion. Because these conditions can persist for days or weeks, significant accumulations of ice can result. Large concentrations of supercooled droplets are not common at air temperatures below about 0°F (−18°C).

In-cloud icing forms rime ice with a density between about 10 and 57 pcf (150 and 910 kg/m³). If the heat of fusion that is released by the freezing droplets is removed by convective and evaporative cooling faster than it is released, the droplets freeze on impact. The degree to which the droplets spread as they collide with the structure and freeze governs how much air is incorporated in the accretion and thus its density. If the cooling rate is relatively low, not all the colliding droplets freeze and the rime accretion will be clear or opaque ice, possibly with attached icicles.

The collision efficiency of a structure is defined as the fraction of cloud droplets in the volume swept out by the structure that actually collide with it. The basic theory of the collision efficiency of smooth circular cylinders perpendicular to the flow of droplets carried by a constant wind was developed by Langmuir and Blodgett [14]. Collision efficiency increases with wind speed and droplet diameter and decreases as the diameter of the cylinder increases. For a given wind speed and droplet size, the theory defines a critical cylinder diameter beyond which accretion will not occur. This concept of a critical diameter has been confirmed by observation.

The amount of rime ice accreted depends on the duration of the icing condition and the wind speed. If, as often occurs, wind speed increases and air temperature decreases with height above ground, larger amounts of rime will accrete on higher structures. The accretion of rime also depends on the flexibility of the structural member, component or appurtenance. If it is free to rotate, such as a long guy or a long span of a single conductor or wire, rime accretes with a roughly circular cross section. On more rigid structural members, components and appurtenances, rime forms in irregular pennant shapes extending into the wind.

Hoarfrost. Hoarfrost is an accumulation of ice crystals formed by direct deposition of water vapor from the air onto a structure. Because it forms when air with a dew point below freezing is brought to saturation by cooling, hoarfrost is often found early in the morning after a clear, cold night. It is feathery in appearance and typically accretes up to about an inch (25 mm) in thickness with very little weight. Normally, hoarfrost does not constitute a significant loading problem; however, it is a very good collector of supercooled fog or cloud droplets and in light winds may accrete rime of significant volume and weight [16].

These four ice accretion categories cover the spectrum of the atmospheric icing phenomenon. The distinctions made in defining each category are not often clearly identifiable in practice. There may be an overlap of more than one type of icing condition, such as snow and freezing rain.

Ice-sensitive structures. Ice-sensitive structures are structures for which the load effects from atmospheric icing control the design of part or all of the structural system. Open structures are efficient ice collectors, so ice accretions can have a significant load effect. The sensitivity of an open structure to ice loads depends on the size and number of structural members, components and appurtenances and also on the other loads for which the structure is designed. For example, the additional weight of ice which may accrete on a heavy wide-flange member will be smaller in proportion to the dead load than the same ice thickness on a light angle member. Also, the increase in projected area for wind loads will be smaller for the wide-flange member than for the angle member. For some open structures other design loads, for example, snow loads and live loads on a catwalk floor, may be larger than the design ice load.

10.2 General

Ice accretions can impose substantial vertical loads on the structural system, present a greater projected area exposed to the wind and affect the lift and drag coefficients. Ice loads on wires, cables, conductors and guys increase both the tension in that component and the load on the rest of the structural system.

Meteorological data suggest that atmospheric ice loads and combined ice and wind loads should be included in the design of ice-sensitive structures throughout most of the United States. This Section provides general guidance on the selection of design ice loads. Where ice accretion data have been compiled for a given area or a meteorologist has been consulted to estimate expected ice loads, that information should take precedence. In the following paragraphs the atmospheric icing risk in each of six regions in the contiguous 48 states is discussed, with particular emphasis on freezing rain. This information was provided by the six regional climate centers of the National Weather Service.

**Northeast Region
(ME,NH,VT,NY,MA,RI,CT,NJ,PA,DE,MD,WV).**
Freezing rain storms can occur anywhere in the 12-state area comprising the Northeastern United States. There is a somewhat greater risk for these storms to occur in the cooler, northern portions of the region than in the Northeast's southernmost states. Also, due to the moderating effect of the Atlantic Ocean, coastal regions are not at as great a

risk as interior areas, more than about 50 mi (80 km) from the coast. The portions of this region most likely to experience freezing rain storms are Pennsylvania (except the southeast) and interior portions of New York and New England. The remainder of the region, although not at as great a risk, is still at a higher risk for freezing rain than many other parts of the country.

Southeast Region (VA,NC,SC,GA,AL,FL). In the southeastern United States freezing rain occurs relatively frequently. A large V-shaped wedge of high event frequency is observed over inland/mountain Virginia and North Carolina. The highest average is over 6 events per year, and occurs at Roanoke and Lynchburg, Virginia; Greensboro, North Carolina; and Washington, D.C. The freezing rain event frequency decreases in the northern coastal regions (except in Washington, D.C.) and in the southern Piedmont and lowlands. Thus the general decreasing gradients of freezing rain events are north to south and mountain to coastal. No freezing rain events have been recorded in Tampa Bay, Key West, and Palm Beach, Florida.

Freezing rain event duration is highest in the northern regions. Roanoke, Greensboro and Dulles Airport have the longest average durations, with the typical winter event lasting over 12 hr. Most of upland Virginia and North Carolina experience events of this length. Asheville and Charlotte have recorded the longest single events of well over 100 hr. The same north-south and mountain-coastal gradients are seen for duration. Florida is not exempt from longer duration freezing rain events. Although few events have been recorded, some have lasted longer than 20 hr.

Midwest Region (IA,IL,IN,KY,MI,MN,MO,OH,WI). Almost all of the Midwest is located in the "glaze belt" where freezing rain events are common. This area experiences frequent interactions between cold polar air from the north and moist tropical air from the Gulf of Mexico which lead to favorable conditions for icing during the colder months of the year.

Despite the economic impacts of these freezing rain events, there have been very few systematic observations of the accumulation of glaze. Based on limited data, it appears that glaze ice accretions greater than 1 in. (25 mm) occur approximately once in 10 years for most of the Midwest. These events are somewhat less likely (perhaps once in

20 years) in the northern regions of Michigan and Wisconsin. Accumulations greater than 2 in. (50 mm) are extremely rare in the Midwest.

Southern Region (AR,LA,MS,OK,TN,TX). Icing conditions due to freezing rain in the Southern Region demonstrate a north-to-south gradient in terms of frequency and severity. This latitudinal trend is further enhanced by the regional geography, with a continental climate dominant across the northern sections of the Southern Region while the Gulf of Mexico produces a moderating maritime influence to the south. Data from the National Weather Service first-order stations indicate that freezing rain storms have been reported at every location across the region in recent years. Even Brownsville, Texas, has reported a handful of events. Freezing rain storms capable of creating significant damage, such as damaging trees, downing power lines and creating transportation hazards can occur virtually anywhere within this region. These severe events tend to be somewhat rare in southern sections, particularly along the coastal margins.

Throughout these six states freezing rain has been observed everywhere during the months of December, January and February. Based on an examination of all January precipitation-hours from National Weather Service stations (i.e., hours with any form of precipitation reported), freezing rain is reported during about 20% of these hours in the plains of Oklahoma and Texas, while being reported during less than 10% of these hours in some of the southern and eastern sections of the Southern Region.

The panhandle regions of Texas and Oklahoma have the highest frequency of freezing rain events relative to precipitation-hours during the winter months with a January maximum of 20%. The percentage of rain-hours with freezing rain is substantially lower in Arkansas and Tennessee, 10–13% for most of Arkansas, falling to well under 10% across most of Tennessee. However, this frequency increases in eastern Tennessee. The ridge and valley complexes of eastern Tennessee may promote the occurrence of freezing rain. Warm-air advection over the ridges can create an environment where liquid precipitation falls along the slopes, while freezing rain occurs in the valley bottoms where cold air drainage has created subfreezing surface temperatures.

Further south the frequency of freezing rain events in central Texas, northern Louisiana and central Mississippi is lower. Proximity to the Gulf becomes more important, particularly in Louisiana and Mississippi. In central Texas freezing rain events account for 10% or less of all winter rain-hours. In the drier sections of Texas, these precipitation events are more uncommon. Coastal stations throughout the entire Southern Region reported only a few events in 20 years.

High Plains Region (ND,SD,NE,KS,CO,WY).
The High Plains Region is characterized by a diverse climate. The west-northwestern portions are the driest, have the greatest elevations, and experience the coldest winter seasons of the High Plains. This area also most frequently experiences a dry continental air mass of polar origin. The southeastern portion of the region is more humid than the north and west, has much longer warm seasons, and is frequently in contact with the warm maritime air mass. Winter snow occurrences and accumulations are common in the northern and western portions, while less common in southeastern portions of the High Plains.

Generally, freezing rain or drizzle is associated with the intrusion of warm moist air aloft from the south together with subfreezing air at the surface intruding from the north. The portions of the High Plains where this situation frequently occurs are in eastern and southeastern Nebraska, in southeastern South Dakota and in central and eastern Kansas. The northern and western portions of the High Plains experience freezing rain less frequently.

Ice loads are sometimes severe.

Western Region (MT,ID,WA,OR,CA,NV,UT,NM,AZ). In the 9 westernmost states, the area most likely to be subject to freezing rain is the Pacific Northwest. Freezing rain occurs most often when incoming warm, moist, precipitating air is rising over domes of trapped cold air lying in valleys and basins. Usually the warm air aloft is slowly eroding away the cold air from the top, eventually reaching the surface at which point the freezing rain changes to rain. This is in contrast to situations near frontal boundaries, where cold air north of a front may be replenished at a rate comparable to that at which the warm air is eroding it away from the top. A similar scenario can occur near the Cascade Mountains when cold air is spilling into river valleys, such as the Columbia and onward into the Willamette Valley, the Fraser River Valley in southern British Columbia, the Rogue and the Umpqua in Oregon, and a few other rivers drain-

ing the west slopes of the Cascades. In these areas freezing rain can continue for quite a while and surface wind speeds may be high while the freezing rain is occurring.

Freezing rain is more likely to occur at lower elevations, from sea level up to 2,000–3,000 ft (600–900 m), and rarely above 4,000 ft (1,200 m). Places such as Walla Walla, Pendleton, and Yakima average about 10 hr of freezing rain in January, and 20–40 hr per year. Mountain valleys in central and northern Idaho and the lower elevation Pacific drainages of western Montana, where cold air can remain trapped, experience about 5 hours of freezing rain in January on average. Missoula, Montana, averages about 10 hr per year, and Kalispell about 20–30 hr. Freezing rain also occurs farther to the south in the northern and central parts of the Sacramento Valley, but less frequently than in Oregon.

Rime occurs very frequently on exposed ridges and slopes in the mountains. Above the mean freezing level, heavy deposits [many inches or even many feet (100 of mm or even meters) thick] can form during the numerous storms that strike the region in winter. Steep cliff faces and any exposed structures or obstacles to the wind can become covered with deep coats of rime. Riming occurs on nearly all mountaintops in the West. At elevations below about 4,000 ft (1,200 m) rime is not common.

10.3 Design for Ice Loads
Applicable standards and guidelines include NESC *National Electrical Safety Code* [18], ASCE 74, *Guidelines for Transmission Line Structural Loading* [2], IEC 826, *Loading and Strength of Overhead Transmission Lines* [11], and ANSI/EIA/TIA-222-E, *Structural Standard for Steel Antenna Towers and Antenna Supporting Structures* [7]. Engineers designing structures for sites near the Canadian border may wish to consult the Canadian tower and transmission line standards [4], [17] for ice load guidance.

Current Industry Practice. Loads associated with atmospheric icing are currently used in the design of communication towers and transmission lines.

The telecommunication and broadcast industries use ANSI/EIA/TIA Standard 222 for the design of towers. It specifies 0.75 of the 50-year return-period wind load on the ice-covered structure. It requires that ice be considered when it is known to occur, but no ice thickness is specified. Typically

196

0.5- or 1-in. (12- or 25-mm) radial ice thicknesses have been applied uniformly over the tower. Thicker ice has been used for towers designed for areas of severe icing such as near large bodies of water or at higher altitudes. This has been generally satisfactory. Problems have occurred, however, when ice loads have not been considered in regions where freezing rain occurs or when insufficient ice has been used in the design of tall towers that, even at low altitudes, are subject to in-cloud icing. The 0.75 factor applied to the wind load on an ice covered structure is appropriate for the EIA/TIA standard due to its other less conservative requirements. This wind and ice combination is generally conservative compared to the combinations that are specified by other standards, for example CAN/CSA S37 [4].

A 1979 survey of design practice for transmission line loadings [1] obtained responses from one-hundred-thirty utilities operating 290,000 mi (470,000 km) of high-voltage transmission lines. Fifty-eight of these utilities specifically indicated 'heavy icing areas' as one reason for special loadings in excess of code requirements. Design ice loads on conductors ranged from no ice, primarily in portions of the southern United States, up to a 2-in. or 2.25-in. (50-mm or 57-mm) radial thickness of glaze ice in some states. Radial glaze ice thicknesses between 1.25 and 1.75 in. (32 and 45 mm) are commonly used. Most of the responding utilities design for heavy ice on the wires with no wind and less ice with wind. Few utilities consider ice on the supporting structures in design.

Selecting design values for ice loads in the United States is difficult because of the absence of a systematically compiled data base.

The Environmental Protection Research Division of the U.S. Army issued a report [3] on the frequency and intensity of freezing rain storms. This report presents the geographical distribution of the occurrence of glaze ice on utility wires from data compiled by various railroad, electric power and telephone associations covering the nine-year period from the winter of 1928–1929 to the winter of 1936–1937. The data in the Bennett study are primarily from glaze ice observations associated with freezing rain or drizzle, but because no distinction was made in the compiled data among the different types of ice that form on wires, wet snow and rime measurements were included as well. Ice thicknesses were measured on wires of various diameters, heights above ground and exposures. No

standardized technique was used in measuring the thickness. The maximum ice thickness observed during the nine-year period in each of 975 squares, 60 miles (97 km) on a side, in a grid covering the contiguous United States is reported. Information on the geographical distribution of the number of freezing rain storms with glaze ice accretions greater than a specified thickness is also included.

In a more recent paper, Tattelman and Grin- gorten [24] reviewed ice load data, storm descriptions and damage estimates in several meteorological publications to extend Bennett's data for severe freezing rain storms to a 50 year period. They calculated the ice thickness for a number of mean recurrence intervals for each of seven regions in the United States. In their eighth region, west of the continental divide, they found very few freezing rain storms and state that in this region in cloud icing should be expected at higher elevations particularly in the coastal ranges.

A base of information of the type included in these two ice load studies is not available for Alaska. What information is available indicates that moderate to severe ice loads of all types can be expected. Several meteorological studies using an ice load model to predict ice loads have been performed for high voltage transmission lines in Alaska [20]–[22], [9], [10]. Predicted 50-year mean recurrence interval glaze ice accretions range from 0.25 to 1.5 radial inches (6 to 38 mm), snow from 1.0 to 5.5 radial inches (25 to 140 mm), rime from 0.5 to 6.0 radial inches (12 to 150 mm) and mixed hoarfrost and rime from 0.5 to 1.0 radial inches (12 to 25 mm). The assumed accretion densities were glaze 57 pcf (910 kg/m^3), snow 31 pcf (500 kg/m^3) and rime 25 pcf (400 kg/m^3). The loads are valid only for the particular regions studied and are highly dependent on the elevation and local terrain features. Large accretions of both wet and dry snow have been observed in most areas of Alaska that have overhead lines.

When ice data are not available, the glaze ice map in Fig. C10–1 for the contiguous United States may be used with great caution. It was originally published in ASCE 74, *Guidelines for Electrical Transmission Line Structural Loading* [2] and is derived from Bennett's map of maximum observed ice thicknesses. Thus it is based on limited observational data on freezing rain ice thicknesses for which the local meteorological and topographical conditions are not available. Wet snow and in-cloud icing will follow different geographical distributions from that shown in this map. The map divides the United States into five zones. For each zone a thickness is estimated for the 50-year mean recurrence interval ice load with no wind, expressed as an equivalent radial thickness of glaze with a density of 57 pcf (910 kg/m³): Zone 1, no icing, 0 in. (0 mm); Zone 2, light icing, approximately 0.4 in. (10 mm); Zone 3, moderate icing, approximately 1 in. (25 mm); Zone 4, heavy icing, approximately 1.6 in. (41 mm), and Zone 5, severe icing, approximately 2.2 in. (55 mm). Consistent 25- and 100-year return-period ice thicknesses are obtained by multiplying the mapped ice thicknesses by 0.86 and 1.14, respectively. Taller structures may accrete additional ice because of higher winds and colder temperatures aloft. The influences of elevation, complex relief, proximity to water and structure size and shape are also highly significant. The following two examples of predicted ice loads differing significantly from those specified in Fig. C10-1 emphasize the need for engineers to conduct a site specific study with the assistance of a meteorologist to determine more accurate design ice loads:

1. A transmission line in the Wasatch Mountains of Utah [zone 3, 1 in. (25 mm) of glaze ice] was designed with input from the state meteorologist for 4 radial inches (102 mm) of 10-pcf rime ice (150 kg/m³) with 40 mph (18 m/s) winds or 2 radial inches (51 mm) of 57-pcf (910 kg/m³) glaze ice. A span of this line descending from a high plateau into a valley was later observed with rime bridging two conductors 18 inches (0.5 m) apart.

2. The micrometeorological conditions along a transmission line that failed under vertical load in the Front Range of Colorado (zone 4) were analyzed after the failure. The study indicated that the map-specified 1.6-in. (41-mm) glaze ice load for the general area would have a mean recurrence interval greater than 300 years at the specific site. The failure was caused by a 1.7-radial-inch (43-mm), 30-pcf (480-kg/m³) wet snow accretion with a 42 mph (19 m/s) wind. The mean recurrence interval of this event was estimated at 25 years [15].

Design ice loads may be estimated using mathematical models based on the physics of the various types of icing and recorded meteorological data (for example, precipitation rate, temperature, and wind speed) that are required as input for these models. Model applications of this type are currently limited to freezing rain and snow accretions because in-cloud icing models require cloud liquid water content and droplet size that are not included in standard weather measurements. An icing model analysis typically gives the calculated maximum ice loads on a specific structure at a specific site for the historical icing storms for which meteorological data are available. Extreme value analysis can then be applied to the calculated ice loads to predict maximum ice loads for specified mean recurrence intervals. Yip [25] produced a freezing rain ice map for Canada using a simple precipitation icing model and more than 10 years of meteorological data at 303 stations.

10.3.2 Wind on Ice Covered Structures

Wind loads on ice covered structures are determined for a 50-year mean recurrence interval. Both the 50-year mean recurrence interval wind speed and the 50-year mean recurrence interval ice thickness are reduced to arrive at a 50-year mean recurrence interval combined load. The lack of data makes it difficult to determine appropriate wind and ice load combinations. The governing combination may depend on the structure type. For Category I and IV structures, 25- and 100-year mean recurrence intervals, respectively, are used instead of 50 years.

10.3.3 Partial Loading

Glaze ice accretions rarely exceed a thickness of a few inches (50 mm) because the associated meteorological conditions typically last no more than a day or two. Horizontal spatial variations over distances of about a thousand feet (300 m) during a freezing rain storm are small. Therefore, partial glaze icing of a structure is usually not significant and partial loading associated with ice shedding will usually be small [6].

In-cloud icing conditions can persist for several days, resulting in rime accretion thicknesses of a foot (300 mm) or more. Because the rime density and thickness increase with increasing wind speed, significant differences in ice loads over the structure are associated with differences in the exposure of the various structural members, components and appurtenances to the wind. The exposure is affected by shielding by other parts of the structure and by the upwind terrain. Partial loading due to rime shedding from only part of the structure may be significant.

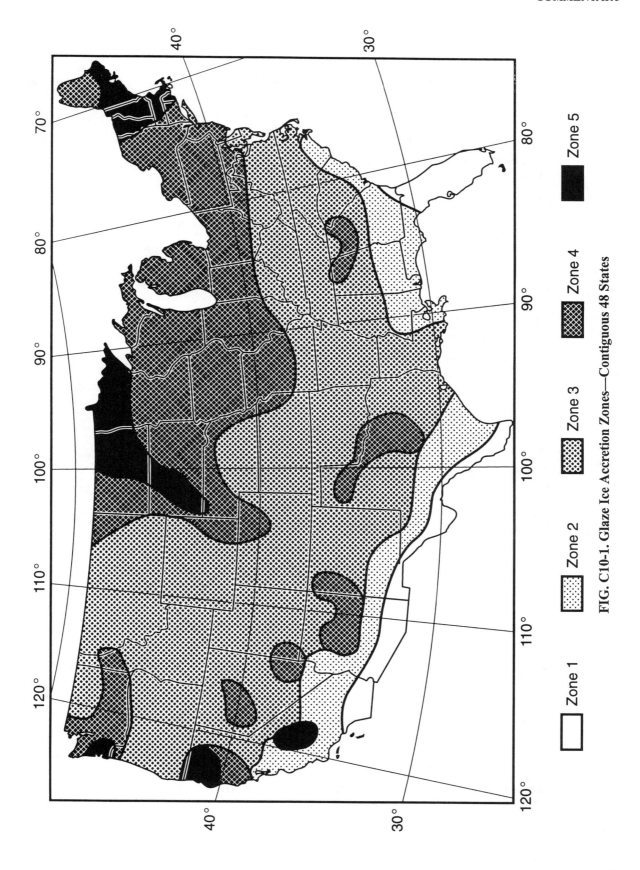

FIG. C10-1. Glaze Ice Accretion Zones—Contiguous 48 States

Zone 1   Zone 2   Zone 3   Zone 4   Zone 5

Partial loading associated with the shedding of a snow accretion from one span or guy but not from adjacent ones may be significant.

References

[1] Loadings for Electrical Transmission Structures by the Committee on Electrical Transmission Structures, *J. of the Structural Division*, 108(5), 1088–1105, 1982.

[2] *Guidelines for Electrical Transmission Line Structural Loading*, ASCE Manuals and Reports on Engineering Practice No. 74, American Society of Civil Engineers, New York, 1991.

[3] Bennett, I. *Glaze; Its Meteorology and Climatology, Geographical Distribution and Economic Effects*, Quartermaster Research and Engineering Center, Environmental Protection Research Division Technical Report EP-105, 217 pages, 1959.

[4] Antennas, Towers and Antenna-supporting structures. CAN/CSA-S37-M86, Canadian Standards Association, Rexdale, Ontario, 1986.

[5] Colbeck, S. C. and Ackley, S. F. Mechanisms for ice bonding in wet snow accretions on power lines, *Proceedings of the First International Workshop on Atmospheric Icing of Structures*, U. S. Army CRREL Special Report 83-17, Hanover, N. H., 25–30, 1982.

[6] Cluts, S. and Angelos, A. Unbalanced forces on tangent transmission structures, IEEE Winter Power Meeting, Paper No. A77-220-7, 1977.

[7] *Structural Standards for Steel Towers and Antenna Supporting Structures*, EIA/TIA-222-E, Electronics Industries Association, Washington D.C., 1991.

[8] Gland, H. and Admirat, P. Meteorological conditions for wet snow occurrence in France—Calculated and measured results in a recent case study on 5 March 1985, *Proc. Third Int. Workshop on Atmospheric Icing of Structures*, pp 91-96, published by Canadian Climate Program in 1991, Vancouver, Canada, 1986.

[9] Gouze, S. C. and Richmond, M. C. Meteorological Evaluation of the Proposed Alaska Transmission Line Routes, Meteorology Research, Inc., Altadena, CA, 1982a.

[10] Gouze, S. C. and Richmond, M. C. Meteorological Evaluation of the proposed Palmer to Glen-nallen Transmission Line Route, Meteorology Research, Inc., Altadena, CA, 1982b.

[11] *Loading and Strength of Overhead Transmission Lines International Standard 826*, International Electrotechnical Commission, Technical Committee 11, Geneva, Switzerland, Second Edition, 1990.

[12] Kuroiwa, D. A study of ice sintering, Research Report 86, U.S. Army CRREL, Hanover, N.H., 8 pages, 1962.

[13] Kuroiwa, D. Icing and snow accretion on electric wires, Research Paper 123, U.S. Army CRREL, Hanover, N.H., 1965.

[14] Langmuir, I. and Blodgett, K. Mathematical investigation of water droplet trajectories, pp 335-393 in *The Collected Works of Irving Langmuir*, Pergamon Press, Elmsford, N.Y, 1946.

[15] McCormick, T. and Pohlman, J.C. Study of compact 220 kV line system indicates need for micro-scale meteorological information, *Proceedings of the Sixth International Workshop on Atmospheric Icing of Structures*, Budapest, Hungary, 1993.

[16] Climatological ice accretion modeling, Canadian Climate Center Report No 84-10, prepared by Meteorological and Environmental Planning Limited and Ontario Hydro for the Atmospheric Environmental Service, 1984.

[17] Overhead lines. CAN/CSA-C22.3 No. 1-M87, Canadian Standards Association, Rexdale, Ontario, 1987.

[18] National Electrical Safety Code, National Bureau of Standards, Washington, D.C., 1993.

[19] Peabody, A. B. Snow loads on transmission and distribution lines in Alaska, *Proceedings of the Sixth International Workshop on Atmospheric Icing of Structures*, Budapest, Hungary, 1993.

[20] Richmond, M.C. Meteorological Evaluation of Bradley Lake Hydroelectric Project 115kV Transmission Line Route, M. C. Richmond Meteorological Consultant, Torrance, CA, 1985.

[21] Richmond, M.C. Meteorological Evaluation of Tyee Lake Hydroelectric Project Transmission Line Route, Wrangell to Petersburg, Richmond Meteorological Consulting, Torrance, CA, 1991.

[22] Richmond, M.C. Meteorological Evaluation of Tyee Lake Hydroelectric Project Transmission Line Route, Tyee Power Plant to Wrangell, Rich-

mond Meteorological Consulting, Torrance, CA, 1992.

[23] Sakamoto, Y., Mizushima, K. and Kawanishi, S. Dry snow type accretion on overhead wires—growing mechanism, meteorological conditions under which it occurs and effect on power lines, *Proc of the Fifth Int Workshop on Atmospheric Icing of Structures*, paper 5-9, Tokyo, Japan, 1990.

[24] Tattelman, P. and Gringorten, I. I. Estimated glaze ice and wind loads at the earth's surface for the contiguous United States, Air Force Cambridge Research Laboratories Report AFCRL-TR-73-0646, 1973.

[25] Yip, T. C. Estimating icing amounts caused by freezing precipitation in Canada, *Proceedings of the Sixth Int Workshop on Ice Accretion on Structures*, Budapest, Hungary, 1993.

B. SERVICEABILITY CONSIDERATIONS

Serviceability limit states are conditions in which the functions of a building or other structure are impaired because of local damage, deterioration or deformation of building components or because of occupant discomfort. While safety generally is not an issue with serviceability limit states, they nonetheless may have severe economic consequences. The increasing use of the computer as a design tool, the use of stronger (but not stiffer) construction materials, the use of lighter architectural elements and the uncoupling of the nonstructural elements from the structural frame, may result in building systems that are relatively flexible and lightly damped. Limit states design emphasizes that serviceability criteria are essential to ensure functional performance and economy of design for such building structural systems (Committee on Serviceability Research, 1986; Commentary A, 1990; Fisher and West, 1990).

There are three general types of unserviceability that may be experienced:

1. Excessive deflections or rotation that may affect the appearance, functional use or drainage of the structure, or may cause damaging transfer of load to non-load supporting elements and attachments.
2. Excessive vibrations produced by the activities of building occupants, mechanical equipment, or the wind, which may cause occupant discomfort or malfunction of building service equipment.
3. Deterioration, including weathering, corrosion, rotting, and discoloration.

In checking serviceability, the designer is advised to consider appropriate service loads, the response of the structure, and the reaction of the building occupants.

Service loads that may require consideration include static loads from the occupants and their possessions, snow or rain on roofs, temperature fluctuations, and dynamic loads from human activities, wind-induced effects, or the operation of building service equipment. The service loads are those loads that act on the structure at an arbitrary point in time. (In contrast, the nominal loads have a small probability of being exceeded in any year; factored loads have a small probability of being exceeded in 50 years.) Appropriate service loads for checking serviceability limit states may be only a fraction of the nominal loads.

The response of the structure to service loads normally can be analyzed assuming linear elastic behavior. However, members that accumulate residual deformations under service loads may require examination with respect to this long-term behavior. Service loads used in analyzing creep or other long-terms effects may not be the same as those used to analyze elastic deflections or other short-term or reversible structural behavior.

Serviceability limits depend on the function of the building and on the perceptions of its occupants. In contrast to the ultimate limit states, it is difficult to specify general serviceability limits that are applicable to all building structures. The serviceability limits presented in Commentaries B.1.1, B.1.2, and B.1.3 provide general guidance and have usually led to acceptable performance in the past. However, serviceability limits for a specific building should be determined only after a careful analysis by the engineer and architect of all functional and economic requirements and constraints in conjunction with the building owner. It should be recognized that building occupants are able to perceive structural deflections, motion, cracking, or other signs of possible distress at levels that are much lower than those that would indicate that structural failure is impending. Such signs of distress may be taken incorrectly as an indication that the building is unsafe and diminish its commercial value.

B.1.1 Vertical Deflections and Misalignment

Excessive vertical deflections and misalignment arise primarily from three sources: (1) gravity loads, such as dead, live and snow loads; (2) effects of temperature, creep and differential settlement; and (3) construction tolerances and errors. Such deformations may be visually objectionable, may cause separation, cracking, or leakage of exterior cladding, doors, windows and seals, and may cause damage to interior components and finishes. Appropriate limiting values of deformations depend on the type of structure, detailing, and intended use [16]. Historically, common deflection limits for horizontal members have been 1/360 of the span for floors subjected to full nominal live load and 1/240 of span for roof members. Deflections of about 1/300 of the span (for cantilevers, 1/150 of length) are visible and may lead to general architectural damage or cladding leakage. Deflections greater than 1/200 of the span may impair operation of moveable components such as doors, windows and sliding partitions.

In certain long-span floor systems, it may be necessary to place a limit (independent of span) on the maximum deflection to minimize the possibility of damage of adjacent nonstructural elements [17]. For example, damage to nonload-bearing partitions may occur if vertical deflections exceed more than about 10 mm (3/8 in.) unless special provision is made for differential movement [11]; however, many components can accept larger deformations.

Load combinations for checking static deflections can be developed using first-order reliability analysis [16]. Current static deflection guidelines for floor and roof systems are adequate for limiting surficial damage in most buildings. A combined load with an annual probability of 0.05 of being exceeded would be appropriate in most instances. For serviceability limit states involving visually objectionable deformations, repairable cracking or other damage to interior finishes, and other short-term effects, the suggested load combinations are:

$$D + L \tag{B-1a}$$

$$D + 0.5S \tag{B-1b}$$

For serviceability limit states involving creep, settlement or similar long-term or permanent effects, the suggested load combination is:

$$D + 0.5L \tag{B-2}$$

Live load, L, is defined in Section 4. The dead load effect, D, used in applying Eqs. (B-1a), (B-1b) and (B-2) may be that portion of dead load that occurs following attachment of nonstructural elements. For example, in composite construction, the dead load effects frequently are taken as those imposed after the concrete has cured; in ceilings, the dead load effects may include only those loads placed after the ceiling structure is in place.

B.1.2 Drift of Walls and Frames.

Drifts (lateral deflections) of concern in serviceability checking arise primarily from the effects of wind. Drift limits in common usage for building design are on the order of 1/600 to 1/400 of the building or story height [8]. These limits generally are sufficient to minimize damage to cladding and nonstructural walls and partitions. Smaller drift limits may be appropriate if the cladding is brittle. An absolute limit on interstory drift may also need to be imposed in light of evidence that damage to nonstructural partitions, cladding and glazing may occur if the interstory drift exceeds about 10 mm (3/8 in) unless special detailing practices are made to tolerate movement [11], [15]. Many components can accept deformations that are significantly larger.

Use of the factored wind load in checking serviceability is excessively conservative. The load combination with an annual probability of 0.05 of being exceeded, which can be used for checking short-term effects, is

$$D + 0.5L + 0.7W \tag{B-3}$$

obtained using a procedure similar to that used to derive Eqs. (B-1a) and (B-1b). Wind load, W, is defined in Section 6. Due to its transient nature, wind load need not be considered in analyzing the effects of creep or other long-term actions.

Deformation limits should apply to the structural assembly as a whole. The stiffening effect of nonstructural walls and partitions may be taken into account in the analysis of drift if substantiating information regarding their effect is available. Where load cycling occurs, consideration should be given to the possibility that increases in residual deformations may lead to incremental structural collapse.

B.1.3 Vibrations.

Structural motions of floors or of the building as a whole can cause the building occupants discomfort. In recent years, the number of complaints about building vibrations has been increasing. This increasing number of complaints is associated in part with the more flexible structures that result from modern construction practice. Traditional static deflection checks are not sufficient to ensure that annoying vibrations of building floor systems or buildings as a whole will not occur [1]. While control of stiffness is one aspect of serviceability, mass distribution and damping are also important in controlling vibrations. The use of new materials and building systems may require that the dynamic response of the system be considered explicitly. Simple dynamic models often are sufficient to determine whether there is a potential problem and to suggest possible remedial measurements [9], [13].

Excessive structural motion is mitigated by measures that limit building or floor accelerations to levels that are not disturbing to the occupants or do not damage service equipment. Perception and tolerance of individuals to vibration is dependent on their expectation of building performance (related to building occupancy) and to their level of activity at the time the vibration occurs [7]. Individuals find continuous vibrations more objectionable than transient vibrations. Continuous vibrations (over a period of minutes) with acceleration on the order of 0.005–0.01 g are annoying to most people engaged in quiet activities, whereas those engaged in physical activities or spectator events may tolerate steady-state accelerations on the order of 0.02–0.05 g. Thresholds of annoyance for transient vibrations (lasting only a few seconds) are considerably higher and depend on the amount of structural damping present [18]. For a finished floor with (typically) 5 percent damping or more, peak transient accelerations of 0.05–0.1 g may be tolerated.

Many common human activities impart dynamic forces to a floor at frequencies (or harmonics) in the range of 2 to 6 Hz [2]–[5]. If the fundamental frequency of vibration of the floor system is in this range and if the activity is rhythmic in nature (e.g., dancing, aerobic exercise, cheering at spectator events), resonant amplification may occur. To prevent resonance from rhythmic activities, the floor system should be tuned so that its natural frequency is well removed from the harmonics of the excitation frequency. As a general rule, the natural frequency of structural elements and assemblies should be greater than 2.0 times the frequency of any steady-state excitation to which they are exposed unless vibration isolation is provided. Damping is also an effective way of controlling annoying vibration from transient events, as studies

have shown that individuals are more tolerant of vibrations that damp out quickly than those that persist [18].

Several recent studies have shown that a simple and relatively effective way to minimize objectionable vibrations to walking and other common human activities is to control the floor stiffness, as measured by the maximum deflection independent of span. Justification for limiting the deflection to an absolute value rather than to some fraction of span can be obtained by considering the dynamic characteristics of a floor system modeled as a uniformly loaded simple span. The fundamental frequency of vibration, f_o, of this system is given by

$$f_o = \frac{\pi}{2\,l^2} \sqrt{\frac{EI}{\rho}} \tag{B-4}$$

in which EI = flexural rigidity of the floor, l = span, and $\rho = w/g$ = mass per unit length; g = acceleration due to gravity (9.81 m/s²), and w = dead load plus participating live load. The maximum deflection due to w is

$$\delta = (5/384)\,(w\,l^4/EI) \tag{B-5}$$

Substituting EI from this equation into Eq. (B-4), we obtain

$$f_o \approx 18 / \sqrt{\delta} \quad (\delta \text{ in mm}) \tag{B-6}$$

This frequency can be compared to minimum natural frequencies for mitigating walking vibrations in various occupancies [6]. For example, Eq. (B-6) indicates that the static deflection due to uniform load, w, must be limited to about 5 mm, independent of span, if the fundamental frequency of vibration of the floor system is to be kept above about 8 Hz. Many floors not meeting this guideline are perfectly serviceable; however, this guideline provides a simple means for identifying potentially troublesome situations where additional consideration in design may be warranted.

B.2 Design for Long-Term Deflection

Under sustained loading, structural members may exhibit additional time-dependent deformations due to creep, which usually occur at a slow but persistent rate over long periods of time. In certain applications, it may be necessary to limit deflection under long-term loading to specified levels. This can be done by multiplying the immediate deflection by a creep factor, as provided in material standards, that ranges from about 1.5–2.0. This limit state should be checked using load combination (B-2).

B.3 Camber

Where required, camber should be built into horizontal structural members to give proper appearance and drainage and to counteract anticipated deflection from loading and potential ponding.

B.4 Expansion and Contraction

Provision should be made in design so that if significant dimensional changes occur, the structure will move as a whole and differential movement of similar parts and members meeting at joints will be a minimum. Design of expansion joints to allow for dimensional changes in portions of a structure separated by such joints should take both reversible and irreversible movements into account. Structural distress in the form of wide cracks has been caused by restraint of thermal, shrinkage and prestressing deformations. Designers are advised to provide for such effects through relief joints or by controlling crack widths.

B.5 Durability

Buildings and other structures may deteriorate in certain service environments. This deterioration may be visible upon inspection (weathering, corrosion, staining) or may result in undetected changes in the material. The designer should either provide a specific amount of damage tolerance in the design or should specify adequate protection systems and/or planned maintenance to minimize the likelihood that such problems will occur. Water infiltration through poorly constructed or maintained wall or roof cladding is considered beyond the realm of designing for damage tolerance. Waterproofing design is beyond the scope of this standard. For portions of buildings and other structures exposed to weather, the design should eliminate pockets in which moisture can accumulate.

References

[1] Structural serviceability: A critical appraisal and research needs. *J. Struct. Div.*, ASCE 112(12), 2646–2664, 1986.

[2] Allen, D.E. and Rainer, J.H. Vibration criteria for long-span floors. *Canadian J. Civ. Engrg.*, 3(2), 165–173, 1976.

[3] Allen, D.E., Rainer, J.H. and Pernica, G. Vibration criteria for assembly occupancies. *Canadian J. Civ. Engrg.*, 12(3), 617–623, 1985.

[4] Allen, D.E. Floor vibrations from aerobics. *Canadian J. Civ. Engrg.*, 19(4), 771–779, 1990a.

[5] Allen, D.E. Building vibrations from human activities. *Concrete International*, 12(6), 66–73, 1990b.

[6] Allen, D.E. and Murray, T.M. Design criterion for vibrations due to walking. *Engrg. J.*, AISC 30(4), 117–129, 1993.

[7] American National Standard Guide to the Evaluation of Human Exposure to Vibration in Buildings (ANSI S3.29-1983). Am. Nat. Stds. Inst., New York, NY, 1983.

[8] Wind drift design of steel-framed buildings: State of the art. *J. Struct. Div.*, ASCE, 114(9), 2085–2108, 1988.

[9] Bachmann, H. and Ammann, W. Vibrations in structures. Structural Engineering, Doc. 3e, International Assoc. for Bridge and Str. Engr., Zurich, Switzerland, 1987.

[10] Commentary A, Serviceability Criteria for deflections and vibrations. National Building Code of Canada-1990, National Research Council, Ottawa, Ontario, 1990.

[11] Cooney, R.C. and King, A.B. Serviceability criteria for buildings. BRANZ Report SR14, Building Research Association of New Zealand, Porirua, New Zealand, 1988.

[12] Ellingwood, B. and Tallin, A. Structural serviceability: floor vibrations. *J. Struct. Div.*, ASCE, 110(2), 401–418, 1984.

[13] Ellingwood, B. Serviceability guidelines for steel structures. *AISC Engr. J.*, 26(1), 1–8, 1989.

[14] Fisher, J.M. and West, M.A. Serviceability design considerations for low-rise buildings. Steel Design Guide No. 3, American Institute of Steel Construction, Chicago, IL, 1990.

[15] Freeman, S. Racking tests of high rise building partitions. *J. Struct. Div.*, ASCE, 103(8), 1673–1685, 1977.

[16] Galambos, T.V. and Ellingwood, B. Serviceability limit states: Deflections. *J. Struct. Div.*, ASCE, 112(1), 67–84, 1986.

[17] Bases for the design of structures—Deforma-

tions of buildings at the serviceability limit states. ISO Standard 4356, 1977.

[18]Murray, T. Building floor vibrations. *AISC Engrg. J.*, 28(3), 102–109, 1991.

[19] Ohlsson, S. Ten years of floor vibration research—a review of aspects and some results.

Proc. Symp. on Serviceability of Buildings, National Research Council of Canada, Ottawa, 435–450, 1988.

[20] Tallin, A.G. and Ellingwood, B. Serviceability limit states: Wind induced vibrations. *J. Struct. Engr.*, ASCE, 110(10), 2424–2437, 1984.

INDEX

209